# Chemistry and Physics of
# INTERFACES

Based on the Symposium on
Interfaces sponsored by
INDUSTRIAL AND ENGINEERING CHEMISTRY
and the Division of Industrial and
Engineering Chemistry of the American
Chemical Society, Washington, D. C.,
June 15 and 16, 1964.
**Sydney Ross** Chairman
Reprinted from INDUSTRIAL AND
ENGINEERING CHEMISTRY, September 1964-
September 1965.

AMERICAN CHEMICAL SOCIETY | PUBLICATIONS | WASHINGTON, D.C.

Library of Congress Catalog Card Number 65-28228
PRINTED IN THE UNITED STATES OF AMERICA

# Contents

# Preface

This Symposium on the Chemistry and Physics of Interfaces stems from the joint venture, entered into in 1964, between the Division of Industrial and Engineering Chemistry and INDUSTRIAL AND ENGINEERING CHEMISTRY. It is the first of what will become an annual summer series of state-of-the-art symposia arranged by the Division on subject areas suggested by the editors.

The subjects are selected from physicochemical phenomena of broad industrial significance. The talks, after updating and expanding, are published in INDUSTRIAL AND ENGINEERING CHEMISTRY (monthly). They are collected here for use as text material in advanced training courses for industrial chemists and chemical engineers with problems in surface chemistry.

We wish to thank the authors for their care in proofreading these long manuscripts and for their willingness to permit us to create unorthodox means of presenting the information. Credit for the final, published form of the articles goes to the editor-artist team, Miss Elspeth Mainland, Assistant Editor, and Leroy Corcoran, Staff Artist.

David E. Gushee, Editor
INDUSTRIAL AND ENGINEERING CHEMISTRY

# Introduction

The articles published in this group are based on a Symposium on Interfaces held in Washington, D. C., June 15 and 16, 1964. The symposium was sponsored by the Division of Industrial and Engineering Chemistry of the American Chemical Society and INDUSTRIAL AND ENGINEERING CHEMISTRY. The topic was specified by these two groups, but the task of organizing the subject matter was offered to me. I accepted it willingly because I saw in it, beyond the occasion itself, an opportunity to construct a badly needed teaching instrument for industrial chemists who, without having had much formal training in the field, are faced with problems in surface chemistry. That the number of such persons is large had been impressed upon me both by my experience as a consultant to industry and as the recipient of letters from personnel managers seeking what must be among the rarest of all professionals—colloid and surface chemists.

Why men with this training should be so rare might be worth a moment's consideration. A recent survey of the undergraduate courses offered in colloid and surface chemistry throughout the nation reported that "a substantial number of universities or colleges have an active teaching program in colloid chemistry" (2). This finding would certainly seem satisfactory, were it not irreconcilable with the known shortage of men trained in that discipline. Let us inquire elsewhere and a different result appears. A survey by the education committee of the Division of Colloid and Surface Chemistry of the American Chemical Society, conducted among 185 major U. S. industrial companies, revealed how large was the number of chemists and chemical engineers engaged in full-time work on projects involving colloid and surface chemistry, and how great the gap in numbers between those that would soon be needed and those that would be available (1). What then of "the substantial number of active teaching programs in the universities of the nation"?

The truth is that the needs of the nation in this important field are not being met by the universities. In the past 15 years the membership of the Division of Colloid and Surface Chemistry has grown tenfold, showing increasing awareness on the part of industrial chemists of how frequently the subject appears in the problems they have to solve. In the universities during the same period no parallel growth has taken place. The leaders of the field in U. S. universities during the years 1920 to 1950 were Bancroft, Bartell, Harkins, Hauser, McBain, and Weiser; to these, add two names of persons still living. It would be invidious to name the corresponding persons of today, but the number of universities offering comparable training is not any greater than existed then.

A professor in the subject may be allowed to supply the answer: students do not come forward. The subject lacks glamor. Foams, emulsions, jellies, gums, glues, or greases—how mundane they are to young people who are thinking of nuclear-powered rockets and interstellar space. A hypothetical graduate student, determined to major in colloid and surface chemistry, finds few graduate schools that offer the subject as a major. He then finds that research assistantships or fellowships are few and far between. He will probably accept a teaching assistantship for four years (normally a one- or two-year stint for his more fortunate friends). The time that this man spends on research for his doctorate is not reimbursed. The graduate student who teaches is, in fact, callously exploited by "the system." A large fraction of the academic research in colloid chemistry in the United States—research often of indirect benefit to industry—is thus carried out at the expense of a small number of young men. Little wonder that so few are to be found who are willing to join them.

But if others are more fortunate in graduate school, they, too, may have to pay the price, and a higher price, later in their careers. Most academic research projects are geared to defense needs, not to industrial problems. The process of reorienting one's training, perhaps one's philosophy of life, is painful to the young graduate, and expensive to the industrial company that hopes to get something of value out of him some day.

The proper independence of the graduate school laboratories requires that their projects should be so selected as to have fundamental scientific value. Such projects need not be entirely disconnected from the great industrial world outside; nevertheless, the lack of industrial support often means that the pure research project is remote from practicality. The result of this isolation sometimes affects the young graduate with a virulent case of intellectual snobbishness, which inclines him to consider problems of applied science as beneath the dignity of so fine a fellow. His professor can save him from this lamentable provincialism—the professor should be the link that connects the two worlds; he should bring back to his laboratory and to his graduate students some glimpses of the complexity of applied problems and of the fascination and excitement that suffuses applied research. To this end, the professor should not be too young himself. Young men possess qualities that fit them to do pure research; even youthful conceit and inexperience contribute to the intellectual adventurousness that is essential for creative work in pure science. Applied research, however, requires qualities that are the fruits of experience, and so is better handled at a later stage in a man's career, when, in Milton's words,

> Old experience doth attain
> To something of prophetic strain.

Young men, meanwhile, vociferate their adherence to their faith with more fervor than grace, as is their wont.

Industry has been unduly neglectful of the whole situation. Government agencies were not challenged by industry as they took over virtually the whole academic research establishment of the nation. The pinch was felt only when men of suitable training became rare, and the need to do something for those with wildly unsuitable backgrounds became more apparent. Industry has expressed itself as willing to support its employees who take summer courses in colloid and surface chemistry, or who attend symposia such as this one (1). But these are inadequate remedies which do nothing to make up for the time lost by men who should have had such courses during their student days.

In addition, more than course work is needed to fit a man to tackle problems in colloid science; the subject has a character of its own, requiring much practical familiarity, as well as a background of information. The difference between the problems that occupy a colloid chemist and those that occupy a physicist, for example, lies in the greater number of variables that the colloid chemist has to consider. The more variables there are, the more possible descriptions one can find of a phenomenon, depending on how one or another of those variables is weighted. Those of us who teach physicists or mathematicians soon discover that we are talking to men who expect to find a single rigorous answer to their questions. To teach colloid science, however, you must make the students familiar with the notion that some effects have more than one possible cause, or sets of causes, though only one answer is right; and that they must develop and use a certain, almost intuitive, kind of judgment about selecting one solution and discarding another.

Neither the specialized pursuits of AEC, NASA, and ONR, nor the fundamental projects favored by NSF are designed to meet the needs of chemical industry; nor are those agencies expected to do so. Colloid science is not the only neglected subject having industrial importance but neglected in the interlocking complex of governmental and defense research activities. Industrial companies should, therefore, insist on their interests being represented in the laboratories of the graduate schools. Unspecified grants-in-aid of research do little good in this connection—they are merely swept into the current programs, which were originally inspired and continue to draw their major support from governmental sources.

At one time, when their influence was not contested, industrial companies specified too closely what they wanted investigated in the academic laboratories; today, the tendency is for them to specify nothing. The former course deprived academic research of its independence; the present course does little to redress the injury already sustained by industrial interests. It is not beyond the wit of an industrial sponsor of research to devise appropriate methods of securing for himself a voice in directing the technical training of men who must, for the most part, look to industry for employment.

The response to the Symposium on Interfaces on the part of the public to whom it was addressed—i.e., industrial chemists—was enthusiastic, and confirmed again the existence of the need to which we have referred. Among the lecturers selected to handle the various topics, the industrial chemists outnumbered the academics, reflecting the emphasis on applied colloid science. Even so, theoretical treatments were not neglected. The people who attended were rather older than college students and, of course, more strongly motivated to make the effort to comprehend the material. Publication of the papers that were delivered increases the size of the audience to whom they were addressed.

Several of the lecturers have much enhanced the value of their contributions since the initial occasion by additions and clarifications, so that the printed paper is not always just what was delivered at the symposium. Those emendations are all to the good and help bring closer to perfection the teaching instrument that I originally envisaged. For industrial chemists and for college students, the present collection is a most useful possession. As a teacher, I plan to use it as my class textbook, as no better one is, in my opinion, at present to be had.

## LITERATURE CITED

(1) *Chem. Eng. News* **42**, No. 31, 42–3 (1964).
(2) Mysels, K. J., *J. Chem. Educ.* **37**, 355 (1960).

# 1
# Attractive Forces
# at Interfaces

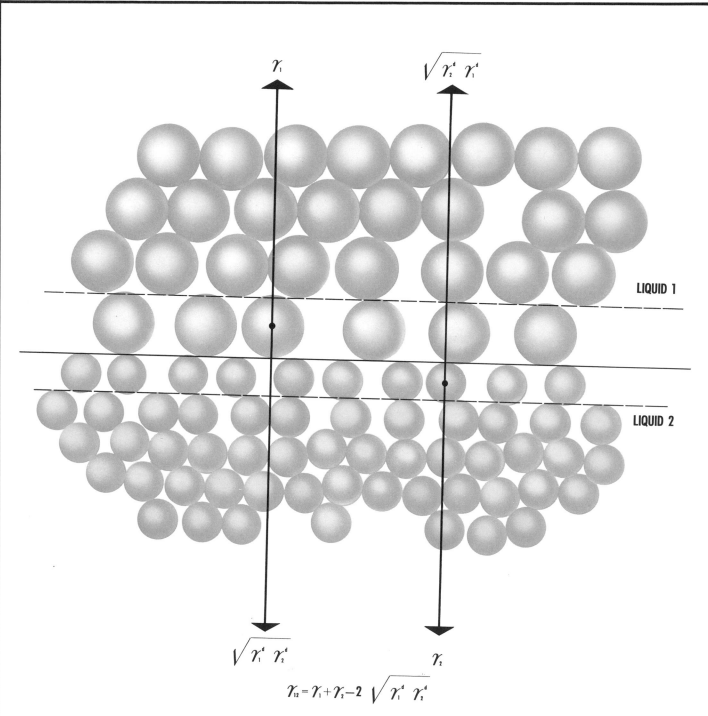

$$\gamma_{12} = \gamma_1 + \gamma_2 - 2\sqrt{\gamma_1^d \gamma_2^d}$$

*Figure 1. Although a very simple model of the interface is used, it gives accurate predictions of wetting, adsorption, and spreading behavior for many fluids. At the interface between mercury and a saturated hydrocarbon the molecules in the two "interfacial regions" are subject to the resultant force field made up of components arising from bulk attractive forces in each phase, and the London dispersion forces operating across the interface itself*

# Attractive Forces at Interfaces

FREDERICK M. FOWKES

*Calculation of a new property unifies several previously unrelated fields of surface chemistry and permits rapid determination of several design variables. Most noteworthy of these are the heats and free energies of adsorption.*

Equations based on a simple model of surfaces and interfaces have been found useful for relating quantitatively several previously unrelated fields of surface chemistry (10–13). These equations introduce a new term—the London dispersion force contribution to the surface free energy ($\gamma^d$)—and make use of this term for the accurate calculations of surface tension, interfacial tension, contact angles, heats and free energies of immersion, heats and free energies of adsorption, and the long-range van der Waals attractive forces. The accuracy of predictions of values verifiable by experiment lead one to expect that predictions of unverifiable quantities, such as the magnitude of attractive forces at solid–solid interfaces, are to be trusted.

This approach should appeal especially to those who need to use the results of surface chemistry and would prefer to calculate from existing values rather than make new experimental determinations. It should also appeal to those teaching surface chemistry in that it relates for the first time several widely separated fields of surface chemistry. Most noteworthy is the ability to calculate heats and free energies of adsorption of gases on solid surfaces directly from measurements of surface tensions and contact angles. The calculation of the long range van der Waals attractive constant, $A$, from values of $\gamma^d$ is also very attractive.

## Model and Basic Assumptions

We will start with a discussion of liquid surfaces and liquid–liquid interfaces and then proceed to liquid–solid, vapor–solid, and solid–solid interfaces. First, it is useful but not necessary to the argument to consider the origin of surface tension in a liquid surface. It is normal to consider that the tension resides in the surface monolayer, although in some systems it has been demonstrated to have contributions from second or third layers. We shall use the term "surface region" or "interfacial region" to represent not only the surface or interfacial monolayers but also those adjacent parts of the bulk liquid in which part of the surface tension resides. Molecules in the surface region of the liquid are subject to attractive forces from adjacent molecules which result in a net attraction into the bulk phase in the direction normal to the surface. The attraction tends to reduce the number of molecules in the surface region, and results in an increase in intermolecular distance. The extension (as in the case of a spring) requires work, and returns work to the system upon release. The analogy with the spring is complete—it explains why tension exists and why there is a surface free energy.

The intermolecular attractions which cause surface tension result from a variety of well known intermolecular forces. Most of these forces, such as the metallic bond or the hydrogen bond, are a function of specific chemical nature. On the other hand, London dispersion forces exist in all types of matter and always give an attractive force between adjacent atoms or molecules no matter how dissimilar their chemical natures may be (28). The London dispersion forces arise from the interaction of fluctuating electronic dipoles with induced dipoles in neighboring atoms or molecules. These forces depend on electrical properties of the volume elements involved and the distance between them, and are independent of temperature. In a liquid such as mercury there are two main interatomic forces, the metallic bond and the London dispersion forces. Consequently the surface tension of mercury can be divided into two parts, the part due to dispersion forces and the part due to metallic bonds.

$$\gamma_{Hg} = \gamma_{Hg}{}^d + \gamma_{Hg}{}^m$$

A similar equation may be written for the surface tension of water or of any other polar liquid.

Let us consider the interface between mercury and a suitable reference liquid, preferably a saturated liquid hydrocarbon, as in Figure 1. Liquid saturated hydrocarbons are useful as reference liquids because the intermolecular attraction in these liquids is, for all practical purposes, entirely due to London dispersion forces.

Furthermore the only appreciable interfacial interactions to which these standard liquids are subject are the London dispersion forces. The interface is composed of the two adjacent interfacial regions, and the interfacial tension must therefore be the sum of the tensions in each of these regions. In the interfacial region of the hydrocarbon, the molecules are attracted toward the bulk hydrocarbon by intermolecular forces which tend to produce a tension equal to the surface tension of the hydrocarbon ($\gamma_1$). However, at the interface there is also an attraction by the London dispersion forces of the mercury for those hydrocarbon molecules in the interfacial region. These molecules are in a different force field than those at the surface of the hydrocarbon because of this interaction, and therefore the tension in this layer is a function of the difference between the surface tension of the hydrocarbon and the attractive force exerted by the London dispersion force interaction between hydrocarbon and mercury. For those acquainted with the success of the solubility parameter for predicting the solubility of nonelectrolytes (23, 24), it is expected that the geometric mean of the dispersion force attractions should predict the magnitude of the interaction between these dissimilar materials, as was done by Girifalco and Good (15). This point is justified in the following section. The effect of interfacial attraction on the tension in the interface can be predicted by the geometric mean of the dispersion force components of the surface tension of the hydrocarbon and of the mercury ($\sqrt{\gamma_1^d\gamma_2^d}$). Thus the tension in the interfacial region of the hydrocarbon is equal to $\gamma_1 - \sqrt{\gamma_1^d\gamma_2^d}$. Similarly in the interfacial region of mercury the attractive force of bulk mercury is partially balanced by the attractive force of the hydrocarbon and the tension in this layer is equal to $\gamma_2 - \sqrt{\gamma_1^d\gamma_2^d}$. Since the interfacial tension $\gamma_{12}$ is the sum of the tensions in these two layers

$$\gamma_{12} = \gamma_1 + \gamma_2 - 2\sqrt{\gamma_1^d\gamma_2^d} \qquad (1)$$

The use of the geometric mean relationship to predict intermolecular forces is based on certain assumptions and has certain limitations. A calculation of these forces by summation of pair potentials illustrates the principle and demonstrates some limitations. The potential for the interaction between volume elements in liquid 1 is given by

$$\mu_{11} = -\frac{3\ \alpha_1^2\ I_1}{4\ r_{11}^6} \qquad (2)$$

where $\alpha_1$ is the polarizability, $I_1$ is the ionization potential, and $r_{11}$ the intermolecular distance. If one sums up the pair potentials of all of the surface volume elements with all of the volume elements below the surface (5, 28), one obtains the following estimate for the dispersion force contribution to the surface energy

$$\gamma_1^d = \frac{-\pi\ N_1^2\ \alpha_1^2\ I_1}{8\ r_{11}^2} \qquad (3)$$

Equation 3 gives the surface energy in electron volts per sq. cm.; when multiplied by $1.602 \times 10^{-12}$ it gives ergs per sq. cm. This equation is realistic in that

insertion of the proper values for water ($\alpha_1 = 1.48$ A.[3], $I_1 = 12.6$ volts, $N_1 = 3.34 \times 10^{22}$, $r_{11} = 2.76$ A.) gives 25.4 ergs per sq. cm. as the dispersion force component of the surface energy of water.

In a similar fashion, one can determine the interaction between dissimilar phases (at an interface) with volume elements of such a size that the volume elements in the surface still have twelve nearest neighbors. Under these conditions the energy of interaction of the volume elements in the surface of phase 1 is.

$$\Sigma_{12}^d = \frac{-\pi\ N_1 N_2\ \alpha_1\alpha_2}{4\ r_{12}^2} \cdot \frac{I_1 I_2}{I_1 + I_2} \qquad (4)$$

If we use the geometric mean relationship of Berthelot, London, Hildebrand, etc., and write

$$\Sigma_{12}^d \cong (\Sigma_{11}^d \Sigma_{22}^d)^{1/2} = \frac{-\pi\ N_1 N_2\ \alpha_1\alpha_2}{8\ r_{11}r_{22}} \cdot \frac{I_1 I_2}{\sqrt{I_1 I_2}} \qquad (5)$$

we may now compare Equation 5 with Equation 6 to see what errors arise in the use of the geometric mean relationship. Obviously if $N_1 = N_2$, $r_{11} = r_{22}$, and $I_1 = I_2$, the two equations are identical. It can be shown that even a 50% difference in ionization potential will cause an error of only 2%. By proper choice of the size of volume elements in the two phases, errors due to a disparity in the interelement distances can usually be made negligibly small. For instance, in the case of saturated hydrocarbons, the volume element to be summed will be the $CH_2$ group, and in the case of aromatics, the CH group. Fortunately, all of these have very nearly the same radius as the water molecule or the mercury atom. However, there may be some difficulty in the case of fluorocarbons where the radius of the $CF_2$ group is a bit larger, and it may be that part of the overestimation of the interaction at interfaces (discussed later) and the overestimation of the solubility of fluorocarbons in hydrocarbons could result from treating these interactions as though the distance between interacting volume elements is negligibly different, when in fact this is not the case.

The above arguments show that, with the possible exception of hydrocarbon–fluorocarbon interactions, the interaction energies due to dispersion forces at an

**TABLE I. DETERMINATION OF $\gamma_1^d$ FOR MERCURY**
(Ergs/Sq. Cm. at 20° C.)

| Hydrocarbon (No. 2) | $\gamma_2$ | $\gamma_{12}$ | $\gamma_1^d$ |
|---|---|---|---|
| n-Hexane | 18.4 | 378 | 210 |
| n-Octane | 21.8 | 375 | 199 |
| n-Nonane | 22.8 | 372 | 199 |
| Benzene | 28.85 | 363 | 194 |
| Toluene | 28.5 | 359 | 208 |
| o-Xylene | 30.1 | 359 | 200 |
| m-Xylene | 28.9 | 357 | 211 |
| p-Xylene | 28.4 | 361 | 203 |
| n-Propylbenzene | 29.0 | 363 | 194 |
| n-Butylbenzene | 29.2 | 363 | 193 |
| Average | | | 200 ± 7 |

$\gamma_1 = 484$ ergs/sq. cm. at 20° C.
*See Reference 11.*

interface can be reliably predicted by the geometric mean of the dispersion force components of the surface energies of the two substances. Since the dispersion force contributions to surface energy calculated with Equation 3 take into account the density (and its change with temperature) these are essentially surface free energy terms (or surface tension terms), and the geometric mean of $\gamma_1{}^d$ and $\gamma_2{}^d$ may be used to give the magnitude of the interfacial attraction resulting from dispersion forces between adjacent dissimilar phases.

### Calculation of Interfacial Tension

Equation 1 can be tested with the known values of surface and interfacial tension for a variety of hydrocarbons with mercury. Since with these hydrocarbons $\gamma_2 = \gamma_2{}^d$, there is only one unknown in the equation, $\gamma_1{}^d$, the dispersion force component of the surface tension of mercury. Table I shows the results of fitting known values of surface and interfacial tension into Equation 1 for a series of ten different hydrocarbons with mercury at 20° C. Although the value of $\gamma_{Hg}{}^d$ is very sensitive to differences in interfacial tension, this value is seen to be remarkably consistent with these ten different hydrocarbons, having a standard deviation of only 3.5%.

A similar test of the equation using the surface and interfacial tensions of several hydrocarbons with water is shown in Table II. The values of $\gamma_{H_2O}{}^d$ obtained by the different hydrocarbons at 20° C. average 21.8 dynes per cm. with a standard deviation of 0.7 dynes per cm. or about 3%. This close agreement of the values of $\gamma_{Hg}{}^d$ and $\gamma_{H_2O}{}^d$ derived from interfacial tensions with a variety of hydrocarbons illustrates the usefulness of the concept of $\gamma^d$ and of the model which leads to Equation 1. This also demonstrates that with Equation 1 we can calculate interfacial tensions between water or mercury and any saturated hydrocarbon of known surface tension.

One may also use the values of $\gamma_{H_2O}{}^d$ and $\gamma_{Hg}{}^d$ in Equation 1 to calculate the interfacial tension between water and mercury on the assumption that the interaction between these two liquids is entirely due to London dispersion forces. The calculated value is 424.8 dynes per cm. with a standard deviation of 4.4 dynes per cm.; this agrees very well with the best experimental values of 426–7 dynes per cm. This result

is evidence that the interaction between water and mercury is almost entirely due to dispersion force interactions, and therefore the dipole–metal image forces are comparatively very weak.

### Calculation of Spreading Coefficients

The spreading coefficient of oil on water is given by the equation

$$S = \gamma_W - (\gamma_O + \gamma_{OW})$$

If we substitute Equation 1 into the above expression:

$$S = 2\sqrt{\gamma_O\gamma_W{}^d} - 2\gamma_O \qquad (6)$$

This equation holds for pure hydrocarbons and shows that the spreading coefficient of an oil on water is a single-valued function of the surface tension of the oil. However, for the case of mixed oils, where there is some degree of adsorption at either the surface or the interface, the results are slightly modified. In Figure 2 we see the results obtained with pure hydrocarbons and some obtained with mixed hydrocarbons. If aromatics are present, the interfacial tension is lowered and the points fall below the predicted line. However, if there are no aromatics present and there is a variety of saturates, the low molecular weight saturates give a low value of the surface tension and the spreading coefficients are seen to fall above the line.

### Calculation of Contact Angles

The Young equation for the contact angle $\theta$ of a liquid $L$ on a plane surface $S$ is

$$\gamma_L \cos\theta = \gamma_S - \gamma_{LS} - \pi_e \qquad (7)$$

where $\pi_e$ is the equilibrium film pressure of adsorbed vapor on the solid surface. For solid–liquid systems interacting by dispersion forces, one can use Equation 1 to predict $\gamma_{LS}$:

$$\gamma_L \cos\theta = -\gamma_L + 2\sqrt{\gamma_L{}^d\gamma_S{}^d} - \pi_e \qquad (8)$$

For the contact angles of a series of liquids on a given solid, such as measured by Zisman (37), where $\gamma_L > \gamma_S$ and consequently (as explained later) $\pi_e$ is zero:

$$\cos\theta = -1 + 2\sqrt{\gamma_S{}^d}\left(\frac{\sqrt{\gamma_L{}^d}}{\gamma_L}\right) \qquad (9)$$

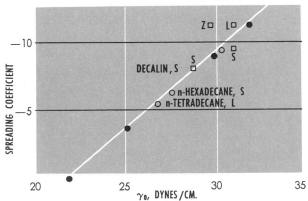

*Figure 2. Relation of spreading coefficient to surface tension of oils. The circles represent pure hydrocarbons, the squares refined oils; Z refers to measurements made by W. A. Zisman, L by I. Langmuir, S by W. M. Sawyer. The open circle at about 31 dynes/cm. is for decalin, measured by Sawyer*

**TABLE II. DETERMINATION OF $\gamma_1{}^d$ FOR WATER**

(Ergs/Sq. Cm. at 20° C.)

| Hydrocarbon (No. 2) | $\gamma_2$ | $\gamma_{12}$ | $\gamma_1{}^d$ |
|---|---|---|---|
| n-Hexane | 18.4 | 51.1 | 21.8 |
| n-Heptane | 20.4 | 50.2 | 22.6 |
| n-Octane | 21.8 | 50.8 | 22.0 |
| n-Decane | 23.9 | 51.2 | 21.6 |
| n-Tetradecane | 25.6 | 52.2 | 20.8 |
| Cyclohexane | 25.5 | 50.2 | 22.7 |
| Decalin | 29.9 | 51.4 | 22.0 |
| White oil (25°) | 28.9 | 51.3 | 21.3 |
| Average | | | 21.8 ± 0.7 |

$\gamma_1 = 72.8$ ergs/sq. cm. at 20° C.
*See Reference 11.*

A plot of $\cos \theta$ vs. $\sqrt{\gamma_L^d}/\gamma_L$ should give a straight line with origin at $\cos \theta = -1$ and with slope $2\sqrt{\gamma_s^d}$. Since the origin is fixed, one contact angle measurement is sufficient to determine the dispersion force component of the surface energy of the solid ($\gamma_s^d$).

Some comment should be made on the reasons for predicting that $\pi_e$ is zero when high energy liquids are brought in contact with low energy solids which have only dispersion force interactions (such as waxes and hydrocarbon polymers). The basic reason for this assumption is that all theoretical and experimental evidence predicts that adsorption of high energy material cannot reduce the surface energy of a low energy material. For example, the surface tension of a liquid hydrocarbon is never reduced by adsorbing water; this point has been verified by experiment. The fact that a given liquid has a contact angle greater than zero degrees on a given low energy solid is evidence that the liquid is a higher energy liquid and therefore $\pi_e$ should be zero. This rule holds for all solids that interact by dispersion force only. It does not hold for high energy solids such as metals or graphite; water doesn't wet these solids but it does adsorb and produce appreciable values of $\pi_e$. The solids on which water produces film pressure $\pi_e$ have surface energies considerably in excess of water.

Zisman and co-workers at the Naval Research Laboratory have accumulated extensive tables of contact angle measurements on low energy solids (37). For each solid surface the contact angles of many liquids have been determined. Many of the liquids are hydrocarbons or esters consisting largely of hydrocarbon structures. When these data are plotted according to Equation 9 as in Figure 3, they give a simple fan of straight lines with common origin, for Equation 9 has only a single parameter (the slope $2\sqrt{\gamma_s^d}$). Here $\gamma_s^d$ is the dispersion force contribution to the surface free energy of the solid, rather than the total surface free energy. This is a most useful concept, for this is a quantitative measure of the available energy of this solid surface for interaction with adjacent media.

Zisman and co-workers plot $\cos \theta$ vs. $\gamma_L$ and the value of $\gamma_L$ at the intercept where $\cos \theta = 1$ is termed the critical surface tension for wetting ($\gamma_c$). If $\gamma_c$ for a given solid has been determined with liquids having only dispersion force interactions (such as hydrocarbons), it equals $\gamma_s^d$, unless long extrapolations have been made. The plot of $\cos \theta$ vs. $\gamma_L$ gives two-parameter straight lines at best and sometimes extrapolation of such lines obtained with a homologous series of hydrocarbons predicts $\cos \theta$ for water $< -1$ and $\cos \theta$ for mercury as low as $-20$ (14). In Figure 3 the value of $\gamma_s^d$ obtained with liquid hydrocarbons on paraffin wax predicts the contact angle of water to be $111°$, in excellent agreement with the experimental $108°–112°$ values (8, 37). On the other hand $\cos \theta$ for mercury is predicted to be $-0.8$ whereas $-0.9$ is observed; it is possible that some wax spread on mercury resulting in a decrease in surface tension and therefore too high a contact angle.

It is also of interest that $\gamma_s^d$ values can be obtained by other measurements such as heats or free energies of immersion or adsorption (as shown later). Thus Equation 9 can be used to predict contact angles quite accurately without any adjustable parameter. For example, Graham's recent adsorption studies of argon and nitrogen on polypropylene predict $\gamma_s^d$ to be 26–28.5 dynes/cm. for this solid at $78°$ to $90°$ K. At room temperature $\gamma_s^d$ should be slightly less; since the surface tension of any liquid hydrocarbon is exactly proportional to the fourth power of the density over a wide temperature range, this principle can predict changes in $\gamma_s^d$ with temperature.

There have been many arguments in the literature against the use of contact angle as a thermodynamic quantity and against the use of the Young equation; since Equations 8 and 9 can be used to calculate contact angles from other thermodynamic measurements, the contact angle is established as a true thermodynamic quantity. Some $\gamma_s^d$ values obtained from contact angle measurements are shown in Table III.

**Calculation of Free Energy of Adsorption of Vapors on Solid**

In most studies of physical adsorption of vapors on solids the adsorbates are nitrogen, argon, or hydrocarbons which interact internally and externally by London dispersion forces. Consequently these interactions can be related quantitatively to $\gamma_s^d$ for the adsorbent and $\gamma_L^d$ for the adsorbate. The easiest relation is obtained when the adsorbate is in equilibrium with liquid adsorbate; under these conditions the total reduction in surface energy of the solid resulting

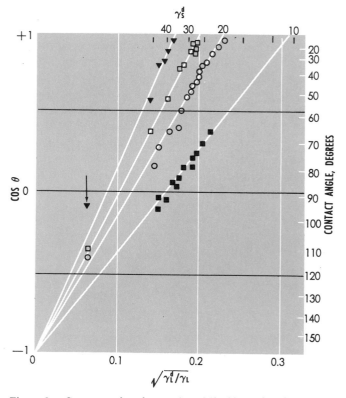

*Figure 3. Contact angles of a number of liquids on four low energy surfaces. Triangles refer to polyethylene, open squares to paraffin wax, open circles to $C_{36}H_{74}$, and black squares to fluorododecanoic acid monolayers on platinum. All points below arrow are contact angles with water*

## TABLE III. VALUES OF $\gamma_S{}^d$ OF LOW ENERGY SOLIDS FROM CONTACT ANGLES

| | |
|---|---|
| $\phi$-Dodecanoic acid on Pt | 10.4 ergs/sq. cm. |
| $\phi$-Decanoic acid on Pt | 13.1 |
| Polyhexafluoropropylene (HFP) | 18.0 |
| Polytetrafluoroethylene (TFE) | 19.5 |
| $n$-$C_{36}H_{74}$ wax crystal | 21.0 |
| $n$-Octadecylamine on Pt | 22.1 |
| Paraffin wax | 25.5 |
| Polytrifluoromonochloroethylene (Kel-F) | 30.8 |
| Polyethylene | 35.0 |
| Polystyrene | 44.0 |

from adsorption is often referred to as $\pi_e$, the equilibrium spreading pressure of the adsorbed film. Harkins (19) has demonstrated that

$$\pi_e = \gamma_S - (\gamma_L + \gamma_{SL}) \qquad (10)$$

If we substitute Equation 1 into 10 we obtain

$$\pi_e = 2\sqrt{\gamma_S{}^d\gamma_L{}^d} - 2\gamma_L \qquad (11)$$

$$\gamma_S{}^d = (\pi_e + 2\gamma_L)^2/4\gamma_L{}^d \qquad (12)$$

It is of interest to compare values of $\gamma_S{}^d$ obtained from $\pi_e$ determinations in adsorption studies with values of $\gamma_S{}^d$ obtained by contact angle measurement. Recent adsorption studies by Graham (16) give $\pi_e$ values of 12 and 13 ergs per sq. cm. for nitrogen ($\gamma_L$ — 10.5 ergs per sq. cm.) and argon ($\gamma_L = 11.9$ ergs per sq. cm.) on polypropylene; with Equation 12 these data give $\gamma_S{}^d$ values of 26 and 28.5 ergs per sq. cm., respectively. These are very reasonable values, as can be seen by comparison with Table III. Another comparison is available with graphite, where various measurements of $\pi_e$ (see Table IV) give $\gamma_S{}^d$ values averaging 122 ergs per sq. cm. These compare with the 109 ergs per sq. cm. obtained with Equation 8 using the contact angle of water (85.7°) (8) and $\pi_e$ of water on graphite (19 ergs per sq. cm.) (19).

Some additional calculations of $\gamma_S{}^d$ with Equation 12 using $\pi_e$ measurements from the literature are shown in Table IV. The $\gamma_S{}^d$ values obtained with various adsorbates on a given adsorbent are seen to agree well.

Table IV is a useful guide in comparing the adsorbent properties of materials. All of the materials listed have higher $\gamma^d$ values than any organic substance measured so far. This means that hydrocarbons will adsorb more strongly on any of these materials than on organic solids. Of the materials listed graphite is the strongest adsorbent ($\gamma_S{}^d = 122$) with tin oxide and titanium oxide (anatase) second best. Surprisingly silica, a favorite adsorbent, is seen to be a much weaker adsorbent than these ($\gamma_S{}^d = 78$), about the same as barium sulfate. There is a rather wide spread for the metals: copper (60); silver (74); lead, tin, and iron (100); and, of course, mercury (200). In the adsorption studies on these metals (21), $\pi_e$ values were determined first on metal powders with oxidized surfaces and then after hydrogen reduction; there was little change but $\pi_e$ values always decreased. The values of $\pi_e$ (in ergs per sq. cm.) went from 33 to 29 ($\gamma_S{}^d = 67$ to 60) for copper, from 38 to 37 ($\gamma_S{}^d = 76$ to 74) for silver, from 51 to 49 ($\gamma_S{}^d = 103$ to 99) for lead, and from 54 to 53 ($\gamma_S{}^d = 110$ to 108) for iron. These values indicate that copper should be the more easily outgassed (of hydrocarbons) in a vacuum system, for it should have the weaker interaction with adsorbed hydrocarbon vapors.

The study of adsorption potentials of metals and oxides should eventually be done on ultraclean surfaces of known orientation. The values calculated from $\pi_e$ measurements of adsorbed vapors on powdered solids are an average of several crystal faces and very probably have a high density of dislocations; however, there is every reason to believe these surfaces to be very clean by virtue of their very large surface area. Perhaps the contact angle method in ultraclean vacuum equipment will prove better for confining measurements exclusively to certain crystal faces.

Table IV shows $\gamma_S{}^d$ values measured at 78° and 90° K., 0° and 25° C. As mentioned earlier these should be easily related by the relation of $\gamma^d$ to the density of the material. One useful relation is the well known dependence of the surface tension upon the fourth power of the density of hydrocarbons (1). This does not

## TABLE IV. VALUES OF $\gamma_S{}^d$ OBTAINED FROM $\pi_e$ MEASUREMENTS FOR ADSORBED VAPORS

| Adsorbent | Adsorbate | Reference | Temperature | $\pi_e$ | $\gamma_S{}^d$, Ergs/Sq. Cm. |
|---|---|---|---|---|---|
| Polypropylene | Nitrogen | (16) | 78° K. | 12 | 26 |
| | Argon | (16) | 90° K. | 13 | 28.5 |
| Graphite | Nitrogen | (29) | 78° K. | 51 | 123 |
| | $n$-Heptane | (3, 6, 20) | 25° C. | 63, 56, 58 | 132, 115, 120 |
| Copper | $n$-Heptane | (21) | 25° C. | 29 | 60 |
| Silver | $n$-Heptane | (21) | 25° C. | 37 | 74 |
| Lead | $n$-Heptane | (21) | 25° C. | 49 | 99 |
| Tin | $n$-Heptane | (27) | 25° C. | 50 | 101 |
| Iron | $n$-Heptane | (21) | 25° C. | 53 | 108 |
| | Argon | (2) | 90° K. | 47 | 106 |
| | Nitrogen | (2) | 78° K. | 40 | 89 |
| Ferric oxide | $n$-Heptane | (21) | 25° C. | 54 | 107 |
| Anatase ($TiO_2$) | $n$-Heptane | (26) | 25° C. | 46 | 92 |
| | Butane | (26) | 0° C. | 43 | 89 |
| | Nitrogen | (26) | 78° K | 56 | 141 |
| Silica | $n$-Heptane | (6) | 25° C. | 39 | 78 |
| Stannic oxide | $n$-Heptane | (3) | 25° C. | 54 | 111 |
| Barium sulfate | $n$-Heptane | (6) | 25° C. | 38 | 76 |

agree with Equation 3, however, for here we have calculated an 8/3 power dependence on density. Of course Equation 3 does not include any configurational entropy change but only a concentration entropy effect. Thus for many solids the 8/3 power may be the more appropriate. However, let us compare these estimates for graphite, iron, and silver. If $\gamma_s{}^d$ is measured at 78° K. with liquid nitrogen, it must be decreased when adjusted to 25° C. The fourth power rule gives a greater decrease than the 8/3 power rule; for graphite $-2.2\%$ vs. $-1.6\%$, for iron $-2.7\%$ vs. $-2.1\%$, and for silver $-4.3\%$ vs. $-3.1\%$. These values are small; however, for soft organic materials much larger decreases may be expected.

### Calculation of Heats of Adsorption

The integral heat of adsorption $\Delta H°_{ads}$ of vapor $L$ on adsorbent $S$ at $p/p_0 = 1$ is easily derived from Equation 11:

$$\Delta F°_{ads} = 2\gamma_L - 2\sqrt{\gamma_s{}^d\gamma_L{}^d}$$

$$\Delta H°_{ads} = \Delta F°_{ads} - T\left(\frac{d\Delta F°_{ads}}{dT}\right) = 2\gamma_L - 2\sqrt{\gamma_s{}^d\gamma_L{}^d} -$$

$$2T\left(\frac{d\gamma_L}{dT} - \sqrt{\gamma_L{}^d}\frac{d\sqrt{\gamma_s{}^d}}{dT} - \sqrt{\gamma_s{}^d}\frac{d\sqrt{\gamma_L{}^d}}{dT}\right) \quad (13)$$

For systems of known $\gamma_s{}^d$, $\gamma_L{}^d$, and their temperature coefficients, $\Delta H°_{ads}$ is easily calculable. Temperature coefficients of $\gamma_L$ are normally available, but in the case of polar liquids and solids the temperature coefficients of $\gamma_L{}^d$ and $\gamma_s{}^d$ must be estimated from the fourth power of the density. Since these are small, errors arising from such estimates must be even smaller.

From measured values of $\Delta H°_{ads}$ with reference adsorbents (having only dispersion force interactions) one can also calculate $\gamma_s{}^d$. For example, Isirikyan and Kiselev (25) have determined $\Delta H°_{ads}$ for n-hexane on Graphon, a graphitized carbon black. From their values of the area per molecule occupied by n-hexane (54 A.) and of 5.0 kcal. per mole for $\Delta H°_{ads}$, Equation 13 gives $\gamma_s{}^d = 108$ ergs per sq. cm. for Graphon. This compares very well with the 109 ergs per sq. cm. obtained from contact angles on graphite crystals and the 122 ergs per sq. cm. obtained from $\pi_e$ measurements on Graphon powder.

### Calculation of Heats of Immersion

The calorimetrically obtained heats of immersion of powdered solids in aqueous and nonaqueous liquids are a very good means of determining solid–liquid interactions; these values are calculable from the free energy of immersion ($\Delta F_i$) in the same manner as for the heats of adsorption:

$$\Delta F_i = \gamma_{SL} - \gamma_S = \gamma_L - 2\sqrt{\gamma_s{}^d\gamma_L{}^d}$$

$$\Delta H_i = \Delta F_i - T\left(\frac{d\Delta F_i}{dT}\right) = \gamma_L - 2\sqrt{\gamma_L{}^d\gamma_s{}^d} -$$

$$T\left(\frac{d\gamma_L}{dT} - 2\sqrt{\gamma_L{}^d}\frac{d\sqrt{\gamma_s{}^d}}{dT} - 2\sqrt{\gamma_s{}^d}\frac{d\sqrt{\gamma_L{}^d}}{dT}\right) \quad (14)$$

This equation can be evaluated from the same information needed for Equation 12, and $\gamma_s{}^d$ values can be readily determined for solids immersed in reference liquids.

Figure 4 shows calculated heats of immersion for graphite and rutile ($TiO_2$) in saturated hydrocarbon liquids for a range of $\gamma_s{}^d$ values. The value of $\Delta H_i$ is shown to be rather sensitive to $\gamma_s{}^d$ but not very sensitive to $\gamma_L{}^d$. Thus $\Delta H_i$ for hexane, heptane, and octane should be nearly identical, as was observed by Healey (22) for rutile (shown as squares), though not for graphite (shown as circles). These observed values of heats of immersion for graphite indicate that $\gamma_s{}^d$ lies between 97 and 120 dynes per cm., which agrees well with the 109 obtained by contact angle measurement, the 108 obtained by heat of adsorption, and the 115 to 132 obtained by $\pi_e$ determinations for adsorbed vapors.

It is interesting to note with two different forms of titanium dioxide the high and reproducible values of $\gamma_s{}^d$ for rutile (139 to 148 ergs per sq. cm.), as compared to the lower values (about 90 ergs per sq. cm.) obtained by $\pi_e$ measurements on anatase.

### Calculation of Long Range Attractive Forces

As has been shown by London (28) and Hamaker (17), dispersion forces operate over longer distances than other intermolecular forces. Between flat plates separated by distance $d$ in vacuum the attractive forces (in dynes per sq. cm.) is $A/6\pi d^3$, where $A$ is the attractive constant (in ergs). The value of $A$ can be calculated by summing the pair potentials ($\mu$) between volume elements having polarizability $\alpha$, ionization potential $I$, and distance of separation $r$:

$$\mu_{11} = \frac{-3\ \alpha_1{}^2 I_1}{4\ r_{11}{}^6}$$

This summation by Hamaker (17) gives

$$A_1 = \frac{3}{4}\ \pi^2\ N_1{}^2\ \alpha_1{}^2\ I_1 \quad (15)$$

where $N$ is the number of interacting volume elements per cubic centimeter.

When particles of substance 2 are immersed in substance 1, according to Hamaker

$$A_{12} = \sqrt{A_1{}^2} - 2\sqrt{A_1 A_2}\left(\frac{2\sqrt{I_1 I_2}}{I_1 + I_2}\right) + \sqrt{A_2{}^2} \quad (16)$$

As pointed out by Vold (35), when $I_1$ and $I_2$ are not too different

$$A_{12} = (\sqrt{A_1} - \sqrt{A_2})^2 \quad (17)$$

The evaluation of these interaction parameters is not simple, however. The use of ionization potential is an approximation in the first place, but to obtain suitable values for ionization potential and polarizability for a wide variety of solids and liquids is nearly impossible. Another means is needed for evaluating the attractive force constant $A$. It now appears that this can be done experimentally by using the dispersion force contribution to surface free energy ($\gamma^d$). An equation for

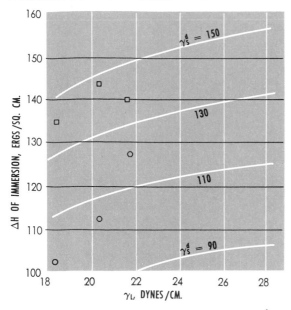

*Figure 4. Dependence of the heats of immersion on $\gamma_S{}^d$ and $\gamma_L$. Squares refer to rutile, circles to graphite*

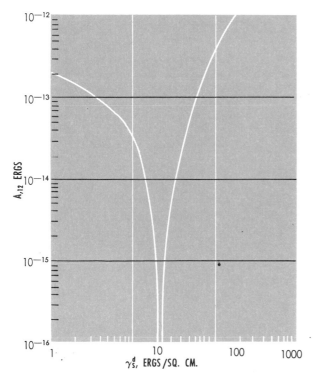

*Figure 5. Long range attractive force constant for solids suspended in water at 20° C., as given by Equation 19*

**AUTHOR** *Frederick M. Fowkes is Director of Research, Sprague Electric Company, North Adams, Mass.*

evaluating $\gamma^d$ by summation of pair potentials has already been developed (Equation 3).

$$\gamma_1{}^d = \frac{-\pi\ N_1{}^2\ \alpha_1{}^2\ I_1}{8\ r_{11}{}^2}$$

It can be seen that substitution of the above equation into Equation 15 cancels out the polarizability $\alpha$ and the ionization potential $I$, which are so difficult to obtain experimentally. The result is

$$A_1 = 6\pi\ r_{11}{}^2\ \gamma_1{}^d \qquad (18)$$

and for two-phase systems where $I_1$ and $I_2$ are not too different

$$A_{12} = 6\pi\ r_{11}{}^2\ (\sqrt{\gamma_1{}^d} - \sqrt{\gamma_2{}^d})^2 \qquad (19)$$

For water and systems with volume elements such as oxide ions, metal atoms, $CH_2$ or $CH$ groups which have nearly the same size, $6\pi r_{11}{}^2 = 1.44 \times 10^{-14}$. Figure 5 shows $A_{12}$ for such materials (2) immersed in water (1) as a function of the $\gamma_2{}^d$ values which have been determined independently, and are listed in Table V.

Obviously $A_{12}$ drops to zero at $\gamma_1{}^d = \gamma_2{}^d$, which is 21.8 ergs per sq. cm. for water, 37 ergs per sq. cm. for glycerol, etc. Three well justified experimental points are found to fall on the predicted curve; one is for arachidic acid solutions (30) where $A_{12} = 3$ to $8 \times 10^{-15}$ and $\gamma_2{}^d$ should be between 25 and 30 ergs per sq. cm., another is the 5 to $6 \times 10^{-14}$ measured for polystyrene by Watillon of Brussels (private communication), and the other is 3 to $5 \times 10^{-13}$ measured for silver iodide (31) where the $\gamma_s{}^d$ has yet to be measured but probably is 80 to 100 ergs per sq. cm., just below the metal oxides.

It is possible to take experimentally determined values of $A_{12}$ from the literature and calculate $\gamma^d$ values from these. For instance, in the paper of Reerink (31) there are listed some values obtained with selenium ($A_{12} = 2 \times 10^{-13}$) and with gold ($A_{12} = 1$ to $6 \times 10^{-12}$). These would correspond to $\gamma_2{}^d$ values of 72 ergs per sq. cm. for selenium and 60 to 120 ergs per sq. cm. for gold. In both cases we have no check yet on the $\gamma_s{}^d$ values by other methods, but the magnitude is very reasonable.

**TABLE V.** $\gamma_2{}^d$ **AND** $A_{12}$ **IN WATER FOR VARIOUS SUBSTANCES AT 20° C.**

| Substance (No. 2) | $\gamma_2{}^d$ (Exptl.), Ergs/Sq. Cm. | $A_{12}$ Calcd. Ergs |
|---|---|---|
| Polyhexafluoropropylene | 18 | $2 \times 10^{-15}$ |
| Polytetrafluoroethylene | 19.5 | $8 \times 10^{-16}$ |
| Paraffin Wax | 25.5 | $2 \times 10^{-15}$ |
| Polymonochlorotrifluoroethylene | 30.8 | $1 \times 10^{-14}$ |
| Polyethylene | 35 | $2 \times 10^{-14}$ |
| Polystyrene | 44 | $5 \times 10^{-14}$ |
| Copper | 60 | $1.4 \times 10^{-13}$ |
| Silver | 76 | $2.5 \times 10^{-13}$ |
| Anatase (TiO$_2$) | 91 | $3.5 \times 10^{-13}$ |
| Iron | 98 | $4 \times 10^{-13}$ |
| Lead | 99 | $4 \times 10^{-13}$ |
| Tin | 101 | $4 \times 10^{-13}$ |
| Ferric oxide | 107 | $4.5 \times 10^{-13}$ |
| Graphite | 110 | $5 \times 10^{-13}$ |
| Stannic oxide | 118 | $5.5 \times 10^{-13}$ |
| Silica | 123 | $6 \times 10^{-13}$ |
| Rutile (TiO$_2$) | 143 | $8 \times 10^{-13}$ |
| Mercury | 200 | $1.3 \times 10^{-12}$ |

### Evaluation of $\gamma_L^d$ for Polar Liquids

It has already been shown how the dispersion force contribution to the surface free energy ($\gamma_L^d$) can be determined for polar organic liquids from interfacial tension measurements between polar liquids and reference (saturated hydrocarbon) liquids. Although this procedure works very well for water and mercury, it is not satisfactory for most polar organic liquids because they are too soluble in the reference hydrocarbons. One way out of this situation is to use solid hydrocarbons as the reference phase and determine $\gamma_L^d$ from contact angle measurements. Some of these are illustrated in Figure 6. In this figure, nine reference solids have been used. The $\gamma_S^d$ values of these solids have been determined with liquid hydrocarbons or with esters which are largely hydrocarbon in nature. By plotting the contact angles of polar liquids on the lines representing the standard reference solids, one obtains from the abscissa the value of $\sqrt{\gamma_L^d}/\gamma_L$. It can be seen from this figure that the measured values are reasonably reproducible. In Figure 6 a calculated scale of $\gamma_L^d$ is inserted below the arrow for each liquid. Thus in the case of water, a scale from 15–30 ergs per sq. cm. is shown and the experimental points for the contact angle of water are shown to predict that $\gamma_L^d$ for water is between 20–25 ergs per sq. cm. This compares well with the 21.8 ergs per sq. cm. obtained from the interfacial tension measurements against liquid hydrocarbons, but shows that the contact angle method is not as precise as the interfacial tension method for measuring $\gamma_L^d$. A summary of such measurements, including the standard deviation of $\gamma_L^d$, is shown in Table VI.

It is of especial interest that for large organic molecules with small polar substituents (such as tricresyl phosphate, $\alpha$-bromonaphthalene, trichlorobiphenyl, and polydimethyl siloxanes) the $\gamma_L^d$ values are not distinguishably different from $\gamma_L$. Although there must be dipole-dipole interactions in some of these liquids, the magnitude of this interaction appears to be negligible when using the contact angle method for determining $\gamma_L^d$. If a method with a standard deviation of 1 or 2% were available, these effects should become measurable, but with several polar liquids the contact angle method gives standard deviations (in $\gamma_L^d$) of about 10%. For some polydimethyl siloxanes there is a large number of contact angle measurements available; here the standard deviation in $\gamma_L^d$ is about 3% and it can be seen that the

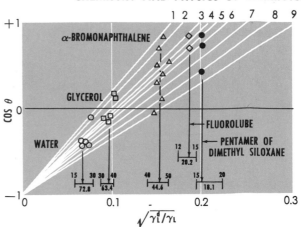

*Figure 6. Method of determining $\gamma_L^d$ of polar liquids by contact angle measurements. Numbers above the grid refer to the following low energy surfaces: 1—polyethylene; 2—Kel-F; 3—paraffin wax; 4—$C_{18}H_{37}NH_2$ monolayer on Pt; 5—$C_{36}H_{74}$; 6—Teflon; 7—polyhexafluoropropylene; 8—$C_9F_{19}COOH$ monolayer on Pt; 9—$C_{11}F_{23}$-COOH monolayer on Pt*

dipole–dipole interaction in this liquid increases the surface energy by 2 ergs per sq. cm. over the 17 ergs per sq. cm. contributed by the dispersion forces.

The $\gamma_L^d$ values for glycerol and formamide (37 and 39.5 ergs per sq. cm., respectively) show that in these liquids the dispersion force interactions are much stronger than in water. In both liquids the dispersion force interactions are somewhat stronger than the sum of the dipole and hydrogen bonding interactions.

### Evaluation of Polar Interfacial Interactions at Liquid/Liquid Interfaces

One of the virtues of expanding surface and interfacial energies into a series of terms for each type of molecular interaction is that we can now evaluate quantitatively the $\gamma^d$ terms for any liquid or solid and then compare these with the total energy observed by interfacial tension, contact angle, and free energies or heats of adsorption or of immersion. In this way we can determine the magnitude (in ergs per sq. cm.) of the polar interactions at these interfaces.

There are many experimental values in the literature for the interfacial tension between mercury and polar organic liquids. Some of these are listed in Table VII. Values of $\gamma_L^d$ are assumed to equal $\gamma_L$; as shown in the previous section, this is a reasonable assumption for many polar organic liquids. For each polar organic liquid the interfacial tension ($\gamma_{12}$) is shown, and this is compared with the interfacial tension ($\gamma_{12}^d$) calculated as if there were only dispersion force interactions. The difference is shown in the right-hand column; a positive value means that there is an interaction between mercury and the organic liquid over and above the dispersion force interaction. Because of difficulties in measuring interfacial tensions with mercury, differences of less than 10 ergs per sq. cm. are not considered significant.

The interactions of mercury with polar organic liquids may be summarized as follows. In all cases the dis-

**TABLE VI. EVALUATION OF $\gamma_L^d$ FOR POLAR ORGANIC LIQUIDS FROM CONTACT ANGLE MEASUREMENTS ON REFERENCE SOLIDS**

(Ergs/Sq. Cm. at 20° C.)

|  | $\gamma_L$ | $\gamma_L^d$ ($\pm$ *std. dev.*) |
|---|---|---|
| Tricresyl phosphate | 40.9 | 39.2 $\pm$ 4 |
| $\alpha$-Bromonaphthalene | 44.6 | 47 $\pm$ 7 |
| Trichlorobiphenyl | 45.3 | 44 $\pm$ 6 |
| Methylene iodide | 50.8 | 48.5 $\pm$ 9 |
| Glycerol | 63.4 | 37.0 $\pm$ 4 |
| Formamide | 58.2 | 39.5 $\pm$ 7 |
| Dimethyl siloxanes | 19.0 | 16.9 $\pm$ 0.5 |
| Fluorolube FCD-330 | 20.2 | 14.0 $\pm$ 0.2 |

## TABLE VII. ENERGY OF MERCURY–ORGANIC LIQUID INTERACTION IN EXCESS OF DISPERSION FORCES

(Ergs/Sq. Cm.²)

| Liquid No. 2 | $\gamma_2$ | $\gamma_{12}{}^d$ | $\gamma_{12}$ | $(\gamma_{12}{}^d - \gamma_{12})$ (Excess Energy) |
|---|---|---|---|---|
| Dichloromethane | 23.0 | 372 | 343 | +29 |
| Chloroform | 27.1 | 364 | 357 | + 7 |
| Carbon tetrachloride | 27.0 | 364 | 359 | + 5 |
| 1,1-Dichloroethane | 24.6 | 368 | 337 | +31 |
| 1,2-Dichloroethane | 32.2 | 357 | 358 | − 1 |
| Chlorobenzene | 33.2 | 354 | 360 | − 6 |
| 1,2-Dibromomethane | 38.7 | 346 | 346 | 0 |
| 1,1,2,2-Tetrabromomethane | 49.7 | 334 | 293 | +41 |
| Bromobenzene | 36.3 | 350 | 350 | 0 |
| Methyl iodide | 30.1 | 359 | 304 | +55 |
| Ethyl iodide | 28.2 | 362 | 322 | +40 |
| Ethyl mercaptan | 23.2 | 370 | 314 | +56 |
| Nitrobenzene | 43.9 | 340 | 350 | −10 |
| Nitroethane | 32.2 | 356 | 306 | +50 |
| Aniline | 42.9 | 341 | 341 | 0 |
| Diisoamylamine | 24.2 | 369 | 372 | − 3 |
| Diethyl ether | 17.0 | 384 | 379 | + 5 |
| n-Butyl acetate | 25.2 | 367 | 375 | − 8 |
| Methanol | 22.6 | 372 | 383 | −11 |
| Ethanol | 22.7 | 372 | 389 | −17 |
| n-Propanol | 23.8 | 370 | 378 | − 8 |
| n-Butanol | 24.6 | 368 | 375 | − 7 |
| Isobutanol | 23.0 | 371 | 343 | +29 |
| Isopentanol | 25.7 | 366 | 374 | − 8 |
| n-Hexanol | 25.8 | 366 | 372 | − 6 |
| sec-Octanol | 26.5 | 365 | 348 | +17 |
| n-Octanol | 27.5 | 363 | 352 | +11 |
| Cyclopentanol | 32.0 | 356 | 365 | − 9 |
| Acetic acid | 27.8 | 363 | 329 | +34 |
| Valeric acid | 27.3 | 363 | 330 | +33 |
| Undecylinic acid | 30.6 | 358 | 353 | + 5 |
| Oleic acid | 32.5 | 355 | 322 | +33 |

## TABLE VIII. ENERGY OF WATER-ORGANIC LIQUID INTERACTION IN EXCESS OF DISPERSION FORCE INTERACTION

(Ergs/Sq. Cm. at 20° C.)

| Liquid No. 2 | $\gamma_2$ | $\gamma_{12}$ | $\gamma_{12}{}^d$ | Excess | $2\sqrt{\gamma_1{}^d\gamma_2}$ |
|---|---|---|---|---|---|
| Benzene | 28.9 | 35 | 51.5 | +16.5 | 50.2 |
| Toluene | 28.5 | 36.1 | 51.5 | +15.4 | 50.0 |
| Mesitylene | 28.8 | 38.7 | 51.4 | +12.7 | 50.1 |
| Carbon tetrachloride | 26.9 | 45.0 | 51.3 | + 6.3 | 48.4 |
| Carbon tetrabromide | 49.7 | 38.8 | 56.5 | + 6.8 | 66.0 |
| Butyronitrile | 28.1 | 10.4 | 51.3 | +23.2 | 49.6 |
| Aniline | 42.9 | 5.8 | 53.7 | +47.9 | 62.0 |
| Di-n-butylamine | 22.0 | 10.3 | 51.0 | +40.7 | 43.8 |
| Octanoic acid | 27.5 | 8.5 | 51.3 | +42.8 | 49.0 |
| Cyclohexanol | 32.7 | 3.9 | 51.9 | +48.0 | 53.6 |
| Polydimethylsiloxanes[a] | 15.7 | 41.3 | 53.9 | +12.6 | 34.6[b] |
| " | 16.8 | 41.3 | 53.6 | +12.3 | 36.0[b] |
| " | 19.4 | 41.3 | 53.2 | +12.1 | 39.0[b] |

[a] $\gamma_2{}^d$ values estimated as $\gamma_2 - 2$ ergs/sq. cm. (see Table VI). [b] Actually $2\sqrt{\gamma_1{}^d\gamma_2{}^d}$

persion force interactions provide most of the energy of interaction (about 120 ergs per sq. cm.). The strongest polar interactions occur with alkyl iodides, mercaptans, and nitro derivatives (50 ergs per sq. cm.). Mercury also interacts with carboxylic acids (33 ergs per sq. cm.) and to a lesser extent with some alkyl chlorides. Negligible polar interactions occur with organic bases (aniline, diisoamylamine, and diethyl ether). The interactions of aliphatic alcohols are also negligible. It appears that maximum interactions occur with highly polarizable organic molecules, especially those which are electron acceptors. Electron donors appear to have no interaction, and in general the interaction of dipoles with mercury appears negligibly small.

In similar fashion the polar interactions at the interface between polar organic liquids and water can be determined. The accuracy of measurement of interfacial tensions for these systems is very much greater than for mercury, and consequently the significance of differences is much greater. Table VIII shows the observed interfacial tensions and the interfacial tension ($\gamma_{12}{}^d$) calculated by considering only dispersion force interactions at the interface. For all the compounds listed, $\gamma_{12}{}^d$ is significantly greater than $\gamma_{12}$ and the excess is a measure in ergs per sq. cm. of the energy of interaction due to interactions involving various polar interactions. In the case of benzene, toluene, and mesitylene, the polar interaction of water involves a pi-bonding interaction which is shown to result in an interfacial interaction of about 15 ergs per sq. cm. In the case of carbon tetrachloride and carbon tetrabromide, the dipole interaction of water with an induced dipole in the organic phase results in an interaction energy of 6 ergs per sq. cm. In the case of butyronitrile, the dipole–dipole interaction gives rise to an interfacial interaction of 23 ergs per sq. cm., whereas in the case of the silicones the dipole–dipole interaction with water gives rise to an interfacial energy of interaction of 12 ergs per sq. cm. Organic molecules capable of hydrogen bonding (aniline, di-n-butylamine, octanoic acid, and cyclohexanol), have the strongest interactions with water (40–48 ergs per sq. cm.). In all examples studied the dispersion force interaction was the largest single contribution to interfacial attraction, although in the case of the hydrogen-bonded materials the attractive forces resulting from dispersion forces and from hydrogen-bonding are approximately equal.

### Evaluation of Polar Interfacial Attractions at Solid/Liquid Interfaces

The interface between polar organic liquids and high energy solids can be evaluated in the same way we have evaluated the liquid–liquid interface, using the $\gamma_S{}^d$ values determined by free energies and heats of adsorption and from heats of immersion. One method of evaluating the interaction of polar organic molecules with polar inorganic solids is to use $\pi_e$ values determined by adsorption of polar organic vapors on powdered solids (19) according to Equation 11

$$\pi_e = 2\sqrt{\gamma_S{}^d\gamma_L{}^d} - 2\gamma_L$$

The above equation applies only when the interfacial interactions are confined to dispersion forces. If additional interactions occur, $\pi_e$ will be larger. Table IX shows some of the $\pi_e$ determinations (from the literature) involving polar interactions at the liquid–solid interface. The values of dispersion force interactions $(2\sqrt{\gamma_s{}^d\gamma_L{}^d})$ are shown in one column and the adjacent column is headed $\pi_e + 2\gamma_L$. If only dispersion force interactions occur, the value of $\pi_e + \gamma_L$ will equal $2\sqrt{\gamma_s{}^d\gamma_L{}^d}$, but if additional interactions occur, the excess, shown in the last column, is a measure of the polar interaction in ergs per sq. cm.

It can be seen from Table IX that benzene interacts with graphite and with oxides with an interaction energy of 20–25 ergs per sq. cm. in excess of the dispersion force interaction. This is probably due to pi-bonding between the benzene ring and the oxide surface. This interaction can be compared with that already discussed for the interaction between aromatics and water where the pi-bonding results in a 15 ergs per sq. cm. increase in interaction energy. It is a little surprising that benzene interacts more strongly with graphite than predicted by dispersion force interactions. This finding suggests that the surface of graphite was not clean but covered with an oxide film for these measurements. Propanol, which is capable of interaction with oxide surfaces by dipole–dipole interaction, ion–dipole interaction and hydrogen bonding, shows a polar interaction energy (in excess of the dispersion force interaction) of 54–96 ergs per sq. cm. The interactions of water with these oxides is extremely strong and probably results from dipole–dipole interaction, ion–dipole interaction and hydrogen bonding. The polar interaction term is remarkably constant for all four oxygen-containing surfaces (336–368 ergs per sq. cm.) and is very much larger than the dispersion force interaction (94–102 ergs per sq. cm.). The magnitude of this interaction is enormous compared with all other interfacial interactions studied so far.

### Fluorocarbon–Hydrocarbon Interactions

The interaction of fluorocarbons with hydrocarbons in solution is not well understood (23). Their deviations from predictions of solubility are much greater than with other nonelectrolytes. Fluorocarbons are poorer solvents for hydrocarbons than predicted by heats of vaporization; this means that the actual interactions are weaker than predicted. The same is observed at interfaces—for example, a fluorinated lubricating oil was found to have a surface tension of 22.4 dynes per cm. (9). If we assume that the intermolecular forces are entirely dispersion forces ($\gamma_L = \gamma_L{}^d$), then the interfacial tension with water should be 50.3 dynes per cm., according to Equation 1; however, the experimental interfacial tension is 57.7 dynes per cm., which indicates a weaker than predicted interaction with water. If $\gamma_L{}^d$ is calculated with Equation 1 using the interfacial tension of 57.7 dynes per cm. the result is 15.4 dynes per cm. as compared with the experimental $\gamma_L$ of 22.4 dynes per cm. These findings, in good agreement with solution studies, do not explain the discrepancy.

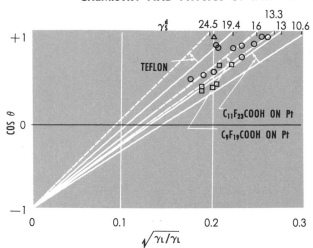

*Figure 7. Contact angles of liquid fluorocarbons on solid fluorocarbons. Solid lines refer to values predicted from $\gamma_L{}^d$ determined with liquid hydrocarbons; dashed lines represent experimental measurements*

Similar findings arise in contact angle studies with solid fluorochemicals (4, 14, 18, 32, 33). Contact angles of hydrocarbons on these surfaces, when graphed as in Figure 3, give very low $\gamma_s{}^d$ intercepts. However, contact angles of highly fluorinated liquids on these surfaces lead to larger $\gamma_s{}^d$ intercepts (Figure 7). One might question which $\gamma_s{}^d$ really involves only dispersion force interactions. It is assumed that the lower value obtained with liquid hydrocarbons is the better measure of dispersion force interaction with all materials other than fluorocarbons and the larger value obtained with liquid fluorocarbons is the proper value to use for predicting interactions with fluorochemicals.

Very similar findings resulted in a contact angle study of a perfluorinated lubricating oil on paraffin wax. The surface tension, $\gamma_L$, was 20.2 dynes per cm., but the contact angles on two wax surfaces gave $\gamma_L{}^d$ values of 13.5 dynes per cm. (see Figure 6).

As discussed earlier in the development of Equation 5, these deviations from predicted values could arise partly from differences in ionization potentials (since fluorocarbons have ionization potentials of about 15 volts as compared with about 10 volts with hydrocarbons) or from the disparity in size of volume elements acting at the interface. As mentioned earlier, the $CF_2$ group is somewhat larger than the $CH_2$ group, and consequently the geometric mean approximation may be slightly in error (see Equations 4 and 5). The magnitude of difference shown in Figure 7 is 3–5 ergs per sq. cm. which corresponds to 20 to 25% of the interaction energy. This difference seems larger than one might explain on the basis of differences in ionization potential or differences in size of volume elements, or both.

### Application to Problems in Adhesion

The foregoing tables and discussion give a background which should be useful in deciding what molecules or chemical groups should bond most strongly to a given substrate, and also what contaminants are most likely to be strongly bonded to surfaces or are capable of penetrating into interfaces.

The predictions of Zisman (*38*) on the importance of wettability in adhesion have been recently confirmed by Sharpe and Schonhorn (*34*) for adhesion to low-energy polymers. The wettability of a solid, $S$, by a liquid, $L$, is predicted by the spreading coefficient, $S$

$$S = \gamma_S - (\gamma_L + \gamma_{SL})$$

and in the case of solid–liquid systems which can interact only by dispersion forces, then

$$S = \sqrt{\gamma_L^d \gamma_S^d} - 2\gamma_L$$

With this equation, we can determine how large a value of $\gamma_S^d$ is required for various liquids to spread on solids when only dispersion force interactions occur. For example, with water positive values of $S$ (which indicates that spontaneous spreading occurs) will result only when $\gamma_S^d$ exceeds 243 dynes per cm. We can see from Table IV that water will not spread on graphite or on any of the oxide-free metal surfaces listed in that table. We can also see from the values in Table VI that with formamide positive values of $S$ will occur only when $\gamma_S^d$ exceeds 85 dynes/cm. Formamide should spread on graphite, lead, tin, and iron, not on copper or silver.

The above predictions on the nonwettability of pure metal surfaces by water have been verified by experiment. White (*36*) of the Bell Telephone Laboratories has found that in ultraclean vacuum systems water will not wet gold. He found that water did wet gold oxide prepared by anodization in nitric acid; however, a heat treatment in the vacuum system removed the unstable gold oxide, and the resulting clean surface was no longer water-wet. Similar results have been obtained by R. A. Erb (*7*) at the Franklin Institute who has found that with rigorously clean metal surfaces the contact angles of water range from 50–85° for rhenium, silver, platinum, palladium, and gold. These findings, made in equipment designed for providing clean metal surfaces, appear to conflict with some observations made in laboratory air. Various investigators have found that freshly "cleaned" metals are immediately wet by water in laboratory air. The type of cleaning used in these experiments is generally to rub a powder (of no particular cleanliness) on these surfaces. It appears that these crude experiments are subject to very much more contamination than those specifically designed for the elimination of adsorbed materials. It is very educational to note that in the case of mercury–water interfaces where exact measurements are available, the adsorption of a monolayer of benzene occurs at the mercury–water interface with a 30 ergs per sq. cm. reduction of interfacial tension (*11*). This decrease is easily calculated and has been experimentally observed. This reduction can increase the spreading coefficient of water on mercury from a value of −14 ergs per cm. to +16 ergs per sq. cm., providing the benzene is present in such small amounts that it is confined to the mercury–water interface. Additional benzene in the system would tend to reduce the surface tension of mercury and prevent spreading. Thus, small amounts of contamination (especially by aromatic hydrocarbons) can be clearly predicted to have the surprising effect of promoting the wetting of metal surfaces by water.

The enhancement of the attractive forces between liquids and solids resulting from hydrogen bonding or dipole interactions are indicated quantitatively from the values shown in Tables VII, VIII, and IX. At interfaces between organic solids having hydroxyl groups in the surface and liquids having similar groups the attraction can be enhanced (over and above the dispersion forces) by about 40 ergs per sq. cm. as shown in Table VIII for the interface between water and butyronitrile, or between water and di-*n*-butylamine. Similarly, the enhancement of the attraction of polar substances to metal surfaces (over and above the dispersion forces) may be estimated by the value shown for the mercury interface with polar organic liquids in Table VII. The much stronger bonds established between polar liquids and ionic solids are shown in Table IX.

Consider adhesion of materials to solid fluorocarbons.

### TABLE IX. POLAR INTERFACIAL INTERACTIONS AT SOLID-LIQUID INTERFACES

| Solid | Liquid | $2\sqrt{\gamma_S^d \gamma_L^d}$ | $\pi_e + 2\gamma_L$ | Excess |
|-------|--------|--------|--------|--------|
| Graphite | *n*-Heptane (std.) | 96 | 96 | 0 |
| | Benzene | 114 | 134 | 20 |
| Anatase | *n*-Heptane (std.) | 99 | 99 | 0 |
| | Benzene | 116 | 142 | 26 |
| | *n*-Propanol | 106 | 162 | 56 |
| | Water | 102 | 446 | 344 |
| Silica | *n*-Heptane (std.) | 100 | 100 | 0 |
| | Benzene | 118 | 138 | 20 |
| | Acetone | 98 | 156 | 58 |
| | *n*-Propanol | 98 | 182 | 84 |
| | Water | 94 | 462 | 368 |
| BaSO₄ | *n*-Heptane (std.) | 99 | 99 | 0 |
| | *n*-Propanol | 106 | 202 | 96 |
| | Water | 102 | 464 | 362 |
| SnO₂ | *n*-Heptane (std.) | 98 | 98 | 0 |
| | Benzene | 108 | 134 | 26 |
| | *n*-Propanol | 98 | 152 | 54 |
| | Water | 102 | 438 | 336 |

These surfaces bond more strongly to other fluorocarbons than to hydrocarbons; the forces of attraction between fluorocarbons are about 25% greater than calculated for dispersion force interactions, using the values of $\gamma_S^d$ and $\gamma_L^d$ shown in these tables.

In a number of the above examples, we see that the simple rule that a low-energy liquid will wet and strongly adhere to a high-energy solid only holds if the intermolecular forces in the solid and liquid can interact with each other. If these forces cannot interact, the simple rule breaks down. Thus the prediction and observation that water will not spontaneously wet an oxide-free metal surface appears to break the simple rule since the surface energy of these metals is much greater than that of water. However, since only the dispersion forces can interact at these interfaces, the simple rule no longer holds and predictions of wettability can only be made by the spreading coefficient calculated with the dispersion force contributions to surface tension.

### Ultimate Tensile Strength of Interfaces

The magnitude of interfacial attraction between two phases interacting by dispersion forces can be estimated from the energy of attraction $(2\sqrt{\gamma_1^d\gamma_2^d})$ between the two interfacial monolayers, by differentiating Equation 5 with respect to intermolecular distance ($r_{12}$):

$$\frac{d\sum_{12}^d}{dr_{12}} = \frac{-3}{r_{12}}\sum_{12}^d$$

where $\sum_{12}^d$ is a best estimate of the value of $\sqrt{\gamma_1^d\gamma_2^d}$. However, this derivation assumes that the number of volume elements per cu. cm. is unchanged during tensile stress and the only change in intermolecular distance occurs at the interface. If the changes in intermolecular distance also occur in the bulk materials, then $N$ of Equations 2, 3, and 4 decreases with increase in $r_{12}$. If $r_{11}$, $r_{22}$, and $r_{12}$ all increase equally under tensile stress,

$$\frac{d\sum_{12}^d}{dr_{12}} = \frac{-4}{r_{12}}\sum_{12}^d$$

while if only $r_{11}$ and $r_{12}$ change (for an elastic material on a rigid substrate), it is reasonable to estimate that

$$\frac{d\sum_{12}^d}{dr_{12}} = \frac{-3.5}{r_{12}}\sum_{12}^d$$

For the ultimate tensile strength of polyethylene

$$2\,(d\sum_{11}^d/dr_{11}) = \frac{8}{r_{11}}\gamma_1^d = \frac{8\times35}{r_{11}}$$

For $r_{11} = 4$ A. this gives $70\times10^8$ dynes per sq. cm. or 105,000 p.s.i. For the polyethylene bond to iron ($\sqrt{\gamma_1^d\gamma_2^d} = 60$ ergs per sq. cm.) the ultimate tensile strength should be:

$$2\,(d\sum_{12}^d/dr_{12}) = \frac{7\sqrt{\gamma_1^d\gamma_2^d}}{r_{12}}$$

or $105\times10^8$ ergs/sq. cm. (157,000 p.s.i.) at $r_{12} = 4$ A. This is greater than that of the polymer, even when the strain is not shared between substances. Of course the measured tensile strengths are an order of magnitude lower, since failures are not the result of concerted breaking of bonds, but of crack initiation.

## NOMENCLATURE

$\gamma_1$ = surface free energy of substance 1
$\gamma_O$ = surface free energy of organic liquid $O$
$\gamma_W$ = surface free energy of water
$\gamma_S$ = surface free energy of solid $S$
$\gamma_L$ = surface free energy of liquid $L$
$\gamma_c$ = Zisman's "critical surface tension for wetting" of given solid
$\gamma_{12}$ = interfacial free energy between substances 1 and 2
$\gamma_1^d$ = dispersion force contribution to the surface free energy of substance 1
$\gamma_{12}^d$ = dispersion force contribution to the interfacial free energy between substances 1 and 2
$\alpha_1$ = polarizability of substance 1
$\mu_{11}$ = London pair potential between two volume elements of substance 1
$I_1$ = ionization potential of substance 1
$r_{11}$ = distance between centers of volume elements in substance 1
$r_{12}$ = distance between centers of volume elements at interface between substances 1 and 2
$N_1$ = number of volume elements per av. cm. of substance 1
$\sum_{12}^d$ = summation of London pair-potentials of a monolayer of substance 1 with adjacent bulk liquid 2
$S$ = spreading coefficient
$\pi_e$ = decrease in surface free energy of substrate resulting from adsorption of another substance
$\theta$ = contact angle
$\Delta F^\circ_{ads}$ = free energy change (per sq. cm.) of solid surface upon adsorbing vapor (in equilibrium with liquid) onto bare solid surface
$\Delta H^\circ_{ads}$ = enthalpy change (per sq. cm.) of above process
$\Delta F_i$ = free energy change (per sq. cm.) of bare solid surface when immersed in liquid
$\Delta H_i$ = enthalpy change (per sq. cm.) of above process
$A_1$ = attractive constant between two bodies of substance 1 (in vacuum)
$A_{12}$ = attractive constant between two bodies of substance 2 (in liquid 1)

## LITERATURE CITED

(1) Adam, N. K., "The Physics and Chemistry of Surfaces," 3rd ed., p. 166, Oxford, London, 1941.
(2) Armbruster, M. H., Austin, J. B., J. Am. Chem. Soc. 66, 159 (1944).
(3) Basford, P. R., Harkins, W. D., Twiss, S. B., J. Phys. Chem. 58, 307 (1954).
(4) Bernett, M. K., Zisman, W. A., J. Phys. Chem. 65, 2266 (1916).
(5) deBoer, J. H., Trans. Faraday Soc. 32 10 (1936).
(6) Boyd, G. E., Livingston, H. K., J. Am. Chem. Soc. 64, 2383 (1942).
(7) Erb, R. A., submitted to J. Phys. Chem.
(8) Fowkes, F. M., Harkins, W. D., J. Am. Chem. Soc. 62, 3377 (1940).
(9) Fowkes, F. M., Sawyer, W. M., J. Chem. Phys. 20, 1650 (1952).
(10) Fowkes, F. M., J. Phys. Chem. 66, 382 (1962).
(11) Fowkes, F. M., Ibid., 67, 2538 (1963).
(12) Fowkes, F. M., in "Adhesion" ASTM, Spec. Tech. Pub. No. 360 (1964).
(13) Fowkes, F. M., Advances in Chemistry 43, 99–111 (1964).
(14) Fox, H. W., Zisman, W. A., J. Colloid Sci. 5, 514 (1950); 7, 428 (1952).
(15) Girifalco, L. A., Good, R. J., J. Phys. Chem. 61, 904 (1957).
(16) Graham, D., J. Phys. Chem. 68, 2788 (1964).
(17) Hamaker, A. C., Physica 4, 1058 (1937).
(18) Hare, E. F., Shafrin, E. G., Zisman, W. A., J. Phys. Chem. 58, 236 (1954).
(19) Harkins, W. D., "Physical Chemistry of Surface Films," Reinhold, N. Y., 1952
(20) Harkins, W. D., Jura, G., Loeser, E. H., J. Am. Chem. Soc. 68, 554 (1946).
(21) Harkins, W. D., Loeser, E. H., J. Chem. Phys. 18, 556 (1950).
(22) Healey, F. H., Chessick, J. J., Zettlemoyer, A. C., Young, A. C., J. Phys. Chem. 58, 887 (1954).
(23) Hildebrand, J. H., Scott, R. L., "Solubility of Non-Electrolytes," 3rd ed., Reinhold, N. Y., 1950.
(24) Hildebrand, J. H., Scott, R. L., "Regular Solutions," Prentice-Hall, Edgewood Cliffs, N. J., 1962.
(25) Isirikyan, A. A., Kiselev, A. V., J. Phys. Chem. 66, 210 (1962).
(26) Jura, G., Harkins, W. D., J. Am. Chem. Soc. 66, 1356 (1944).
(27) Loeser, E. H., Harkins, W. D., Twiss, S. B., J. Phys. Chem. 57, 251 (1953).
(28) London, F., Trans. Faraday Soc. 33, 8–26 (1937).
(29) Melrose, J. C., Advances in Chemistry 43, 172 (1964).
(30) Ottewill, R. H., Wilkins, D. J., Trans. Faraday Soc. 58, 608 (1962).
(31) Reerink, H., Overbeek, J. Th. G., Disc. Faraday Soc. 18, 74 (1954).
(32) Schulman, F., Zisman, W. A., J. Colloid Sci. 7, 4 5 (1952).
(33) Shafrin, E. G., Zisman, W. A., Ibid., 7, 166 (1952).
(34) Sharpe, L. H., Schonhorn, L., Advances in Chemistry 43, 189 (1964).
(35) Vold, M., J. Colloid Sci. 16, 1 (1961).
(36) White, M. L., J. Phys. Chem. 68, 3083 (1964).
(37) Zisman, W. A., Ind. Eng. Chem. 55, 19 (1963).
(38) Zisman, W. A., in "Adhesion and Cohesion," ed. by P. Weiss, pp. 176–208 Elsevier, Amsterdam, 1962.

# 2

# Aqueous Interfaces

# Methods of Study
# and Structural Properties

# Part I

WALTER DROST-HANSEN

# Aqueous
# Interfaces

*Methods of Study
and Structural Properties*

## Precise measurements of surface and interfacial tension can provide clues to liquid structure

The purpose of this, the first part of this article, is to present a review of the more frequently used methods for precise surface and interfacial tension determinations. In the second part of the article, to appear in the April issue of INDUSTRIAL AND ENGINEERING CHEMISTRY, some structural aspects of surface and interfacial properties of water and aqueous solutions will be considered. Because the author's interest is primarily in aqueous systems, the present discussion of methodology is mainly restricted to systems suitable for measurements on water and aqueous solutions of simple electrolytes and nonelectrolytes. Also, in the interest of brevity, interfacial properties of aqueous systems containing surface active agents will not be discussed. Furthermore, in the discussion of interfacial phenomena, we shall restrict our attention primarily to the water-hydrocarbon interface.

A very large number of methods have been proposed for the determination of surface tension of liquids in general. Here we shall deal primarily with the methods which are most commonly used for precise measurements. The relative merits and shortcomings and some of the more obvious pitfalls in each method are discussed. Pertinent references which can be consulted for more detailed, practical instructions are provided.

### Surface and Interfacial Tension Measurements

The methods for surface and interfacial tension measurements can be divided conveniently into two groups: static methods and dynamic methods. The capillary rise and the pendant drop method are two static methods. Examples of dynamic methods are the DuNoüy ring and the drop volume methods, in which the surface is ruptured in the process of making the measurement. Truly dynamic methods for determining surface tensions, which can be applied to very freshly formed surfaces, also exist—we shall deal briefly with these in the second part of this paper. The advantage of the static methods is that, in theory at least, true equilibrium values may be obtained from such measurements. Because dynamic techniques such as the du Noüy ring or the drop weight or drop volume methods cause the surface to rupture in the process of making the measurement, considerable care must be taken in order that one may safely assume that the surfaces are in equilibrium and that the numbers obtained represent reproducible and thermodynamically meaningful quantities.

Another important classification of methods can be made—the case of two-phase versus three-phase systems. For instance, in the determination of surface tension by the pendant drop, only the interface between the liquid and air (saturated with the vapor) is of importance, while in methods such as the capillary rise height or the du Noüy ring method, effects due to the contact between the gas phase, liquid, and solid may play a role. Thus the method to be preferred in a particular situation is determined by the specific nature of the system to be studied. In many cases, the capillary rise method, for instance, is satisfactory while in other cases it may be difficult or even impossible to use (if the contact angle is not known, for example.)

### Capillary Rise Method

One of the most commonly used methods for determining surface tension is that of the capillary rise height. A very wide range of precision and accuracy is possible with this method. It can be used as a quick means of obtaining moderately reliable results, or it can be worked into a method of measurement of extremely high precision and good accuracy. One of the most instructive reviews of methods for measuring surface (and interfacial) tensions by the capillary rise method—as well as by a large number of other methods—can be found in an article by Harkins and Alexander (59).

The equations governing capillary rise in the simplest case are well known. The force acting along a (vertical) capillary due to the upward pull of the surface tension is balanced by the oppositely directed force of gravity acting on the mass of liquid in the capillary above the outside level of the liquid (Figure 1). Thus:

$$2\pi r \gamma \cos \theta = \pi r^2 h(\rho - \rho_v)g \qquad (1)$$

where $\gamma$ is the surface tension (dynes/cm.), $r$ the capillary radius (cm.), $h$ the capillary rise height (cm.) as measured from the liquid level in the containing vessel to the bottom of the meniscus in the capillary, $\rho$ the density of the liquid (g./cc.), $\rho_v$ the density of the air (vapor), $g$ the acceleration of gravity, and $\theta$ the contact angle. In the following discussion it will be assumed that $\theta = 0$. In other words, the liquid wets the glass completely. Since we are primarily restricting our attention to pure water and dilute aqueous systems, this restriction does not lead to any serious loss of generality. Hence from Equation 1 the equivalent expressions are obtained:

$$\gamma = \frac{1}{2} rh(\rho - \rho_v)g = \frac{1}{2} a^2(\rho - \rho_v)g \qquad (2)$$

or
$$h = \frac{2\gamma}{r(\rho - \rho_v)g} \qquad (3)$$

where $a$ is sometimes referred to as the capillary constant. Some authors define $a^2 = (1/2) rh$ while others have chosen to use $a^2 = rh$.

In the capillary rise method there is immense room for latitude in precision and accuracy. It may vary from the obvious "quick and dirty" method in which a standard, low quality capillary tube and a dime store ruler are used, to some sophisticated and indeed ingenious variation of the same method such as proposed by Harkins and Gross (54), Harkins and Jordan (61) and Jones and Ray (67).

The height to which the liquid rises in a capillary is normally determined with a cathetometer. An ordinary cathetometer is usually capable of reading to

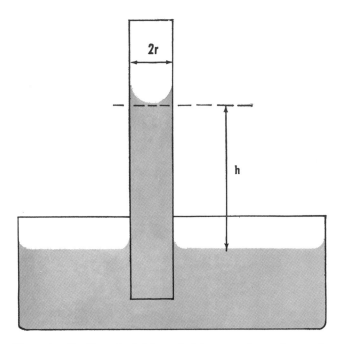

*Figure 1. Capillary rise height method for measuring surface tension*

within 20 to 50 $\mu$, while a good cathetometer can be used to measure to within 1 to 2 $\mu$ (for distances of less than 10 cm.). Two problems are of importance here: it is not always easy to "define" optically the position of the bulk meniscus sufficiently uniquely, and the vessel from which the "outside" level is obtained should be at least 8 to 10 cm. in diameter in order to reduce or eliminate the capillary rise effect on this meniscus.

To overcome these difficulties, an important modification of the capillary rise method is often used. In the so-called differential rise method, the difference in rise height is determined for two capillaries of different diameters. The advantage of this method lies in the high precision with which the difference in rise heights can be measured with the cathetometer. The differential rise method is a superb method, although somewhat laborious corrections are usually required; a condensed but lucid description of these are given in a text by Champion and Davy (*17*).

The capillary or double capillary method for determining surface tension can be used for very fast determinations of moderate precision, for measurements of extremely high precision and good accuracy, or for both. However, while an excellent method for pure liquids, the capillary rise height method requires more attention when used for aqueous solutions. In particular, care is required when using this method for surface tension measurements on aqueous solutions of nonelectrolytes (contact angle and adsorption problems). The capillary method is also applicable to measurements on aqueous solutions of surface-active agents, but in this case, particular care must be exercised to ensure that equilibrium is attained.

While in principle the capillary or double capillary method for surface tension measurements is quite simple, considerable effort is required before the method can

yield very precise results, and in particular before very accurate results can be obtained. As indicated above, we shall restrict our attention to aqueous systems and pure water for which it may safely be assumed that the contact angle is equal to zero. One of the difficulties in the capillary rise height method is the accurate determination of the volume of liquid contained in the meniscus above the point of the minimum rise height (shaded area in Figure 1). In the simplest case of very narrow capillaries, this correction can be neglected; however, in the case of extremely narrow capillaries (less than 20 $\mu$ in diameter) the possibility exists that the capillary is so narrow that specific influences of the capillary wall on the properties of the liquid will affect the determination. Such capillaries are ordinarily avoided in practical work. For capillaries with a radius of about 0.02 cm. or less, it is customary to assume that the shape of the meniscus is hemispherical. Hence, it is necessary to correct for the volume of liquid above the bottom of the meniscus in the capillary simply by adding to the total rise height one-third of the capillary radius. Thus Equation 2 becomes $\gamma = 1/2\, r(\rho - \rho_v)g(h + 1/3\, r)$. However, for larger capillaries up to a radius of 0.05 cm., a considerably more complex expression must be used (derived by Poisson and also by Rayleigh), while for even larger tubes the corrections become extremely complicated. For an excellent discussion of this very important point, the reader is referred to the article by Harkins and Alexander (*59*) and the book by Champion and Davy (*17*). Precautions must also be taken to ensure minimum ellipticity of the capillary tubes used, and a careful determination of the radius must be made. The latter is usually done by measuring the length and weight of a mercury string in the capillary. An ingenious way of avoiding the error introduced by varying diameter of ellipticity along the capillary tube is achieved in the precise but painfully elaborate method of Jones and Ray (*67*). In this method, the volume of liquid in the apparatus is adjusted so that the capillary is always filled to the same point; in this manner, a relative precision of a few thousandths of one percent is claimed.

Another variation of the capillary method was developed by Ferguson and Dowson (*33*). The pressure which is required to force the meniscus in the capillary level with the outside liquid is determined. In this way one avoids the uncertainty due to variations in the capillary radius. For relative determinations this is probably a very sensitive method. Its sensitivity may possibly be further improved if, rather than leveling the capillary meniscus with the outside "bulk" level, a leveling is made with the meniscus in a second, separate, and somewhat larger diameter capillary tube. The calculations involved here become somewhat cumbersome, however, because of the meniscus correction. For most studies requiring good but not extreme precision, capillary tubing of high quality is now commercially available. Such tubing greatly facilitates capillary studies but does not eliminate the need for accurately determining the radius of each piece of tubing. Again, attention is called to the very careful discussion and references found in Harkins and Alexander (59).

The capillary (or double capillary) rise method is very rarely used for interfacial tension measurements even on pure liquids; however, the method can be applied and the reader is referred to Harkins and Alexander (57, page 773), Champion and Davy (17, page 158), and K. L. Wolf (104, page 160).

For interfacial tension measurements, Gordieyeff and Hackley (51) have recently proposed a modification of the method of Ferguson and Dowson. This is a micromethod which appears to be capable of giving results of excellent accuracy with a minimum of manipulation when a rather simple equation is used for the calculation of the interfacial tension from the experimentally measured quantities. The method may be used with extremely small amounts of sample, down to as little as 0.25 mm.[3]

### Ferguson's Horizontal Capillary Method

While most methods ordinarily used for determining surface tension require moderate amounts of liquids, say 10 to 100 ml., the horizontal capillary method of Ferguson (32) requires but a few microliters. In this method a short column of the liquid to be measured is placed in a capillary tube as in Figure 2. By applying pressure to the one side of the liquid string in the capillary, the liquid is forced to the open end of the capillary and the pressure is then adjusted to the point where the meniscus is just at the end of the capillary and changes from a nearly hemispherical shape to a planar one. That this condition has been achieved is easily checked by deflecting a light beam from the surface. The point of balance is thus attained when the applied pressure equals the surface tension forces acting on the right hand meniscus of the liquid string. Since no forces are acting on the liquid at the plane surface of the open end of the capillary, the surface tension forces can be determined directly from the pressure applied to maintain the equilibrium. This pressure is read on a manometer. In the equilibrium position the circumference of the capillary times the surface tension (multiplied by cosine of the contact angle if the liquid does not wet the capillary surface completely) equals the applied pressure. The chief advantages of this method are that it requires

but a minute amount of sample, and that density of the sample does not need to be known, since it does not enter into the calculations. Also, the method makes possible a minimum of contamination in the cleaning and charging of the apparatus. The method is hardly to be considered as one of high precision, however, but it is certainly convenient. The method has also been used to determine interfacial tensions (see Champion and Davy, 17, page 132). The largest sources of error are probably due to the less-than-perfect mobility of the meniscus in the closed end of the capillary (hysteresis) and to the uncertainty of measuring the very small pressure head (of the order of 1 to 10 cm. of water). The interfacial resistance to moving the meniscus is probably not much more of a problem here than it is in the capillary rise height method. Recently, very precise and accurate pressure gages (such as the Texas Instrument Company's Quartz Bourdon Gauge), and high sensitivity, high precision strain gages have become available for use in this pressure range. With these newer instruments, it is possible that Ferguson's method may be considerably improved. Indeed, it may be found that it provides a fast and moderately precise way of determining surface tension. The problem of the mobility of the meniscus in the capillary tube and its deformation due to gravity may still require some attention.

### Drop Weight and Drop Volume Method

The so-called drop weight and drop volume methods for determining surface and interfacial tension are probably among the most precise and accurate methods available. The primary virtue of these methods is undoubtedly the high precision and accuracy with which measurements can be made. However, they are not necessarily the easiest methods to use, as the instrumentation can become quite laborious to construct and operate. Also, because of the complexity of the instrumentation, contamination can easily occur in the cleaning and charging procedures.

The essence of the drop weight or drop volume method is the measurement of the weight or volume of a drop allowed to fall in a controlled manner from a capillary of known outside diameter. The method is not an absolute one, however, in that the geometry which

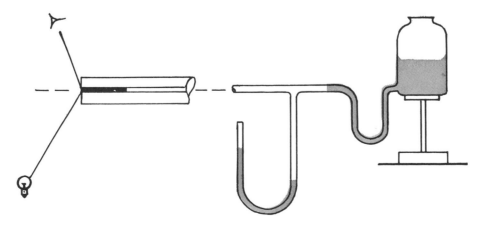

*Figure 2. Ferguson's capillary method for surface (and interfacial) tension measurements*

enters into the determination does so in a manner which has been explored in a largely empirical manner.

By the "principle of similitude" one can show that the mass, $M$, of the liquid drop which detaches from a capillary tip multiplied by the acceleration of gravity, $g$, must equal a force which depends on the surface tension, $\gamma$, and upon some non-dimensional function of the capillary radius. Harkins (59) has shown that

$$Mg = 2\gamma\pi r f\left(\frac{r}{a}\right) = 2\gamma\pi r f\left(\frac{r}{V^{1/3}}\right) \qquad (4)$$

where $a = \sqrt{rh}$ is the capillary constant (see Equation 2) which has the dimension of length. From their studies on water, benzene, carbon tetrachloride, and ethylene dibromide, Harkins and Brown (60) determined the shape of the function $f(r/V^{1/3})$ and this function turns out to be the same for all four liquids; it is very closely that of a cubic equation. Because of the identical form of the function, $f$, for four different liquids, it is reasonable to assume that this function is applicable to all liquids. Measurements of the weight of the drop of any liquid and the radius of the capillary can, therefore, be used to calculate $r/V^{1/3}$ and the tables of Harkins and Brown can be used to find the value of $f(r/V^{1/3})$. Surface or interfacial tension can then be calculated (Equation 4).

The situation is not quite so simple as outlined above, however. For one thing, although we may have a considerable degree of faith in the curves and tables of Harkins and Brown, there are several details which need to be considered. For instance, it is known that the drop does not break off cleanly. In his recent monograph, "Physik and Chemie der Grenzflächen," K. L. Wolf (104) has shown a series of photomicrographs of falling drops. From these, it is easily seen—as indeed one may observe directly by watching the falling drop—that not only does one big drop fall, but that a much smaller drop detaches itself shortly after the main drop has fallen. The illustration in Wolf's book shows very dramatically the breakup of the drop; one is impressed by the dynamic, turbulent action involved in the breaking away of the drop from the surface. Thus, although the drop initially might almost have reached equilibrium shortly before it detaches, this state will not last during the final stages of the determination.

While in the above description we were basing our surface tension determination on the weight of the drop, one can instead measure the volume. The drop volume method for surface tension determinations is a moderately convenient method which is capable of yielding results of high precision and good accuracy. It is, however, particularly useful for interfacial tension determinations between pure liquids and has been used by many authors, for instance Gaddum (47), whose paper should be consulted for details. The method also has been elaborated by B. Adinoff (4). A particularly convenient setup was employed by Franks and Ives (44) and later by the present author (27). The same function, $f(r/V^{1/3})$, that was used with the drop weight method for surface tension determinations applies here; however, it is now necessary to use the density difference between the two phases in Equation 4. Many excellent quality microsyringes such as those manufactured by the Manostat Corporation or by the Burroughs Wellcome and Co., Ltd., England (the Agla micrometer syringe) have become available for accurately and precisely measuring small volumes. The use of the drop volume or drop weight method makes possible a precision of a few parts in ten thousand or better, and accuracies of the order of 0.1%.

Another modification of the drop volume technique has been suggested by Brown and McCormick (13). In this method the drop is allowed to form from a solid cone fed by capillary flow. Since all drops have the same shape, the correction factor is eliminated.

For anyone required to make an intensive study by the drop volume or drop weight method, the discussions by Harkins and Alexander (59) or K. L. Wolf (104) and the review by Dunken (29) are recommended.

### The Ring Method—du Noüy Tensiometers

The ring method and its variations are probably the methods which are most widely used in industrial laboratories. Various kinds of commercial apparatus for determining surface and interfacial tension by a ring method using a torsion balance are sold under the name of du Noüy Tensiometers; for speed and ease of operation, this method is excellent. In fact, when properly used, the surface tension of pure liquids may be determined within 0.3% or better. The method is based on the determination of the maximum pull necessary to detach a ring from the surface of a liquid. This is accomplished either by means of a suitably modified analytical balance, such as a chainomatic balance, or by means of a torsion balance. The rings are usually made of platinum or platinum-iridium wire. The ring should be made of good, circular cross-section wire and must be as close as possible to circular. Both the diameter of the wire and of the ring must be known. As was the case with the drop volume or drop weight method, a correction is necessary. This has been determined and is listed in many places such as in Harkins' (59) article. Freud and Freud (46) have worked out the theory and calculated theoretical values for the correction factor; these values agree quite well with the empirically determined values of Harkins and coworkers, within the experimental accuracy of about 0.25%. The method is probably a very satisfactory one, especially for relative values, such as surface tension of water vs. aqueous solutions of electrolytes (which are not surface-active).

**AUTHOR** *This article was written while Walter Drost-Hansen was Senior Research Chemist, Jersey Production Research Co., Tulsa, Okla. He is now Associate Professor of Chemical Physics at the Institute of Marine Science, University of Miami, Miami, Fla. He wishes to express his sincere appreciation to Henry S. Frank, Felix Franks, and Paul D. Cratin for many helpful suggestions, and to Edward B. Butler and Lynwood Heaver for their help in editing the original manuscript. The experimental assistance of R. W. Myers is also gratefully acknowledged.*

Dole and Swartout (*23*) have described a ring method involving two rings, each ring suspended from the arm of a balance. In use, the weight is determined which must be added to one side to cause the two rings to be pulled out of the liquids simultaneously. In this manner relative measurements can be made with a precision of about 0.002%. This is undoubtedly the best set of relative surface tension measurements ever made by the ring method. While this is possible in principle, it is hardly recommended for routine use. In the particular case of the measurements by Dole and Swartout, however, a need existed for a method that was independent of the problems associated with the capillary rise height method. This was useful in order to verify the interesting and anomalous results obtained by Jones and Ray (*67*), to which we shall refer in the second part of article.

Great care must be exercised to maintain the ring in true circular shape, as horizontal as possible, and as clean as possible. The cleaning is usually effected by flaming the ring over a Bunsen burner before use. It is interesting to note that the maximum pull under certain conditions is not necessarily the pull at which the liquid film breaks. In an ordinary routine determination, however, where the ring is removed moderately quickly from the liquid, this amounts only to a very minor error. The method has often been used indiscriminately, as in studies of solutions of surface-active agents. For this purpose, extreme care must be exercised because of the problem of the accumulation (and variable rate of accumulation) of the surface-active agent at the water-air and liquid-metal interfaces.

The method has also been used by various authors to determine interfacial tensions. They have placed the ring (for instance) in the lower, heavier liquid, overlaying this liquid with the light liquid. The ring is subsequently lifted through the interface. It is the experience of the author that the method is quite difficult to adapt to give reproducible results and the method is not recommended for precision measurements. The main difficulty is undoubtedly the problem of the wettability of the ring. Recently, Krynitsky and Garret (*73*) have suggested the use of hydrophobic rings.

Several commercial instruments of the du Noüy type are available, some with automatic devices for lifting the ring out of the liquid at a controlled rate. Manufacturers' literature should be consulted for details of operation and the estimated precision and accuracy.

### Wilhelmy Slide Method

Another detachment method—a method in which the force is measured which is required to detach an object from the surface of the liquid—is the Wilhelmy slide method. In this method a thin slide, such as a thin platinum plate or a thin microscope slide, is suspended from one arm of a balance with the plate dipping into a dish containing the liquid. The surface tension is determined by measuring the pull at the moment the slide is detached from the surface. The detachment is accomplished either by lowering the vessel with the

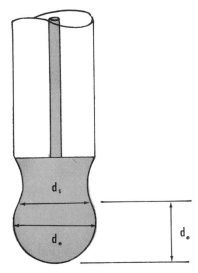

*Figure 3. Geometric dimensions used for calculation of surface or interfacial tensions by the drop volume method*

liquid (i.e., lowering the surface) or raising the balance. Without the use of any tables of correction factors, an accuracy of about 0.1% can be obtained by this method. The Wilhelmy Slide can also be used as a static method. In this form it is a highly sensitive and precise means for studying surface films. Adams (*1*), Harkins (*58*), and Alexander (*5*) give details.

### The Pendant Drop Method

The pendant drop method for determining the surface tension or interfacial tension relies on the geometry of a drop. The method consists of expelling partly a drop from a capillary tip (often referred to only as a "tip") and measuring the dimensions indicated on Figure 3. Here $d_e$ indicates the largest diameter of the drop (extremum diameter) while $d_s$ is the diameter of the drop measured at a point $d_e$ from the lowest part of the drop.

Normally these dimensions are measured from a photograph of the drop which has been obtained with a carefully collimated light beam. The pendant drop method is particularly well suited for interfacial (rather than surface) tension work. In principle, the accuracy of the measurements is within ±0.5% if the linear dimensions of the drop can be measured to within ±0.1%. However, although this accuracy is theoretically possible, it is rarely attained due to the difficulty in measuring all the required distances to within 0.1%. The slight "fuzziness" in the silhouette of the drop makes it difficult to measure within the required accuracy. The method has been thoroughly studied by Andreas, Hauser, and Tucker (*6*), and for practical information, the review article by Harkins and Alexander (*59*) is again recommended. Very recently, Butler (*16*) has made an extensive study of interfacial relations in the water-benzene-mercury system using an ingenious modification of the pendant drop method; this paper should also be consulted. The most important use, however, for the pendant drop method is for the study of interfacial tensions in the presence of a surface-active agent. If the diffusion to the interface of the surface-active species proceeds at a reasonably low rate, the pendant drop method is a superb, quantitative tool for studying the time dependence of the adsorption process. Since we have chosen not to elaborate on surface-active agents in this paper, we shall leave the subject with the recommendation that the papers by Fordham (*34*) and by Ward and Tordai (*102*) be studied for more details.

### Sessile Drop Method

Another method which is based on the shape of drops is the so-called sessile drop method in which the surface tension or interfacial tension is calculated from a measurement of the geometry of a stationary drop resting on a flat surface. Although on some occasions this method may be the only one possible, it generally does not find use in precision measurements on water or aqueous systems.

### Bubble Pressure Method

Among other methods which have been used to give surface tensions with very good precision is the bubble pressure method. This method was suggested more than one hundred years ago by Simon, as described in Partington (*86*). It consists of measuring the maximum gas pressure necessary to blow bubbles of an inert gas slowly into the liquid. Here, as in several other methods, considerable precision and fair accuracy can be obtained only by sustained determination and effort.

### Comparison of Methods

Before leaving the subject of the various methods for measuring surface tension, your attention is invited to an article in the papers from the Third International Congress of Surface Activity in Cologne. In this publication, Padday (*84*) reports on measurements of surface tension of pure liquids and solutions using the capillary rise method, the Wilhelmy plate method (both as an equilibrium and as a detachment method) and two ring methods (including the use of a commercial Du Noüy apparatus). Seven different liquids and a number of solutions of surface-active agents were studied. The article provides a good insight into the variation and quality of data obtained by these different methods.

### Preparation of Pure Water

The problem of providing very pure water for surface and interfacial tension measurements deserves mention. High purity water is an exceedingly rare commodity. Furthermore, water obtained from ion exchange resins has been of considerable value for much electrolytic conductance work, but such water is not necessarily useful for surface and interfacial studies. It is believed that ion exchange resins tend to contaminate the water with organic substances and, furthermore, a test of the specific conductivity of water is obviously far from a satisfactory test for the presence of nonionic, surface-active impurities. For that matter, it is probably not even a good test for the presence of ionic detergents (because of large variations in conductivity alone due to traces of $CO_2$). Franks (*42*) has measured the surface tension of water at 25 °C. obtained from tap water which had been passed through Elgastat deionizers. In spite of the fact that this water—from the point of conductivity studies—was

of extremely good quality (10 megohm resistivity i.e., conductivity $10^{-7}$/ohm cm.), its surface tension was as low as 68 to 70 dynes/cm. at 25 °C. Franks showed that it decolorized alkaline potassium permanganate.

Other authors have doubted the permissibility of using water obtained from ion exchange resins for surface and interfacial studies (see for instance J. A. Kitchener *70*). Thus, it seems fair to insist that water for surface studies must be obtained by distillation. Suitable apparatus for this purpose has been described by various authors. The apparatus devised by Franks (*loc. cit.*) seems very practical. A somewhat similar device has been described by J. E. Taylor (*96*) while a more laborious scheme for purifying water has been described by Butler (*loc. cit.*). The essential element of Butler's method is the recycling in a vacuum of each batch of water. The water obtained with this apparatus has extremely good resistive properties and is evidently also of excellent quality for studies of surface phenomena. The disadvantage of the system described by Butler is the rather low rate of production (say 25 to 50 ml. per hour). A very sophisticated apparatus for production of extremely good water has been described by Eigen and DeMaeyer (*30*). The water obtained in this manner has a specific conductance of only $5.7 \times 10^{-8}$/ohm cm. at 25 °C. The authors do not state any value for the surface tension of this water; however, from the description of the apparatus, it appears that the water would be excellently suited for surface studies. Again, the limitations are the low rate of production and the complicated apparatus.

### LITERATURE CITED

The references cited in Part I of this article are listed below. A more complete, bibliography follows Part II.

(1) Adam, N. K., "The Physics and Chemistry of Surfaces," 3rd ed., Oxford, 1941.
(4) Adinoff, B., Ph.D. thesis, University of Chicago, 1943.
(5) Alexander, A. E., in "Physical Methods of Organic Chemistry," A. Weissberger, ed., 3rd ed., p. 732, Interscience, New York, 1959.
(6) Andreas, J. M., Hauser, E. A., Tucker, W. B., *J. Phys. Chem.* **42**, 1001 (1938).
(16) Butler, E. B., *J. Phys. Chem.* **67**, 1419 (1963).
(17) Champion, F. C., Davy, N., "Properties of Matter," 3rd ed., p. 129, Philosophical Library, New York, 1959.
(23) Dole, M., Swartout, J. A., *J. Am. Chem. Soc.* **62**, 3039 (1940).
(27) Drost-Hansen, W., Myers, R. W., Abstract 5F, 144th National Meeting ACS, Los Angeles, 1963.
(29) Dunken, H., *Z. Physik. Chemie* **47**, 195 (1940).
(30) Eigen, M., DeMaeyer, L., *Z. für Elektrochemie* **59**, 986 (1955).
(32) Ferguson, A., *Proc. Phys. Soc. (London)* **36**, 37 (1923); **44**, 511 (1932).
(33) Ferguson, A., Dowson, P. E., *Trans. Faraday Soc.* **17**, 384 (1922).
(34) Fordham, S., *Proc. Roy. Soc. (London)* **A194**, 1 (1948).
(42) Franks, F., *Chem. Ind.*, **1961**, p. 204.
(44) Franks, F., Ives, D. J. G., *J. Chem. Soc. (London)* **1960**, p. 741.
(46) Freud, B. B., Freud, H. Z., *J. Am. Chem. Soc.* **52**, 1772 (1930).
(47) Gaddum, J. H., *Proc. Roy. Soc. (London)* **B109**, 114 (1931).
(51) Gordieyeff, V. A., Hackley, E. B., *J. Chem. Educ.* **17**, 301 (1960).
(54) Gross, P. L. K., Ph.D. thesis, University of Chicago, 1926.
(57) Harasima, A., in "Advances in Chemical Physics," Vol. **I**, p. 203, Prigogine, ed., Interscience, New York, 1958.
(58) Harkins, W. D., "The Physical Chemistry of Surface Films," Reinhold, New York, 1952.
(59) Harkins, W. D., Alexander, A. E., in "Physical Methods of Organic Chemistry," A. Weissberger, ed., 3rd ed., p. 757, Interscience, New York, 1959.
(60) Harkins, W. D., Brown, F. E., See Harkins and Alexander.
(61) Harkins, W. D., Jordan, H. F., *J. Am. Chem. Soc.* **52**, 1751 (1930).
(64) Henniker, J. C., *Rev. Mod. Phys.* **21**, 322 (1949).
(67) Jones, G., Ray, W. A., *J. Am. Chem. Soc.* **59**, 187 (1937).
(70) Kitchener, J. A., *Nature* **182**, 1667 (1958).
(73) Krynitsky, J. A., Garret, W. D., *J. Colloid Science* **18**, 893 (1963).
(84) Padday, J. F., Third Internat. Congr. of Surface Activity, Cologne, Vol. **I**, p. 233, Academic, New York, 1960.
(86) Partington, J. R., "An Advanced Treatise on Physical Chemistry," Vol. **II**, Longmans, Green and Co., London, 1951.
(96) Taylor, J. E., *J. Chem. Educ.* **37**, 204 (1960).
(102) Ward, A. F. H., Tordai, L., *Rec. trav. Chim.* **71**, 396 (1952).
(104) Wolf, K. L., "Physik und Chemie der Grenzflächen," p. 105, Springer Verlag, Berlin, 1957.

# 3

# Aqueous Interfaces

# Methods of Study
# and Structural Properties

# Part II

# AQUEOUS

## Methods of Study and Structural Properties

In Part I of this article, published in INDUSTRIAL AND ENGINEERING CHEMISTRY in March, a number of methods which have been used for the study of surface and interfacial properties of water and aqueous systems were examined. The present article is concerned with some aspects of the energetics and structural properties of aqueous interfaces. Much effort has been expended on measurements of aqueous surface and interfacial properties; however, the wealth of information which is currently available in the literature notwithstanding, very few studies have done justice to this subject. In fact, the complexity of the problem appears far greater than is generally recognized. The difficulties arise to a large extent from our ignorance about the structure of water; this is the point which will be the center of the discussion in the following paragraphs.

One of the simplest assumptions we can make with regard to liquid surfaces and interfaces (and of course, the aqueous interface in particular) is that the bulk structure extends right up to the surface layer. This assumption immediately leads to trouble, as we are now faced with two problems: What is the bulk structure and how do we define the surface layer. The surface layer is a surface of immense turbulence and disturbance on the molecular scale. Incessant evaporation and recondensation takes place at the air-liquid interface, and it is only in our most abstract thinking that we can afford the luxury of treating this as a mathematical plane. [See, for instance, the discussion by Adamson (2), pp. 60–61. However, even some very recent theoretical treatments of surface tension, for instance Ree et al. (88A), are still being based on the assumption that little or no disturbance occurs in the layers of liquid adjacent to the surface.] The surface layer obviously has thickness. Certainly it must be at least a molecular layer thick and there is fairly general agreement that normally the disturbed, changed layers extend at least a few molecular layers into the bulk of the liquid. That the forces acting in the surface layer are different from those in bulk is obvious, since the surface layer must provide the necessary lateral tension which maintains the liquid rather than the gaseous state of matter.

It is the need for making some assumptions regarding the thickness and structure of the surface layer which introduces extra-thermodynamic features into the treat-

*The model at the right represents a Pauling-type clathrate cage—a pentagonal dodecahedron. Each corner represents the location of a water molecule, with hydrogen bonds along the connecting edges. The cage contains a water molecule in the "guest" position. In the present article, the available evidence from aqueous interface phenomena is examined, and it is concluded that a considerable amount of surface structure is present, although aqueous surface layers are characterized by a considerable degree of turbulence. The depth of the surface structure appears to be at least five to ten molecular layers, and possibly considerably more. The elements of structure appear to be of a separate, discrete nature. Possibly these discrete units are polyhedra, such as the dodecahedron illustrated here, possibly they are specific types of flickering clusters of the Nemethy-Scheraga variety. At low concentrations, the discreteness implied in this model may determine the specific adsorption of ions at the interface (see the discussion of surface potentials). Also, small nonelectrolyte molecules may be incorporated into such structures, becoming part of the cooperative water structure at the interface (see the discussion of the behavior of alcohol at interfaces).*

# INTERFACES

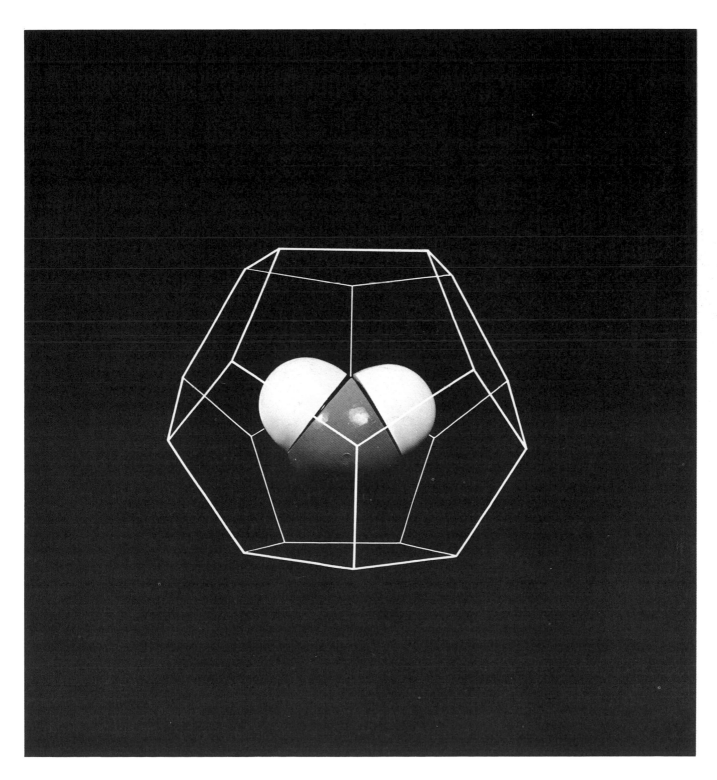

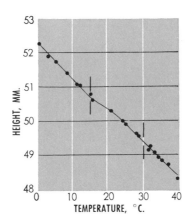

*Figure 4. Capillary rise height data for water obtained by Brunner, 1847. Capillary diameter 0.58548 mm.*

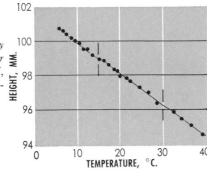

*Figure 5. Capillary rise height data for water obtained by C. Wolf, 1857. Capillary diameter 0.3098 mm.*

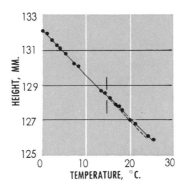

*Figure 6. Capillary rise height data for water obtained by C. Wolf, 1857. Capillary diameter 0.2346 mm.*

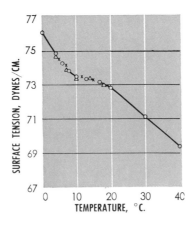

*Figure 7. Surface tension data for water obtained by Timmermans and Bodson, 1937. Circles represent data taken by the capillary rise method, triangles by drop weight, crosses by bubble pressure*

ment of interfaces and thus reduces the utility of a purely thermodynamic approach. At the same time, our "molecular insight" is unfortunately far from satisfactory, and hence no kinetic theory of surface tension is presently capable of treating accurately the properties of aqueous interfaces. The complexity of aqueous interfaces is readily appreciated when one reviews a number of measurements of surface and interfacial tensions made on water or aqueous solutions in contact either with air or hydrocarbons. However, it is appropriate first to describe briefly some problems characteristic of surface studies on water and aqueous systems.

With regard to terminology, strictly speaking, there exist only *bulk phases* and *interface phases*, but the contact between liquid and gas (air, saturated vapor) is often referred to as the *liquid surface* as a distinction from the contact between a liquid and a solid or between two immiscible liquids. The term *liquid interface*, however, can be used generically quite correctly to denote *all* interfaces including the liquid-gas (air vapor) contact as well as the *liquid-solid* or *liquid-liquid* contact.

### Water as a Surface Tension Standard

Water is often taken as a standard reference liquid for surface tension measurements (see Harkins and Alexander, *59*). Apart from the advantage of availability, this is probably one of the poorest choices of standard that one could possibly make. Water has a very high surface energy and consequently is readily contaminated. Usually this results in a considerable lowering of the surface tension. One of the interesting results of this phenomenon is that the more elaborate the equipment for very accurately determining the surface tension of water, the more likely the introduction of impurities. As a result, it is my belief that the currently accepted standard values for water are in error. In fact, the "holy" values of Harkins and co-workers, obtained with both literally and figuratively "gold plated" instruments and reported to five significant figures, may possibly be about one per cent in error. Table I shows values for the surface tension of water at 25° C. The determinations recorded here were all made by reliable investigators, yet some of the values are considerably in excess of the "standard" values given by Harkins, Landolt-Börnstein or K. L. Wolf.

### Temperature Coefficient of the Surface Tension of Water—Older Data

Several temperature studies of the surface tension of water have been published over the past 117 years. Precise data for the temperature variation of the surface tension of water were obtained as long ago as 1847 by Brunner (*14*). Figure 4 shows the height of the capillary rise for water obtained by Brunner. He did not convert his capillary rise height data to absolute surface tensions, but gave only the directly observed rise heights as a function of temperature. One sees immediately that the points do not fall on a single straight line but rather exhibit an inflection point in the vicinity of 17° C. It is interesting to note the excellent precision obtained by Brunner as manifested in the minimal amount of scatter around the curve drawn through the observed points. Figure 5 shows somewhat similar data obtained by Wolf (*103*) in 1857. Like Brunner, Wolf gave the directly observed rise heights and did not convert his measured values to surface tension in dynes/cm. As in Figure 4, one notices an inflection point in the vicinity of 15 to 17° C. When displayed on a suitably enlarged scale, the data also reveal the possible existence of an anomaly in the vicinity of 30°. Again the precision appears excellent—of the order of ±0.02%. The data presented in Figure 6 were also obtained by Wolf, with another capillary. The anomaly near 15° C. can also be observed here although the illustration does not really do justice to the precision of the data. Assuming that the acceleration of gravity in Germany is 981.5, the values for the surface tension calculated from Wolf's data turn out to be 71.6 and 72.2 dynes/cm. at 25° C. for the two sets of data shown in Figures 5 and 6, respectively.

It is the unexpected inflection points in the surface tension *vs.* temperature curves with which we shall mainly concern ourselves in the next few paragraphs. It is interesting—though somewhat disappointing—that although the data by Brunner and Wolf clearly suggest the existence of anomalies, these authors, as well as practically all subsequent writers on this subject, have chosen to neglect the phenomenon. This has occurred despite the fact that sometimes the evidence for the reality of these anomalies clearly is outside the limit of error.

Early in this century Morgan and McAfee (*79*) made a careful study of the temperature dependence of the surface tension of water. These authors reported their results in the form of a second-order polynomial, and it is instructive to look at the difference between their observed and calculated capillary constants, $a^2$ (for a capillary, $a$ is equal to $rh$ as in Equation 2)]. An inspection of their data shows that the differences are not random, but on the contrary, show significant trends (as a function of temperature) which include a notable minimum near 15° C., a maximum between 33° and 36° C., and a very sharp maximum in the vicinity of 60° C. While Morgan and McAfee did not comment on this behavior, they did notice that their data differed somewhat from those of Volkman and of Brunner. They also indicated that the relationship between the data of these authors, as reported in Landolt-Börnstein-Meyerhoffer (1950), seemed to be "nearly" linear and sharply divided into two distinct portions of differing slope, joining at 40° C.

## "Kinks"

The anomalies in the temperature dependence of the surface tension of water bring to mind similar anomalies which have been postulated for bulk water and bulk aqueous solutions. Over the years, several authors have independently suggested the existence of anomalies in the properties of water at a number of different, discrete temperatures. Magat (*78*), for instance, proposed that anomalies exist in the properties of water near 40° C., and demonstrated their existence by referring to measurements of solubility, viscosity, compressibility and specific heat. Dorsey (*24*), in his monograph "Properties of Ordinary Water Substance," points out that the measurements of magnetic susceptibility seem to indicate anomalies in the vicinity of 35° and 55° C. Tammann (*95*) has also suggested the existence of anomalies in the properties of water, and both Antonoff (*7*) and Forslind (*35*) have studied these in more detail. Ives and co-workers (*31, 44*) have perhaps provided some of the most convincing evidence for the reality of an anomaly in the vicinity of 30° to 35° C. The present author and co-workers (*25–28*) have over the years discussed a number of these anomalies, which—for want of a better name—have become known as "kinks" in the properties of water. These kinks, we believe, are evident in a large number of properties of both pure water and aqueous solutions, and in biological systems; the anomalies owe their existence to structural transitions of the nature of higher-order phase transitions. The temperatures around which the anomalies appear to be centered are roughly 15°, 30°, 45°, and 60° C., each extending over, say ±1° to 2° C. on either side of the temperatures listed.

### TABLE I. VALUES FOR THE SURFACE TENSION OF WATER AT 25° C.—STANDARD AND OTHERWISE

| | Surface Tension | |
| *Investigators* | *Dynes/Cm.* | *Reference* |
| --- | --- | --- |
| Harkins | 72.01 | (*59*) |
| Landolt-Börnstein | 71.96 | (*74*) |
| Wolf | 71.98 | (*104*) |
| Smith and Sorg | 73 | (*91*) |
| Bordi and Vannel | 73.57 | (*10*) |
| Drost-Hansen and Myers | (∼72) to 73 | (*21*) |
| Wolf C. | 72.2 | (*103*) |

### Newer Surface Tension Data

Figure 7 shows the surface tension *vs.* temperature data of Timmermans and Bodson from 1937 (*99*). In this case, there is no doubt of the existence of a pronounced inflection point in the vicinity of 13° C.; in fact, the tangent at the inflection point is almost horizontal. Figure 8 shows surface tension *vs.* temperature for pure $D_2O$; in this case the inflection point is also present, but displaced to the vicinity of 17° to 18° C. Timmermans and Bodson commented on the apparent reality of the inflection points but do not seem to have pursued the anomaly further. The anomaly, however, was sufficiently distinct and unequivocal to be mentioned by Dorsey (*24*) in his monograph in the section on thermal anomalies of water (page 651, see also page 514).

Other authors have noticed anomalous variations in the surface tension of water as a function of temperature. Tammann (*95*) has pointed to an anomaly in the surface tension of water near 60° C., while more recently another anomaly in the surface tension of water was suggested by Hacker (*56*). In a study of the surface tension of supercooled water, Hacker claimed an inflection point in the surface tension *vs.* temperature between 0° C. and 8° C. Later, Good (*49*) pointed out an apparent anomaly in

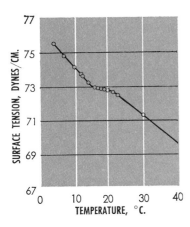

*Figure 8. Surface tension data for heavy water (D₂O) obtained by Timmermans and Bodson, 1937. Circles represent capillary rise data. Squares represent data by Flood and Tronstad*

*Figure 9. Surface tension increments for water at 5° C. intervals obtained by Teitelbaum et al., 1951*

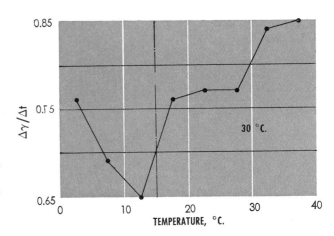

the vicinity of −11° C. in Hacker's data. A careful inspection of Hacker's data also suggests the possible existence of an anomaly very close to 15° C.

The anomaly near 15°C. is also apparent in the measurements by Teitelbaum (*97*) and co-workers, as quoted by Timmermans (*98*). These authors determined the surface tension of water and of aqueous solutions of acetone. Their data were obtained at 5° C. intervals between 0° C. and 40° C. Figure 9 shows the temperature coefficient of the surface tension for pure water, differentiated numerically. The marked minimum near 13°C. agrees very well with the inflection point in the data obtained by Timmermans and Bodson.

Figure 10 shows a set of surface tension data for water obtained by Bordi and Vannel (*9*). These authors have found evidence for anomalies in the properties of aqueous surfaces in the vicinity of 30° C., not only by surface tension measurements, but also in studies of surface potentials of water and aqueous solutions. The surface tension data shown in Figure 10 are also shown in part in Figure 11, in which we have also plotted our own surface tension data. In both sets of data the anomaly near 30° C. is quite distinct. A second anomaly is evident in our own data in the vicinity of 45° C. The data by Bordi and Vannel were obtained using a commercial tensiometer. This throws some doubt on the absolute value of the surface tension; however, it is interesting to note that their value far exceeds the standard value quoted by Harkins, or by Landolt-Börnstein. Our own data were obtained by a capillary rise height method with careful consideration of all experimental details and we believe they represent a very reliable set of surface tension data. Details of these determinations will be published elsewhere. At 25° C. a value of 72.11 dynes/cm. was obtained; however, in other runs which we have made values considerably in excess of 72 dynes/cm. at 25° C. have often been obtained. The inflection points have invariably shown up in all of these data.

An analysis has been made of the data by Bordi and Vannel, our own data, and also a set of data obtained by Moser (*80*). In this analysis, we have numerically differentiated the actual observed data to obtain the variation in surface tension with temperature. It is customary, since this is a derivative of a surface-free

energy, to refer to this as the surface entropy per unit area (ergs per sq. cm. per °C.). The result is shown in Figure 12 and we believe the result to be unique. (In this figure the values obtained from Moser's data are plotted to the same scale, but displaced vertically by an arbitrary amount.) For all three sets of data, the surface entropy is seen to decrease abruptly in the vicinity of 27° C. This is followed by a very notable increase at 30° or 31° C., followed by a precipitous drop in the vicinity of 35° to 37° C. The entropy again rises rapidly in all three sets of data to reach a maximum in the vicinity of approximately 42° to 43° C. We feel that the fact that three different teams of investigators have independently found this extent of similitude lends support to the notion that the phenomenon is indeed real. Thus the surface entropy data indicate *an immense complexity at the aqueous interface.*

A careful analysis of the surface entropy data that we have obtained from the various sources of published data would be highly desirable at this point; however, only in the three cases shown have data been obtained at sufficiently closely spaced intervals to make such an analysis even partly feasible. Even more closely spaced data would be desirable if one is to be concerned with the second derivative, i.e., with the specific heat of the surface. On looking at the curves for the entropy of surface formation, one sees that differentiating these curves once more will lead to an exceedingly complicated specific heat *vs.* temperature curve. For the present, however, we have to be content with the far simpler qualitative statement—that considerable complexity prevails at the interface. We are unable to go much beyond this point now, not only because of the experimental difficulties in obtaining very precise surface tensions at very closely spaced temperature intervals, but also because of the difficulties in attaching specific physical significance to the differentiated surface tension data. As the structure, and therefore the density, of the surface layer is not known, nor is its depth, one must be content with an "apparent" value of entropy of surface formation in terms of ergs per sq. cm. per degree. In other words, we are unable to convert to the standard entropy units of calories per gram mole per degree. Furthermore, merely differentiating the surface tension data with

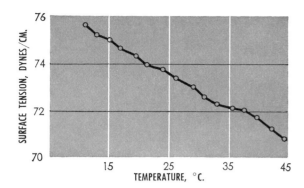

*Figure 10.   Surface tension data for water obtained by Bordi and Vannel, 1962*

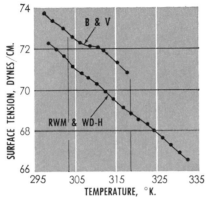

*Figure 11.   Surface tension data for water obtained by Bordi and Vannel, 1962, and by Myers and Drost-Hansen, 1963*

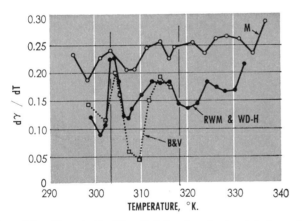

*Figure 12.   Numerically differentiated surface tension data for water, based on measurements by Bordi and Vannel, Moser (1927), and Myers and Drost-Hansen*

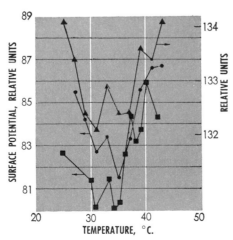

*Figure 13.   Surface potentials (in relative units) for pure water, obtained by Bordi and Vannel, 1962*

respect to temperature does not necessarily give anything but a hint of the true entropy of the surface. Indeed, to do any kind of justice, one must relate $-d\gamma/dT$ to the entropy by means of an expression such as the one derived by Guggenheim (55), which contains not only the temperature variation of the surface tension and the entropy of the surface ($S^\sigma$) but also reference to the mean molar entropies ($S$) of the bulk liquid and gas, the mean molar volumes of the gas and liquid, the thickness ($\tau$) of the interfacial layer and the surface concentration ($\Gamma$).   It is the latter two quantities about which we have very little information.   The expression given by Guggenheim is:

$$-\frac{d\gamma}{dT} = (S^\sigma - \Gamma S_m{}^L) - (\tau - \Gamma V_m{}^L)\frac{S_m{}^G - S_m{}^L}{V_m{}^G - V_m{}^L}$$

### Anomalous Surface Potentials

Before proceeding, we call attention to some relative electric surface potentials measured by Bordi and Vannel (9) on three different samples of water.   Figure 13 shows the observed potentials in relative units, measured essentially as the potential difference between a condenser plate and a surface of water.   The most interesting feature is the fact that in the region from about 30° to 36° C. one finds a distinct minimum in the surface charge.   It is probably also worth noticing that in all three sets of determinations, one actually observes a *double* minimum: one located near 31° C. and one in the vicinity of 34° to 35°C.   Had one set of results alone been available, these details of variation would not have looked very convincing—on the contrary, they might very likely have been taken as being within the limits of experimental error.   However, the fact that all three independent determinations show this degree of consistency, I believe, is again suggestive of something real and indeed something very complex.   It is instructive to compare the details of the entropy of surface formation, as determined from the three independent sets of surface tension data, with the "structure" in the surface charge curves; I believe we are entitled to draw the conclusion that some very specific structural rearrangements take place in the vicinity of 30° to 35° C.   Furthermore, it appears very likely that at least two distinct structures play a role in determining the surface properties in this region, and that these structures are possibly quite different from each other as well as from the ordinary surface structure at temperatures below about 27° C., or above about 37° C.

### Molecular Theories of Surface Tensions of Water

A number of attempts have been made to derive a theory of surface tension of liquids from purely fundamental considerations.   These studies range from fairly simple treatments in terms of easily visualized physical concepts such as the Theory of Significant Structures in liquids [see for instance Ree (88A) or as in Chang (18)] to more rigorous attempts.   The latter category of theories has been thoroughly reviewed recently by Ono and Kondo (82).

While the theoretical attempts to formulate a molecular theory of surface tension for the simplest liquids have met with some degree of success, it is not unexpected that very little has been accomplished in this direction in the case of water. In general, the problem of calculating surface tension involves both the problem of calculating the molecular energies of interaction and the entropy of the surface layer (or layers) since the surface tension is the free energy of the layer (or layers). Calculating the energy of interaction of water molecules—be it in bulk or at an interface—presents an immense problem, particularly if we must take into account the fact that liquid water undoubtedly consists of fairly large aggregates (clusters or "cages") the nature of which have not yet been elucidated. Harasima (57) has pointed out that the calculation of the surface entropy may constitute an even more difficult problem. In the simplest case, the surface entropy (in terms of the free volume theory) is made up in essence of two terms. One term is due to the fact that the molecules at the interface are surrounded by fewer neighbors than are molecules in the bulk (and consequently each molecule is acted upon by weaker forces than prevail in the bulk). The other contribution comes from the way in which we can distribute the molecules over the available "sites" at the interface. It is this latter factor which will present the most difficulties until and unless we learn more about the nature of the structural arrangements in the bulk and at the surface.

### Order at Interfaces

The problem of structural orientation near a liquid interface has been the subject of much controversy. It is fair to say that there exists presently an extreme divergence of opinion. The "classical" view is that only one or a few molecular layers near the surface need be oriented, even in polar liquids. At the other extreme, various authors have claimed that orientation is effected to a depth of, for example, a thousand molecules from the interface. The view that considerable ordering can occur has in particular been advocated by Low (77), Deryjagin (20, 21), and Henniker (64). The best known review of the possibility of liquid orientation near an interface is the article by Henniker; this excellent review, however, is to a very large extent concerned with the liquid-solid interface rather than the air-liquid interface. The review by Low (74, 77) is also of interest.

Most theoreticians have adopted, presumably for convenience, the view that only very limited orientation exists near the interface. It is interesting that one of the truly outstanding theoreticians in the field of liquid structure, Green (53), does not seem to share this opinion. In this survey article, "The Structure of Liquids," Green accepts the likelihood of the postulates made by Henniker. I quote from Green:

*"The Surface Zone in Polar Associated Liquids"*

"There is a considerable body of direct and indirect experimental evidence concerning the surface zone in liquids which is the subject of an excellent review by Henniker."

"In many liquids other than liquid crystals, there is evidence for molecular orientation extending 1000 A. or more below the surface, the precise depth depending on the nature of the material with which the liquid is in contact."

"Surface tension is due to changes in the structure of the liquid in the surface zone, and in polar liquids may be attributed only partly to the rapid change, accompanied by a change in density, which occurs within a few molecular diameters of the interface. There is, in addition, a more gradual change of structure across the surface zone in which the orientations of the molecules become more and more ordered as the interface is approached. Contribution to the surface tension from this zone might be expected to decrease, or at least to be considerably modified, in very thin films; and again this expectation appears to be experimentally realized."

### Jones-Ray Effect

We now turn briefly to an aspect of the surface tension of aqueous electrolyte solutions. Theory and much experimental work indicate that the addition of an electrolyte to water increases the surface tension of the solution over the pure solvent; ions are said to be surface

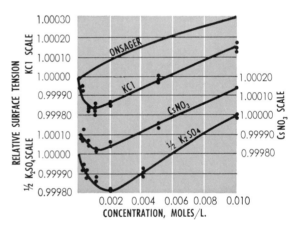

*Figure 14. Relative surface tension data for dilute aqueous solutions obtained by Jones and Ray, 1937*

inactive. However, Jones and Ray (67) have studied the surface tension of very dilute solutions of electrolytes; in particular, they have studied the lowering of surface tension of water upon adding potassium chloride, potassium sulfate, and cesium nitrate. This study, which is indeed a classic in experimental surface chemistry, reveals a noticeable minimum in the relative surface tension (surface tension of solution divided by surface tension of solvent) of all three electrolytes in the concentration range below roughly $10^{-2}$ molar. This is illustrated in Figure 14. Several very interesting features of their results should be pointed out. First, for the three electrolytes there is a minimum in the relative surface tension amounting to approximately two parts in 10,000; second, the lowering is almost exactly the same for all three electrolytes studied. After having passed through the minimum, the surface tension increases as the concentration increases, and for all three electrolytes studied, attains the relative value of 1.0000 at practically the same concentration, namely, $5.5 \times 10^{-3}$ molar. For higher concentrations, up to 0.1 molar, the increase follows quite closely the increase predicted by the Onsager-Samaras [see Harned and Owen (62)] theory of surface tension of electrolyte solutions.

The effect discovered by Jones and Ray has been the subject of considerable controversy. A remarkable confirmation of their results has been obtained from a study of the surface tension of dilute solutions using a relative ("null") method system using the DuNoüy ring as described by Dole and Swartout (23). However, a similar study of apparently good precision has been made using the bubble pressure method. In this case the Jones-Ray effect was not verified. Among the explanations which have been offered for the results of Jones and Ray is the proposal by Langmuir (75) that the anomalous results are due to a change in the effective diameter of the capillary owing to the layer of electrolyte immediately adjacent to the glass capillary wall, related to the zeta potential. Onsager (see Harned and Owen, page 541) has worked this into a quantitative theory and from the relative lowering of the surface tension (as observed by Jones and Ray) has predicted (assuming that the Onsager-Samaras theory is correct) the "correct" value for the zeta potential of glass.

Schäfer and co-workers (89) have studied the surface tension of a number of solutions by means of a detachment method, namely, the measurement of the force required to pull a straight horizontal wire out of the surface. The precision of the method was very satisfactory—the difference between the surface tension of the solutions and of pure water averaged 0.4 dyne/cm., which could be determined with a relative error of about 1%. Measurements were made on sodium and potassium chloride, bromide, and iodide, and on hydrochloric acid and potassium perchlorate solutions. It is interesting and somewhat puzzling that in these very careful measurements the Jones-Ray effect was not confirmed. This is so much more amazing because the Jones-Ray effect had been confirmed earlier by the measurements by Dole and Swartout, who also used a detachment method (differential ring method). On the basis of the presently available experimental data alone, no decision can be made as to the possible mechanism for—or perhaps even the reality of—the Jones-Ray effect. However, in view of the results which are presented in this paper, the present author believes it is reasonable to accept the existence of a Jones-Ray effect and to consider its existence a manifestation of structural peculiarities of the aqueous surface. This implies an intrinsic failure of the Onsager-Samaras theory for dilute solutions although an effect due to a change at the glass-water interface may possibly also be present. One must remember that, notwithstanding the immense sophistication of the mathematical treatments of electrolyte solutions by Onsager and co-workers, one here deals with another case where the highly developed mathematical treatment is applied only to an obviously oversimplified conceptual model. This model neglects, among other things, the detailed structural features of the solvent (the water), and this neglect can only result in a treatment which can hardly be any better than an approximation.

### Dynamic Surface Tensions

We shall now briefly consider the problem of dynamic surface tensions both from the point of experiment and theory. "Unsteady state" surface tension values have often been obtained for aqueous solutions. Here the particular interest usually centers around the behavior of surface-active agents in the vicinity of a freshly formed surface. Because of the lag due to the finite rate of diffusion of the surface-active agents, a freshly formed surface will generally not have the same surface tension as that obtained after sufficient time has elapsed to establish equilibrium.

The problem of the surface tension of a freshly formed surface of a pure liquid has been studied in far less detail and with far less precision than has the corresponding case of solutions. The reason is obviously that experimentally it is difficult to create a surface and measure its properties within, say, milliseconds after its formation. Nevertheless, methods are available which permit such determinations; for instance, the oscillating jet or surface potential measurements can be used to estimate dynamic surface tensions.

The oscillating (or vibrating) jet method is based on the hydrodynamic analysis of an undulating stream emerging from an elliptic orifice, as described by Addison (3). From the shape of the stream the surface tension can be calculated; this method is particularly useful for surfaces from 2 milliseconds to about 20 milliseconds old.

Another method is the study of the bell-shaped sheet of liquid formed upon directing two streams of liquid to collide vertically head on. This method is rather laborious and hardly useful for high precision work. Pallasch (85) determined the surface tension of water by means of a bell method and found that at velocities of less than 200 cm. per second exit speed from the inlet tube the static values were obtained. However, at values of about 300 cm. per second, the surface tension was 14% higher than the static value and seemed to increase linearly with the velocity in this range. In other words, the surface tension is inversely proportional to the time required to generate the surface. If one assumes that the higher surface tension under dynamic conditions is due to a lag in the formation of the surface structure we obtain in this way a qualitative estimate for the time of molecular reorientation and reorganization at the surface.

The surface potential method for determining dynamic surface tensions is based on the monitoring of the interfacial potential between the air and a freshly created surface. An electric potential exists at most aqueous interfaces, either due to the water dipole orientation alone, or due to the preferential adsorption of negative or positive ions. We shall briefly discuss the possible water dipole orientations of the surface of pure water in a later section, as well as the possible adsorption of ions at the surface due to this dipole orientation. Loeb (76) has discussed surface potentials in considerable detail and the reader is referred to his monograph for details and to the text by Davies and Rideal (19); see also the extensive writings on the subject by Kamiensky (69) and the review article by Sparnay (92).

As the water structure changes in a freshly created surface from that resembling the disrupted bulk structure to the "equilibrium" surface structure, the surface potential changes due to the changed dipole orientations. In addition, rearrangement or redistribution of the H$^+$ ion and the OH$^-$ ion will contribute to the changes in surface potential. Finally, any added ions, especially of surface active species, will affect the observed potentials. Due to the generally much slower diffusion rates of the larger surface active ions, the potential monitoring method for determining dynamic surface tensions of solutions of surface active electrolytes is a particularly sensitive method, for which see Posner and Alexander (88). In practical work, the potential above the surface is measured as the liquid leaves a free orifice (as a jet of liquids) or flows in an open trough.

Posner and Alexander have studied the changes in surface potential using three different types of approach, namely, the measurement of the potential difference between a solution placed in a trough and an air electrode, the potential in a channel made of Perspex (which allows for more rapid flow and hence is useful for determining potentials of surfaces of ages between 0.02 to 1 sec.), and finally the measurements of the potential between a jet of liquid and the air by means of a movable air electrode connected to a high impedance electrometer. These authors have also discussed the translation of the observed potentials into surface tensions (and into calculated amounts of ions adsorbed at the interface). The articles by Kamiensky should also be consulted in connection with such calculations, as it appears that some electrolytes (such as α-bromo-propionic acid) can lower the surface tension but increase the surface potential.

The measurement of the potential difference between an aqueous surface and a metal electrode placed over the free surface is often facilitated by use of a radioactive probe. The problem here is to make the air gap conductive in order to minimize the otherwise exceedingly high impedance. A radioactive material, such as polonium (an alpha emitter), is frequently used and serves to ionize the air gap. However, because it is almost impossible to control the extent and direction of the ionization, considerable "leakage currents" may also occur and the method can hardly be considered a highly precise one. Another method is based on the vibrating of a metal disk over the free surface to be studied. In this manner an alternating potential is induced on the vibrating plate (condenser) and this potential can be measured with an external circuit. A high impedance device is required to measure the (a.c.) potential.

There is rather little agreement with regard to the total potential across a pure air–water interface. Loeb

(76) accepts the data by Chalmers and Pasquill who measured a potential of 0.26 volt. From this potential, and assuming that the dipole moment of water is $1.9 \times 10^{-14}$ e.s.u. cm., one obtains the estimate that one in every 30 dipoles is oriented so as to be normal to the surface. A large number of assumptions enter into the estimation of this number, but it probably represents the correct order of magnitude. Alty has arrived at a somewhat larger number of oriented dipoles at the interface. In theory, the problem is confounded by the inevitable presence of hydrogen and hydroxyl ions, and experimentally the situation is usually even more difficult, due to the almost unavoidable contamination, which generally tends to change the surface potential drastically.

Available data for the dynamic surface tension of pure water are few and not particularly reliable. Schmidt and Steyer (90) continued measurements by a method

## TABLE II. DYNAMIC SURFACE TENSION VALUES IN WATER

| $t$, ° C. | Calculated | Method |
|---|---|---|
| 20 | 206 | Condensation coefficient |
| 20 | 109 | Eötvös rule |
| 20 | 128 | Stefans rule |

| $t$, ° C. | Observed | Author |
|---|---|---|
| 20 | 87 | Schmidt and Steyer |
| 12 | 81 | Buchwald and König |
| | (Not virgin surface) | |
| 12 | 180 | Kleinmann |
| 20 | 83 | Pallasch |
| | (Not virgin surface) | |

*This table is taken from the data of Stuke together with the experimental data by other authors quoted in this paper.*

first suggested by Hiss (65). These authors found a value for water of about 100 dynes/cm. at 12° C. This compares with the "standard" value of 73.9 dynes/cm. (Landolt-Börnstein). Kleinman (71) suggests a value of 180 dynes/cm. These dynamic surface tensions presumably are for very "freshly created" surfaces. In fact, after 10 milliseconds, the surface tension has returned almost completely to the static equilibrium value. In the thirties, Buchwald and König, as reported by Stuke (94), determined the dynamic surface tension for water by another experimental approach and obtained a value of 81 dynes/cm. at 12° C. Since their data could not be extrapolated to "time zero" the value obtained is thus likely to be intermediate between that determined by Schmidt and Steyer and the equilibrium value. We shall return shortly to the experiment of Schmidt and Steyer because of the unusual temperature dependence which they observed for the dynamic surface tension. Before we proceed, however, attention is directed to an article by Stuke (94). In this article,

Stuke in essence proposes three alternative ways for theoretically estimating the dynamic surface tension of water by means of a modification of already existing theories. The three equations used are, respectively, an expression for a condensation coefficient derived by Knacke and Stranski (72), a method using the Eötvös rule, and a third method based on a modified expression due to Stefan. For a discussion of the Eötvös rule see the texts by Partington (86) or Wolf (104). Table II shows a comparison of the dynamic surface tensions, both calculated and experimental.

Although one must, of course, be exceedingly careful in accepting the validity of the three equations on which the calculations were based, it is interesting that there is this extent of agreement between the estimated and the observed values for the dynamic surface tension. In view of this agreement, which Stuke cautiously accepts, it is possible to calculate that 0.7 more hydrogen bonds per molecule must have been formed in the surface (if

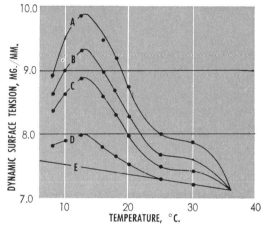

*Figure 15. Dynamic surface tension of water, redrawn from data by Schmidt and Steyer, 1926. Curve A, surface age 0 millisecond; Curve B, 0.5 millisecond; C, 1.0 millisecond; D, 3 milliseconds; E, static values*

we assume a hydrogen bond energy of 5 kilocalories per gram mole). This is impossible since the degree of association is undoubtedly already so large that there is not available another 0.7 hydrogen bond per molecule for further bonding. Furthermore, comparing the surface energy (roughly converted to calories per gram mole) with the heat of fusion of ice, we find that about 2.7 layers of ice would be required to account for the observed energy difference. Indeed, the three outer layers of the water would have to be "icelike" in order to provide the necessary energy. This also is a highly unlikely situation; yet, if the numbers have any significance, we must then accept considerable ordering at the temperature of the maximum dynamic surface tension. Thus, rather than to assume that the three outermost layers were icelike, it seems far more reasonable to distribute the effect in some "cooperative" manner over a far larger number of surface layers. In this connection, it is of interest to recall the observation made by Errera that the water immediately adjacent to an advancing (growing) ice crystal is preceded by a change in the index of refraction of the liquid to almost

that of the solid ice, while the apparent macroscopic viscosity of this layer retains the low water value. The thickness of the layer was claimed to be of the order of one micron. Independent evidence for the likelihood of the existence of such a layer possibly may be inferred from the behavior of the freezing potentials of very dilute solutions of the alkalide halide. Potentials of the order of 10 to 30 volts are generated when dilute solutions, in the concentration range from $10^{-6}$ to $10^{-4}$ molar, are frozen at a moderate rate, say one tenth to one cm. per minute [the Workman-Reynolds (105) effect]. These potentials are temporarily eliminated upon moderately vigorous stirring. This observation can be interpreted as a disturbance of a layer of water adjacent to the ice crystal which has already assumed some of the properties of the ice, including the ability to selectively fit the halide ions into the mobile "quasi-lattice," while selectively rejecting the cations.

### The Entropy of Surface Formation and Dynamic Surface Tensions

As you will recall, we have earlier observed that the entropy of surface formation in the vicinity of 30° C. underwent remarkable and rapid transitions while the data by Timmermans and Bodson suggested a notable minimum in entropy of surface formation in the vicinity of 13° C. for pure water, 18° C. for $D_2O$. These observations may now be compared with the temperature dependence of the dynamic surface tension as obtained by Schmidt and Steyer (90). Figure 15 shows the values obtained for the dynamic surface tensions after various times since the generation of the fresh surface. One sees that a notable maximum in the dynamic surface tension occurs at 13° C. and possibly another one in the vicinity of 30° C. If we consider the region around 13° C., we may conclude, by comparison with the data of Timmermans and Bodson, that the high dynamic surface tension is associated with low entropy of surface formation. In other words, the entropy change in going from the molecular arrangement of the interior liquid to the geometry at the surface goes through a minimum, and thus represents at this temperature a more ordered structure at the interface; this minimum in entropy (and maximum of ordering) corresponds to the maximum dynamic surface tension.

The author tentatively proposes the following explanation. Below 15° C. a certain type of molecular association predominates in the bulk liquid; above 15° C. another type predominates. Around 13° to 15° C. the lower-temperature type of "clusters" ("cages," polyhedra, associated complexes, or whatever they are) suffer a thermal breakdown. In the transition region of conversion from one bulk structure to another it becomes easier to attain a molecular arrangement of higher order (that is, an ordering) perhaps more resembling a close packing of spheres at the interface. Furthermore, to satisfy the energetics as evaluated by Stuke, we must conclude that many layers are indeed ordered at the interface, certainly more than three, and possibly as many as 10 or 20.

### Hydrogen Bonding Versus Dispersion Forces

It is of interest in this connection to compare the apparent contribution of the hydrogen bonding in water to the surface tension with the calculations made by Fowkes (36). This work has been described in a previous article in the Interface Symposium, "Attractive Forces at Interfaces" by Frederick M. Fowkes, INDUSTRIAL AND ENGINEERING CHEMISTRY, December 1964. Fowkes splits the surface tension of a number of liquids into the contribution due to dispersion forces and the contribution due to the hydrogen bonding (or other types of polar interactions). From observed values of the interfacial tension between various saturated hydrocarbons and water, Fowkes calculates the contribution of dispersion forces to the total surface tension of water. The result is the amazingly low value of 21.8 ± 0.7 dynes/cm. at 20° C. (compare the total standard value of 72.8 dynes/cm.). Thus, the contribution to the total surface tension of water due to the hydrogen bonding is more than 50 dynes/cm. In other words, the forces which we believe are responsible for the highly

Ives (44) as a function of temperature. One notices a marked inflection point in the vicinity of 33° or 34° C. The data were obtained by a drop volume method; the probable error on the interfacial tension determinations was estimated to be about ±0.08%. Drost-Hansen and Myers (27) have subsequently modified the instrumentation of Franks and Ives and made a series of measurements of interfacial tensions with equal (or better) precision. We have in particular studied the interfacial tension between water and decane; Figures 17 and 18 show some of our results. Figure 17 gives the interfacial tension data obtained while increasing the temperature from 20° to 40° C., while Figure 18 shows the data obtained with the same system upon lowering the temperature from 40° to 0° C. The two curves superimpose to within 0.1 dyne/cm. or 0.2%. Again, one notices a very complex behavior in the vicinity of 30°. However, rather than just one inflection point as obtained by Franks and Ives, no less than two inflection points are observed. In view of the immense complexity of the surface entropy data for water in the

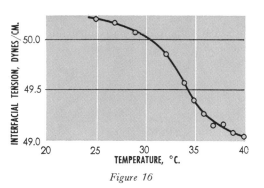
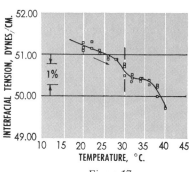
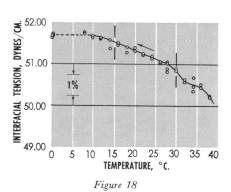

Figure 16                                Figure 17                                Figure 18

*Figure 16 (left). Interfacial tension between n-hexane and water, measured by Franks and Ives, 1960. Figure 17 (center). Interacial tension between n-decane and water, measured while increasing*

*the temperature. Figure 18 (right). Interfacial tension between n-decane and water, measured while decreasing the temperature. Same system as shown in Figure 17*

developed structure account for two thirds of the surface energy.

A further contribution to the understanding of the structure at liquid interfaces is found in an article by Good (50), who has made a study of the surface entropy and surface orientation of polar liquids. Good finds that considerable surface orientation occurs in strongly hydrogen-bonded liquids, as indicated by the energetics and the low surface entropy of such liquids.

### Interfacial Tensions

The complexity of the air-water interface—as manifested in the thermal anomalies of the surface tension and the surface charge—appears firmly established. We now call attention to some other examples of highly anomalous properties of aqueous interfaces which are believed also ascribable to structural transitions at the interface. Figure 16 shows the interfacial tension between water and hexane as determined by Franks and

range from about 27° to 37° C., one should perhaps not be surprised at this degree of complexity in the interfacial tension. Unfortunately, the data are not quite good enough to support comments regarding the apparent temperature-independent behavior between roughly 13° and 0° C. In several other runs on different samples of normal decane vs. water, we have sometimes observed similar inflection points in the vicinity of 30° C. while at other times only one inflection point could be established with certainty.

Figure 19 shows the surface tension of carefully dried n-decane. As well as one can tell, the temperature dependence is here strictly linear. However, admitting a small amount of water through the vapor phase gives the results shown in Figure 20. Here one sees a noticeable anomaly in the form of an inflection point at 30° C. Finally, bulk water was added to this sample to ensure complete saturation with water, and the results are shown in Figure 21. There is now considerable curvature over the range of temperature investigated, but the inflection point near 30° C. is still present.

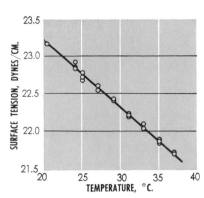

*Figure 19. Surface tension of pure dry n-decane*

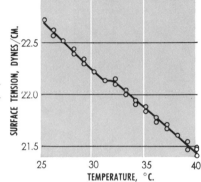

*Figure 20. Surface tension of partially water-saturated n-decane*

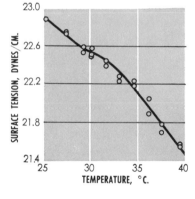

*Figure 21. Surface tension of water-saturated n-decane*

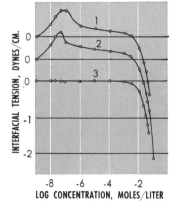

*Figure 22. Interfacial tension between n-hexane and water in the presence of ethyl alcohol at various temperatures: Curve 1 at 10° C., Curve 2 at 25° C., Curve 3 at 40° C. Data by Franks and Ives*

### Effects of Solutes on Interfacial Tensions

In their studies of interfacial tension, Franks and Ives have gone further than merely studying the interfacial tension for the pure system hexane-water. To the hexane-water phases they added various alcohols over a wide range of concentrations. Figure 22 shows the change in interfacial tension as a function of concentration of ethyl alcohol at three different temperatures (10°, 25°, and 40° C.). At the lower two temperatures, the addition of minute amounts of alcohol results in a very notable increase in interfacial tension, of the order of 0.7 dyne/cm. However, at 40° C.—in other words, well above the anomalous temperature range of 30° to 35°—this increase in the interfacial tension is absent. The concentration at which the effect attains its maximum at 10° C. and 25° C. is of the order of $3 \times 10^{-8}$ molar. Frank and Ives also studied this type of behavior with methanol and propanol. For methanol the concentration of the maximum surface tension increase was of the order of $3 \times 10^{-11}$ molar, while for a propanol the maximum occurred around $3 \times 10^{-5}$ molar. It is interesting that pure butanol does not exhibit any anomalous effects on the interfacial tension over the same wide range, from $10^{-9}$ up to $10^{-4}$ mole/liter.

I do not agree in all details with the conclusions drawn by Franks and Ives—primarily because I have found, subsequent to the work of these authors, that the complexity of the air-water and water-hydrocarbon interfaces is far greater than assumed by Franks and Ives. However, it is of interest to quote these authors, on the subject of cooperative actions at water interfaces: "Harkins and McLaughlin [*J. Am. Chem. Soc.*, **47**, 2083 (1925)] have calculated that in dilute electrolyte solutions there is a solute-free surface layer, one molecule thick, into which ions may be forced as the concentration is increased. No information is available about possible preferred orientations in the surface layer or about the effect of temperature. In this case, it is the forces of solvation of ions which are responsible. For the case of the alcohols, the forces of hydrogen bonding come to mind, but these are very much weaker. Something more seems to be needed, and is found in the suggestion that the lower alcohols can, at low enough concentrations, be tolerated as components of the cooperative water structure. Then, over quite a narrow range of rise in temperatures, release of the alcohol molecules might be expected."

Franks and Ives reviewed the literature and also made some pertinent remarks about anomalous properties of water. They state, "Although these effects are embarrassingly various, they all go to confirm the complexity of the water structure problem and support the view that the temperature range 30° to 40° C. is a critical one in which something rather decisive happens." In discussing the sharp peaks in $\Delta S$ of surface formation they note ". . . . the comparative sharpness of the peak suggests that it is caused by something akin to a phase transition, or order-disorder transformation, perhaps leading to a modified interface." Thus, the simplest way of considering the large $\Delta S$ observed in the vicinity of, say 30° to 31° C., is to assume that this corresponds to some kind of "melting."

Finally, Franks and Ives state, "There is no doubt that alcohols interact with water by hydrogen bonding and it is possible that at very low concentrations the molecules of the alcohol may be able to build into the water structure. This is almost certainly true of methanol which is the least abnormal of the alcohols with regard to its entropy of vaporization from aqueous solution (reference to Frank and Wen, *Discussions of the Faraday Society*, No. 24, 1947, p. 133). If this can be accepted then in the lower temperature range where there can be little doubt that water has a cooperative, pseudocrystalline structure, a sudden breakdown might be expected within quite a narrow range of conditions, in particular, of alcohol concentration."

### Solute Effects on Surface and Interfacial Tensions

While Franks and Ives have studied the effects of small amounts of alcohols on the interfacial tension of water-hexane, no one seems to have studied the surface tension of water in the presence of very low concentrations of alcohol. Hence the present author (unpub-

alcohol-water system (at low concentrations of sucrose). However, an extrapolation of Jones and Ray's data shows, when plotted on a logarithmic scale (Figure 24), that instead of an increase, a lowering of the relative surface tension may indeed occur at concentrations below $10^{-3}$ molar. The extrapolation we have performed here (dashed line) can hardly be said to be more "daring" than the one implied by Jones and Ray when they claim that no lowering occurs.

We now compare Franks and Ives data concerning the effects of ethyl alcohol on interfacial tension with the data on the effect of alcohol on the surface tension of water. Quantitatively the numbers are quite interesting. The relative surface tension of water containing alcohol goes through a maximum as the amount of alcohol in solution is increased and the maximum occurs at a far greater concentration than the one observed for the maximum in the water-hexane system; in the later case the maximum occurs at about $3 \times 10^{-8}$ moles $C_2H_5OH$ per liter as compared to $17 \times 10^{-3}$ moles $C_2H_5OH$ per liter for the maximum surface tension of the water-alcohol mixture. It is interesting to note, however, that the concentration at which the

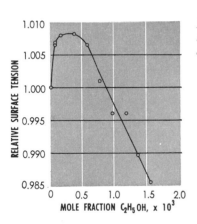

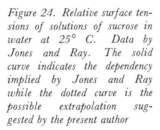

Figure 23. Relative surface tensions of solutions of ethyl alcohol in water at 26° C.

Figure 24. Relative surface tensions of solutions of sucrose in water at 25° C. Data by Jones and Ray. The solid curve indicates the dependency implied by Jones and Ray while the dotted curve is the possible extrapolation suggested by the present author

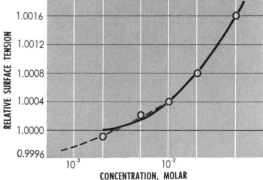

lished data) has made such determinations and the results are shown in Figure 23. Relative surface tension goes through a rather sharp maximum at a mole fraction of approximately $3 \times 10^{-4}$ (corresponding roughly to a $17 \times 10^{-3}$ molar solution). Note also that the value for which the relative surface tension has again decreased to 1000 is approximately $0.8 \times 10^{-3}$ (mole fraction) or roughly $44 \times 10^{-3}$ molar.

In the previously cited study by Jones and Ray, limited attention was also given to the effect on surface tension of the addition of a nonelectrolyte in small amounts. The authors state that they did not find any lowering of the surface tension of water when adding sucrose in the same concentration range for which they studied the electrolytes. The sucrose, while a nonelectrolyte, is certainly likely to interact very strongly with the water structure through the large number of OH groups and perhaps one might guess that the behavior of sucrose should be "in between" the behavior of an electrolyte and the alcohols. Certainly, it would not seem unreasonable that an increase in the surface tension could occur, akin to the one observed for the

increase in interfacial tension has vanished (the relative interfacial tension decreased to 1.0000) is approximately $60 \times 10^{-3}$ mole for the water-hexane system while the relative surface tension for the water-alcohol system became 1.0000 at $44 \times 10^{-3}$ mole. In other words this occurs at quite similar concentrations. It is also interesting that the increase in interfacial tension and the increase in surface tension of water at the optimum concentration of alcohol are about the same, namely 0.7 dyne per centimeter in the case of the interfacial tension of water-hexane and roughly 0.6 dyne per centimeter in the case of surface tension of water alcohol.

The apparent discrepancy between the alcohol concentrations producing maximum interfacial tension or surface tension may not be as serious as would at first appear ($3 \times 10^{-8}$ compared to $17 \times 10^{-3}$). As indicated above, the reason may be that the aqueous phase, in the case of the interfacial tension measurements, was saturated with hexane. If the hexane can substitute for the alcohol in the ability to interact with the water (participate in the cooperative water structure or perhaps simply occupy "sites" in the "water lattice" at the interface), we should add to the low alcohol concentration, the concentration of the hexane in the water, which, for a saturated solution at 25° C., is approximately $0.12 \times 10^{-3}$ molar (E. G. Baker, personal communication). A "total concentration" of $0.12 \times 10^{-3} + 3 \times 10^{-8} \cong 0.12 \times 10^{-3}$ molar is still 100-fold lower than the optimum concentration for the surface tension effect, but not 600,000 times too low.

If the above explanation is correct, we might be led to the prediction that a number of other nonelectrolytes, when added in suitably small concentrations, should result in the same type of surface tension versus concentration dependence. Also, if the added nonelectrolyte does not seriously interfere with the water structure, we would expect that the maximum increase in surface tension should be rather independent of the nature of the dissolved species. Furthermore, the concentration of the maximum surface tension should not vary greatly from one substance to another. We would also suggest that the value for which the relative surface tension has again decreased to 1.0000 should also be about the same for all substances. As was pointed out in an earlier section of this article, it is interesting indeed that in the

**TABLE III. CONCENTRATIONS AT WHICH THE RELATIVE SURFACE TENSION IS 1.00000**

| Compound | Concentration |
|---|---|
| LiF | 0.0050 |
| KClO₃ | 0.0057 |
| CsI | 0.0058 |
| KSCN | 0.009 |
| BaCl₂ | 0.0035 |
| LaCl₃ | 0.0023 |
| K₃Fe(CN)₆ | 0.0015 |
| K₄Fe(CN)₆ | 0.009 |

case of the Jones-Ray effect (notwithstanding the fact that the added electrolyte causes a decrease in relative surface in relative surface tension rather than an increase), the concentration for which the relative surface tension is 1.0000 is approximately the same ($5.5 \times 10^{-3}$ gram mole per liter) independent of the choice of electrolyte (potassium chloride, potassium sulfate, or cesium nitrate). Furthermore, in the comparison of the three electrolytes studied by Jones and Ray, the maximum change (i.e., lowering of the surface tension) is roughly the same, independent of the type of electrolyte studied. However, it appears as if the concentrations at which the relative surface tension is a minimum do vary—from approximately $0.9 \times 10^{-3}$ to $1.7 \times 10^{-3}$ mole per liter, or roughly by a factor of two.

In a second paper, Jones and Ray (68) reported relative surface tension measurements on a number of other electrolyte solutions. For all of the solutions studied, the surface tension goes through a notable minimum after which it rises again, later to become more nearly what would be predicted on the basis of the Onsager-Samaras theory. In Table III are listed the interpolated values of concentration for which the relative surface tension has again increased to 1.00000 subsequent to passing through the minimum in the relative surface tension vs. concentration curve.

Between the time Jones and Ray's first paper appeared and the time of the second paper, Dole (22) had proposed a theory to account for the minimum in the relative surface tension curves. In Dole's theory it is assumed that on the average the dipoles of the water at the interface are oriented so as to expose the protons to the air at the air-water interface. In order to account for the experimental data obtained by Jones and Ray, Dole makes the following assumption: "The property of the solvent of which we find necessary to assume the existence is the special orientation or grouping of water molecules in a limited number of locations or 'active spots' on the water surface, and in such configuration that *negative* ions will be attracted to these spots from the interior of the solution, i.e., a configuration with the proton ends of several contiguous surface water molecules pointing inward." Dole also states: "We do not assume that these active spots are fixed in one place, but appear from time to time at different points of the surface. Liquid water, thanks to the work of Stewart [reference to T. W. Stewart, *Physical Reviews* **35**, 1426 (1930); **37**, p. 9, (1931)] and others and to the calculations of Bernal and Fowler and of Debye [reference to P. Debye, *Chemical Reviews* **19**, 171 (1936)] is now known to have a definite structure which differs from that of the solid chiefly in that it is a function of time. Frumkin [reference to A. Frumkin, *Zeit. für physik. Chemie* **111**, 190 (1924)] first advanced the idea that a certain unspecified number of water molecules were oriented with their proton ends inward, and Ariyama [reference to *Bulletin Chemical Society of Japan* **12**, page 109 (1937)] recently has made use of the same idea in developing a theory for the surface tension of inorganic acids. From the quantitative application of this postulate as given below, it is necessary that there be about four 'active' spots for every hundred thousand water molecules, a number that certainly seems to be within the realm of possibility, and a number that is the same for all data published by Jones and Ray."

When one considers the anomalous concentration dependencies observed by Bordi and Vannel for the surface potentials, it may be recalled that these potentials are determined to a large extent by orientation of the water molecules near the interface. As suggested by Dole, "active" spots—or islands—of dipole orientation might occur at the water interface and the orientation of these "sites" may be opposite to the bulk orientation at the interface. It is hard, however, to see how this suggestion of Dole's could possibly be extended to account for the existence of the *two* minima in the surface potential curves. Instead, it seems more natural to propose that there exists at the interface different structural units which may—with different degrees of ease—incorporate ions or at least be "less inconsistent" with the presence of the ions in these places.

The similarities in the effects of various salts on the relative surface tension and the theoretical difficulties these data present were discussed by Jones and Ray (*68*) in their second paper on the problem of the maximum value of the depression in the relative surface tension *vs.* concentrations curve: "The depth of the minimum does not vary greatly among the eleven salts studied. It is least for potassium ferricyanide, about 0.01% less than that of water, and greatest for potassium thiocyanate, about 0.02% less than that of water." Jones and Ray go on to discuss the shape of the typical surface tension–concentration curve, which is quite complicated. They indicate that: "It has a steep negative initial slope, then passes through a minimum at about 0.0001 molar and then becomes approximately linear with a positive slope and positive curvature. The surface tension becomes equal to that of water at about 0.005–0.006 molar for univalent salts (except for potassium thiocyanate at about 0.009 molar) and at lower concentrations for salts containing a polyvalent ion. There is a point of inflection below 0.02 molar, followed by a slight negative curvature. Although it is difficult to locate the point of inflection very definitely because the curvature on both sides is so slight, in all cases it seems to be below the concentration at which the surface tension becomes equal to that of water. Before a maximum appears, if the salt is sufficiently soluble, there is another point of inflection followed by a positive curvature at higher concentrations. *It is evident that a function adequate to express the curve accurately must have a quite complicated form*" (italics by the present author). It is hard to envision a straightforward extension of any of the existing theories of surface tension of electrolyte solutions which would be capable of reproducing the observed curves. However, while at the moment we are unable to work out the mathematics of the model implied in this paper, it is certainly far easier to see how the postulated existence of various water structures in the bulk and at the interface could account for an exceedingly complex surface tension *vs.* concentration curve.

Precise relative surface tension data on such substances as are known to form well defined clathrate hydrates (such as argon, methane, and ethylene oxide) might contribute significantly to furthering our understanding of the structural characteristics of aqueous surfaces. As we have mentioned, one difficulty in the interpretation of the anomalous behavior of the alcohol-water system is the fact that we ordinarily do not think of the alcohol as participating in clathrate hydrate formation. Instead the alcohol molecule is normally considered likely to upset the water structure in unique fashion. However, we must remember that in the light of Frank's (*37, 39*) theory or the Nemethy-Scheraga (*81*) theory of hydrophobic bonding, the alcohols should be considered bifunctional in their effects on water structure. That is, both the hydrocarbon tail and the OH group must be considered active in influencing the water structure.

In the preceding paragraphs, it was tentatively predicted that some nonelectrolytes, when added in suitably small concentrations, should result in an initial increase relative surface tension *vs.* concentration curve of the aqueous solutions. The data by Jones and Ray

on sucrose do not fit this prediction. However, the disagreement may not necessarily be very serious as the sucrose molecule is of far greater size than the molecules which we normally associate with clathrate hydrate formation. Furthermore, while it may be somewhat difficult to understand how a methyl or ethyl alcohol molecule may participate in the cooperative structure of water near the interface, these molecules are at least of appropriate sizes compared to the ordinary clathrate cage structures known. In addition, the sucrose molecule has not only one, but a large number of hydroxyl groups, and has no exposed "hydrocarbon tails." It therefore may not be able to promote water structure stabilization by hydrophobic bonding as envisioned for the alcohols according to the Nemethy-Scheraga theory of water structure.

Anomalies in the partial molar volume of ethyl alcohol in water have been discussed by Franks and Johnson (*45*). On this basis D. N. Glew (*48*) has proposed the existence of definite clathrate hydrates of nonelectrolytes in solution. While the existence in bulk solution of such definite discrete entities as clathrated hydrate species remains unproved, their existence at the water surface or interface seems more likely in view of the arguments presented in this paper.

Henry Frank (1964) has made the tentative suggestion that a useful classification of the effects of solutes on the surface tension of aqueous solutions is as follows: "Ionic charges tend to be structure breaking, non-polar groups structure-making, and OH and $NH_2$ groups tend to have little effect either way. For polyfunctional solutes (e.g., aminoacids, aliphatic alcohols) the effects of the functions seem often to be more or less additive. The first order effect of sucrose, therefore, would be expected to be a 'mere' size effect, which would probably not be very strong."

Although there is no doubt that some ions are structure breakers while others appear able to promote the water structure, our information about the effects of ions on the structure of water and the problem of hydration of ions are still in an extremely unsatisfactory state. Thus, Vaslow (*101*) has recently proposed that the "classical" view of ion hydration may not necessarily be valid; in other words, the view that "the dipole of a water molecule adjacent to a small or highly charged ion points directly at the center of the ion" may not be correct. In its place, Vaslow suggests: "It appears not unreasonable then that the hydration of small ions could be consistent with normal hydrogen bonded structural groupings of liquid water. Assuming now that this is so, some possible speculative consequences can be discussed. Firstly, as to the nature of the structural groups, water has an open structure with many holes. It is possible that structure forming ions (reference to R. W. Guerney, 'Ionic Processes in Solution,' McGraw Hill, Inc., New York, N. Y., 1953, page 258) as $Li^+$ or $Na^+$ can fit into these holes, distorting but not disrupting the structure, while $K^+$ and large ions which are structure-breaking would presumably not fit into these holes."

While Vaslow's notions will require considerable

further study before they can be accepted, they do suggest a possible answer to the question of the mechanism by which the thermal anomalies (kinks) discussed by the present author are equally frequently observed for both pure water and very concentrated solutions, such as $2M$ sodium chloride. If the ions—even when present in high concentrations—can take part in the cooperative water structure, the temperatures of the structural anomalies may not be significantly altered by the presence of the ions. This problem will be considered elsewhere. For the time being, it is of interest to note here that we may on this basis predict that the thermal anomalies (kinks) observed in surface properties of both pure water and dilute aqueous solutions will also be manifested in the surface properties of more concentrated aqueous solutions of electolytes.

### Possible Direct Evidence for Discreteness at Interfaces

We have discussed the likelihood of the surface of water possessing structural units with individual stability and

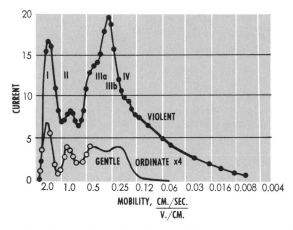

*Figure 25. Current (related to abundance) due to various, negatively charge "micro-droplets" of water, plotted versus mobility (related to size) from results by Chapman (quoted by Loeb). "Violent" and "gentle" refer to the degree of mechanical agitation (spraying) by which the micro-droplets were produced. In the lower curve, many data points have been omitted for clarity. Courtesy of Springer-Verlag*

discreteness. The evidence which we have quoted for the reality of this proposition has been primarily indirect. A possible direct indication of the existence of discrete units, at least in the presence of ions, may be obtained from the studies by Chapman, as quoted by Loeb (76) in his monograph "Static Electrification." In essence, Chapman measured the mobility of "microdroplets" derived from spraying water or solutions in a "poor man's mass spectrograph." In this device, which was operated at atmospheric pressure, the current in the gas phase due to the migration of ionized droplets could be measured between two electrodes. From these data Chapman could calculate the mobility and frequency of occurrence of various species of charge carriers. Thus, a number of "spectra" were obtained showing the distribution of abundance (proportional to the current) of various species *vs.* their mobility. Thus, depending upon the degree of agitation of the water in the proc-

ess of evaporating and breaking up the water surface, at least four different species seem to exist as shown in Figure 25. For aqueous solutions of electrolytes such as potassium chloride and for solutions of sucrose, several "peaks" were observed in the spectra of current *vs.* mobility. It is indeed interesting that for a $3 \times 10^{-4}$ molar sucrose solution, five different species of negatively charged droplets could be detected (see Figure 26). On the other hand, a $3 \times 10^{-3}$ molar sucrose solution gave essentially only two negatively charged carriers and again only one positively charged species (see Figure 27). It is also of interest to note that the distribution of charge carriers changes in the direction of lower mobility (i.e. larger mass) as we go from pure water to $3 \times 10^{-4}$ molal sucrose. Larger structural units thus seem present at the interface in the presence of the sucrose. No such effect appears to occur with KCl solutions.

It would seem from the results of Chapman's studies that we may here have direct evidence for the separate and discrete existence of structural units which can be removed from the surface, possibly intact, although each aggregate must of necessity carry a charge in order to be detected in the apparatus used by Chapman. The very noticeable change in the appearance of the "spectra" for the two dilute sucrose solutions occurs in the concentration range just below the range accessible to Jones and Ray in their study of the surface tension of dilute solutions. This is the range of concentration in which there is doubt about the extrapolation of the relative surface tension data. Incidentally, the charge which was inevitable on these aggregates in the gas phase may not necessarily be due to any externally added ions but rather to the inevitable hydrogen or hydroxyl ions.

### Other Concentration Effects

Bordi and Vannel have studied many surface properties of aqueous solutions. Figure 12 showed the surface potentials of pure water as a function of temperature and the anamalous behavior observed in the vicinity of 30° to 33° C. Bordi and Vannel (9) have also studied the surface potential of potassium chloride solutions as a function of concentration from 0.05 to 3.3 millimoles per liter. This is the concentration range where we found the anomalous surface tension dependence on alcohol concentration. This is also the concentration near which Jones and Ray observed the anomalous decrease in surface tension. In the surface potential measurements on potassium chloride solutions, one observes no less than two distinct minima, as shown in Figure 28.

The existence of two closely spaced minima—such as were observed for the surface entropy as a function of temperature in the vicinity of 30° and 35° C. or in the surface potentials in the vicinity of the same temperatures—is suggestive of the existence of a number of different, discrete entities with individually characteristic properties. In the present case of two distinct minima in the surface potential as a function of concentration the simplest explanation would be the existence of two distinct types of "sites" in the surface which can be occupied by the ions. On the basis of only the present material

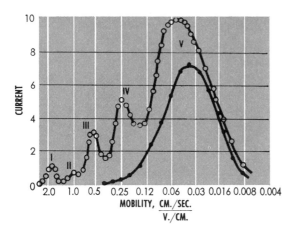

*Figure 26. Curent (related to abundance), mobility of various charged "micro-droplets" formed from a $3.10^{-4}$ molal sucrose solution by spraying. Data by Chapman. The curve with several maxima refers to negatively charged particles; the lower curve refers to positively charged species. Some data points have been omitted. Courtesy of Springer-Verlag*

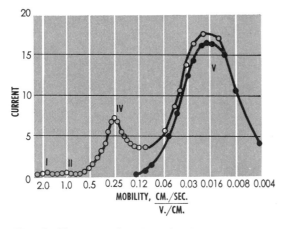

*Figure 27. See Figure 26; data shown in this graph obtained with a $3.10^{-3}$ molal sucrose solution. Note the marked effect on size distribution due to the change in concentration. Some data points have been omitted. Courtesy of Springer-Verlag*

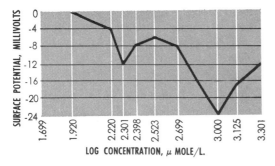

*Figure 28. Surface potentials of potassium chloride solutions vs. concentration. Note existence of two minima. Data by Bordi and Vannel, 1962*

this proposition remains, of course, highly speculative—yet it would at least seem a strong argument for repeating a considerable number of surface measurements, at closely spaced intervals, of both temperature and concentration. Experiment and theory are no longer "neck and neck" for theory has fallen far behind.

Additional evidence for the existence of discreteness at the water surface may also be implied in the results obtained by Bordi and Vannel (11) on the surface conductivity of aqueous solutions of mixtures of $CdCl_2$ and KCl. The surface conductance of these systems varies rather abruptly with concentration, and this Bordi and Vannel interpreted as due to the formation of ion-ion complexes at the interface. An alternative explanation, however, can be made by ascribing the variations with concentration to structural discreteness; in other words, the abrupt changes are caused by the successive "filling in" of appropriate sites at the surface—different types of sites (in different concentrations) for the various ions. Later, Bordi and Vannel (10) studied the surface potentials and surface conductivity of solutions of $CdCl_2$ and $Na_2SO_4$ (separately) as a function of temperature, and the results indicate the presence of marked thermal anomalies near 30° to 35° C., especially in the surface potentials. These findings further support the likely reality of the thermal anomalies in the surface tension data on pure water obtained by Bordi and Vannel.

### Anomalies at Higher Concentrations

We have discussed some of the anomalous properties of highly dilute, aqueous alcohol solutions. Apparently anomalies also exist at higher concentrations of alcohols in water. Some of these anomalies have been reviewed recently by Felix Franks (43), while Brown and Ives (12) have discussed particular aspects of bonding in the system *t*-butyl alcohol–water mixtures. These anomalies have been observed on several occasions both in transport and equilibrium properties. As an example, Figure 29 shows the diffusion coefficient of ethyl alcohol in water as determined by Franke (41) in 1932. One observes a marked minimum near 10 weight % alcohol. Franke, incidentally, also observed the existence of two minima in the diffusion constant for methyl alcohol in water, namely, near 2 and 10 weight %. The anomalies in the properties of the alcohol-water system in this concentration range are also manifested in the surface behavior. Figure 30 shows the temperature coefficient of the surface tension of water-alcohol mixtures from Hoffman and co-workers (66). One notices here the pronounced maximum in the temperature coefficient at a concentration of approximately 8 to 9 weight %. This corresponds roughly to a molar ratio of water to alcohol of about 35 to 1, and this is the same concentration range as found for the minimum in the diffusion coefficient measurements by Franke.

Thus, the properties of water-alcohol mixtures appear abnormal. They still reflect, nevertheless, the peculiarities of the water with regard to thermal stability (kinks). This is demonstrated in Figure 31 which shows the temperature dependence of the surface tension of a 1% alcohol in water mixture [Porwik (87)]. An inflection point is clearly present near 30° C. and possibly also one near 15° to 17° C. It should be noted here, though, that the 1% concentration is far in excess of the concentration for which the relative surface tension exceeds the value of pure water, yet is below the concentration for which the anomaly is observed in the temperature coefficient of surface tension versus concentration (and for which the diffusion coefficient exhibits a minimum).

Teitelbaum and co-workers, as quoted by Timmermans (97), have determined the surface tension of a number of solutions of acetone in water as a function of temperature from 0° to 40° C. Numerically differentiating their data for the 0.5 mole % solution of acetone (at 5° temperature intervals) one again finds a notable minimum in the temperature coefficient in the vicinity of 17° C. Thus, neither alcohol nor acetone (in 0.5 mole % concentration), destroy or even

of the differential capacity at different potentials, they observe: "Without added organic materials, the inflection (in the differential capacity versus surface charge) is much slighter, though in certain systems one or two 'humps' are visible. These must reflect rather discontinuous changes in the adsorption layers, in which may be found, according to the applied potential, strongly polarized anions, water dipoles only, or hydrated cations. The 'hump' observed at 5° C. with NaF when the mercury is slightly positive, becomes smoother at 25° C. and disappears at higher temperatures (reference to, articles by Graham), these effects being independent of the concentration of NaF." The observations by Davies and Rideal of the more or less discontinuous changes with potential and also as a function of temperature may now be seen as reflection of the discreteness we have postulated in liquid water. While we have only claimed the existence of discrete structural elements in bulk water, and in surface and

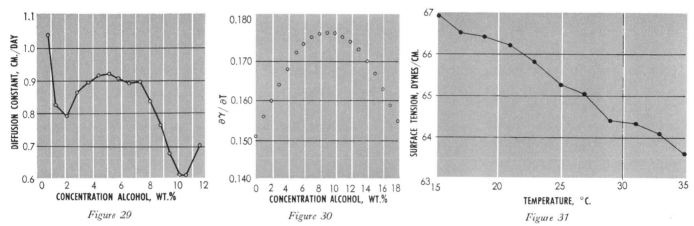

*Figure 29*                          *Figure 30*                          *Figure 31*

*Figure 29 (left). Diffusion constant of ethyl alcohol in water. Data of Franke, 1932. Figure 30 (center). Temperature coefficient of surface tension vs. concentration for ethyl alcohol in water*

*Data by Hoffman et al., 1953. Figure 31 (right). Surface tension of 1% by weight of ethyl alcohol in water vs. temperature. Data by Porwik et al., 1959*

significantly "disturb" the structural units of water which are responsible for the thermal anomalies observed in both bulk properties and surface properties.

### Example—The Mercury-Water Interface

The mercury-water interface has been studied in great detail over many years. We have already mentioned one of the more recent studies by Butler (16). The influence of applied electric potentials on the interfacial tension and on the differential capacity of the double layer at the mercury-water interface has been the subject of extensive studies since the last century. While even an elementary discussion of the main characteristics of the water-mercury interface is outside the scope of the present article, the attention of the reader is invited to the measurements by Graham (52) on the differential capacity as a function of applied potentials of the mercury-aqueous interface in the presence of sodium fluoride. Davies and Rideal (19) have discussed the findings of Graham, and in connection with the problem

interfacial phenomena at the air-water and water-hydrocarbon interfaces, it seems reasonable to propose that similar discreteness in the water structure also occurs at the water-mercury interface and may there be responsible for the intriguing results obtained by Graham.

### Example—Surface Film Studies

So far we have concentrated our attention on relatively simple systems such as pure water and dilute aqueous solutions, either in contact with air or with an organic liquid. However, to illustrate the generality of the qualitative findings of the preceding sections regarding the complexity of the aqueous surfaces, we shall now briefly discuss the extensive and interesting studies by A. A. Trapeznikov (100) on surface films.

Trapeznikov has measured the two-dimensional pressure versus temperature of equilibrium monolayers of palmitic acid spread on very dilute solutions of silver nitrate. (The melting point of palmitic acid is 64° C.) He finds that for the more dilute solutions ($10^{-5}$ and $5 \times$

$10^{-5} N$) the film pressure is zero up to 35° C., above which temperature the pressure exhibits a number of breaks. For a $10^{-3} N$ solution of $AgNO_3$ the film pressure is zero up to 57° C. Trapeznikov states: "It was found earlier that the curve for equilibrium pressure, $F_e = f(t)$, for palmitic acid on a solution of $CaCl_2$ has a break at $t = 34°$ to 35° C. A break at $t = 35°$ was also observed in conductometric experiments on bulk crystals of stearic acid in $Ba(OH)_2$ solution. It must, therefore, be concluded that this temperature corresponds to some new, hitherto unobserved, polymorphic transformation in the acid crystals or in the hydrates, in addition to the transformation observed at $t = 45–48°$ and at $t = 58–59°$ C.

"Thus, the study of the kinetics of formation of monolayers and the temperature dependence of the two-dimensional pressure of 'equilibrium' monolayers and electrolytic solutions has brought to light new phenomena of sorption of electrolytes by crystals of fatty acids out of aqueous solutions and new phase transformations in acid crystals due to hydration and the influence of adsorbed ions."

In his second study reported at the Second International Congress of Surface Activity, Trapeznikov described the electrical conductivity of solutions of silver nitrate in the presence of bulk crystals of palmitic acid. He showed that the conductivity of these solutions changed with time as the silver ions were adsorbed on the palmitic acid crystals and that the rate of adsorption was highly sensitive to the temperature. The change in conductivity was due to the initial loss of silver ions leading to the evolution of hydrogen ions (which possess greater mobility). From his data Trapeznikov concluded: "It is evident from the curves that $\tau_{min}$ (the time at which minimum conductance was observed) changes discontinuously at $T = 31°$ to 33°, 45° to 48° and 58° to 59° C., i.e., at the same characteristic temperatures that were observed in the earlier experiment and which should be connected with phase transformations in the crystals."

Trapeznikov finally describes how a direct microscopic observation under the polarizing microscope of single flakes of palmitic acid, when heated in a solution of thorium nitrate, changes in characteristic steps: "The crystal remains practically unchanged throughout its bulk up to $t = 43°$ C. whereas the edges begin to darken already at ordinary temperatures. At $t = 40°$ to 45° C., dark spots appear in the crystal surface; these grow darker as the temperature is raised to $t = 58°$ C.; however, the penetration of thorium ions into the crystal still proceeds comparatively slowly. At $t = 59°$ to 61° C., darkening of the crystals is sharply intensified, thus confirming that the total rate of the process increases irregularly leading to the transformation of the crystal of acid into a polycrystal of thorium soap, in agreement with the data in the electrical conductivity."

In the light of our present discussion of thermal anomalies, we believe it is reasonable to suggest that what Trapeznikov considers "new, hitherto unobserved, polymorphic transformations" is but a manifestation of the influence on the interfaces of the different water structures, changing more or less abruptly near 30°, 45°, and 60° C. [Drost-Hansen (25–28)].

## Summary

We believe it is safe to insist that the observed anomalous temperature and concentration dependencies of the surface and interfacial tension of water and aqueous solutions are real; likewise that the surface tension of pure water is apparently a very complicated function of temperature. The observed anomalies reflect the structural changes which we have claimed occur in bulk water; at the same time, the properties of aqueous surfaces seem to reflect additional peculiarities due to the different states of aggregation near an interface. The thickness of the surface layer is probably considerably larger than generally accepted; it may well be of the order of 10 to 20 molecular layers and possibly even greater. High values for dynamic surface tensions seem to be associated with low entropies of surface formation, at least near 15° C. It is our conviction that the surface tension of aqueous solutions of electrolytes cannot be predicted from the Onsager-Samaras theory. Furthermore, no theory at all is presently available to predict the observed surface tension or interfacial tension behavior of dilute solutions of alcohols. The addition of salts lead to marked anomalies in the surface potentials at more or less discrete concentrations.

The picture which emerges of water near a water-air interface (and also near a water-hydrocarbon interface) is thus one of considerable structure. The structure of the surface at 25° C. for example, contains elements of structure similar to the structures present in the bulk liquid. At the temperature of the thermal anomaly near 30° C., the large entropy of surface formation near 30° to 31° C. is undoubtedly due to the "melting" of structural clusters or "cages." The minimum in the entropy at a slightly higher temperature in turn corresponding to a state of greater ordering such as found, say, in a more nearly close packing of spherical molecules. For low concentrations of alcohol in solution, the structured clusters or "cages" are "reinforced" by incorporating alcohol molecules in low concentrations and a similar stabilization can possibly be achieved by the mere presence of hydrocarbon molecules, as in the case of the interfacial tension for water-hydrocarbon systems. Thus, the essential elements of the surface structure of water are probably clusters or "cages" which may serve as sites for solutes and possess individual stability and discreteness.

**AUTHOR**   *This article was written while Walter Drost-Hansen was Senior Research Chemist, Jersey Production Research Co., Tulsa, Okla. He is now Associate Professor of Chemical Physics at the Institute of Marine Science, University of Miami, Miami, Fla. He wishes to express his sincere appreciation to Henry S. Frank, Felix Franks, and Paul D. Cratin for many helpful suggestions, and to Edward B. Butler and Lynwood Heaver for their help in editing the original manuscript. The experimental assistance of R. W. Myers is also gratefully acknowledged.*

The sizes of the units involved are probably similar to those postulated by many authors as occurring in bulk water—the order of 20 to 200 molecules per cluster. See Frank and Quist (*39*), Nemethy and Scheraga (*81*), Buijs and Choppin (*15*), Drost-Hansen (*25*).

We have presented a variety of seemingly unrelated although individually quite interesting phenomena regarding the behavior and properties of aqueous surfaces and interfaces.   It is unfortunate that at the present time it is impossible to put all these individual observations into an overall scheme.   Yet the very diversity of the observations indicates the great complexity which prevails at the interface and which indeed makes a more unified treatment impossible at the present time.   However, the anomalies in the surface properties are of sufficiently general occurrence to suggest that these exist in all aqueous systems which are in contact with other phases.   Thus, the underlying structural transitions are probably of particular importance in those cases for which the surface-to-volume ratio is large as in biological systems, porous media (subsurface formations), emulsions, and colloids.

## LITERATURE CITED

(1) Adam, N. K., "The Physics and Chemistry of Surfaces," 3rd ed., Oxford, 1941.

(2) Adamson, A. W., "Physical Chemistry of Surfaces," p. 60, Interscience, New York, 1960.

(3) Addison, C. C., *J. Chem. Soc. (London)* **1943**, p. 535, Part I ; *J. Chem. Soc. (London)* **1945**, p. 354; and subsequent papers.

(4) Adinoff, B., Ph.D. thesis, University of Chicago, 1943.

(5) Alexander, A. E., in "Physical Methods of Organic Chemistry," A. Weissberger, ed., 3rd ed., p. 732, Interscience, New York, 1959.

(6) Andreas, J. M., Hauser, E. A., Tucker, W. B., *J. Phys. Chem.* **42**, 1001 (1938).

(7) Antonoff, G., in "Colloid Chemistry," Alexander, ed., Vol. VII, p. 83, 1950.

(8) Bordi, S., Vannel, F., *Ann. Chim.* **52**, 80 (1962).

(9) Bordi, S., Vannel, F., "Electrolytes," p. 196, Symposium, B. Pesce, ed., Pergamon, New York, 1962.

(10) Bordi, S., Vannel, F., *Gaz. Chim. Ital.* **92**, 82, 1962.

(11) Bordi, S., Vannel, F., *Ric. Sci.* **28**, 2039 (1958).

(12) Brown, A. C., Ives, D. J. G., *J. Chem. Soc. (London)* **1962**, p. 1608.

(13) Brown, R. C., McCormick, H., *Phil. Mag.* **39**, 420 (1948).

(14) Brunner, C., *Ann. der Physik und Chemie (Poggendorff's Annal.)* **70**, 481 (1847).

(15) Buijs, K., Choppin, G. R., *J. Chem. Phys.* **39**, 2035, 2042, (1963).

(16) Butler, E. B., *J. Phys. Chem.* **67**, 1419 (1963).

(17) Champion, F. C., Davy, N., "Properties of Matter," 3rd ed., p. 129, Philosophical Library, New York, 1959.

(18) Chang, S., Ree, T., Eyring, H., Matzner, I., in "Prog. in Intern. Research on Thermodynamics and Transport Properties," p. 88, Masi and Tsai, eds., Academic, New York, 1962.

(19) Davies, J. T., Rideal, E. K., "Interfacial Phenomena," Academic, 1961.

(20) Deryjagin, B. V., "Surface Chemical Compounds and their Role in Adsorption Phenomena," Conference Proc., Moscow, 1957, A. V. Kiselev, ed., AEC-translation-3750.

(21) Deryjagin, B. V., Fedyakin, N. N., *Doklady Akad. Nauk SSSR* **147**, 403 (1962). See also *Acta Physicohim. URSS* **10**, 25 and 153 (1939).

(22) Dole, M., *J. Am. Chem. Soc.* **60**, 904 (1938).

(23) Dole, M., Swartout, J. A., *J. Am. Chem. Soc.* **62**, 3039 (1940).

(24) Dorsey, N. E., "Properties of Ordinary Water Substance," Reinhold, New York, 1940.

(25) Drost-Hansen, W., Abstract 2I, 145th National Meeting ACS, New York, 1963; also New York Academy of Sciences Annals, Conference Monograph "Forms of Water in Biological Systems," 1965; also paper in preparation, First Int. Desalination Conf., October 1965.

(26) Drost-Hansen, W., Lavergne, M., *Naturwissenschaften* **43**, 511 (1956).

(27) Drost-Hansen, W., Myers, R. W., Abstract 5F, 144th National Meeting ACS, Los Angeles, 1963.

(28) Drost-Hansen, W., Neil, H. W., *Phys. Rev.* **100**, 1800 (1955).

(29) Dunken, H., *Z. Physik. Chemie* **47**, 195 (1940).

(30) Eigen, M., DeMaeyer, L., *Z. für Elektrochemie* **59**, 986 (1955).

(31) Feates, F. S., Ives, D. J. G., *J. Chem. Soc. (London)* **1956**, p. 2798.

(32) Ferguson, A., *Proc. Phys. Soc. (London)* **36**, 37 (1923); **44**, 511 (1932).

(33) Ferguson, A., Dowson, P. E., *Trans. Faraday Soc.* **17**, 384 (1922).

(34) Fordham, S., *Proc. Roy. Soc. (London)* **A194**, 1 (1948).

(35) Forslind, E., Handlingar, "Svenska Forskningsinstitute för Cement och Betong vid Kungl. Tekniska Högskolan, Stockholm," No. 16 (1952).

(36) Fowkes, F. M., *J. Phys. Chem.* **67**, 2538 (1963), and Fowkes, F. M., IND. ENG. CHEM. **56**, No. 12, 40–52 (Dec. 1964).

(37) Frank, H. S., personal communication, 1964.

(38) Frank, H. S., Evans, M. W., *J. Chem. Phys.* **13**, 507 (1945).

(39) Frank, H. S., Quist, A., *J. Chem. Phys.* **34**, 604 (1961).

(40) Frank, H. S., Wen, W-Y., *Discussions Faraday Soc.* No. **24**, 133 (1947).

(41) Franke, G., *Ann. Physik* 5te Folge, **14**, 675 (1932).

(42) Franks, F., *Chem. Ind.*, **1961**, p. 204.

(43) Franks, F., *Quart. Rev. (London)*, 1964, in press.

(44) Franks, F., Ives, D. J. G., *J. Chem. Soc. (London)* **1960**, p. 741.

(45) Franks, F., Johnson, H. H., *Trans. Faraday Soc.* **58**, 656 (1962).

(46) Freud, B. B., Freud, H. Z., *J. Am. Chem. Soc.* **52**, 1772 (1930).

(47) Gaddum, J. H., *Proc. Roy. Soc. (London)* **B109**, 114 (1931).

(48) Glew, D. N., *Nature* **195**, 698 (1962).

(49) Good, R. J., personnal communication.

(50) Good, R. J., *J. Phys. Chem.* **61**, 18 (1956).

(51) Gordieyeff, V. A., Hackley, E. B., *J. Chem. Educ.* **17**, 301 (1960).

(52) Graham, D. C., *J. Am. Chem. Soc.* **76**, 4819 (1954), and *J. Chem. Phys.* **23**, 1725 (1955).

(53) Green, H. S., in "Handbuck der Physik," vol. X, "Strucktur der Flüssigkeiten," p. 80–81, Flügge, ed., Springer Verlag, Berlin, 1960.

(54) Gross, P. L. K., Ph.D. thesis, University of Chicago, 1926.

(55) Guggenheim, E. A., "Thermodynamics," North-Holland Publ. Co., Amsterdam, 1959.

(56) Hacker, P. T., Proc. Conf. Interfacial Phenomena and Nucleation, Geophysical Research Paper, No. 37, Geophysics Research Director, Air Force Research Center, H. Reiss, ed., 1955.

(57) Harasima, A., in "Advances in Chemical Physics," Vol. I, p. 203, Prigogine, ed., Interscience, New York, 1958.

(58) Harkins, W. D., "The Physical Chemistry of Surface Films," Reinhold, New York, 1952.

(59) Harkins, W. D., Alexander, A. E., in "Physical Methods of Organic Chemistry," A. Weissberger, ed., 3rd ed., p. 757, Interscience, New York, 1959.

(60) Harkins, W. D., Brown, F. E., see Harkins and Alexander.

(61) Harkins, W. D., Jordan, H. F., *J. Am. Chem. Soc.* **52**, 1751 (1930).

(62) Harned, H. S., Owen, B. O., "The Physical Chemistry of Electrolytic Solutions," 3rd ed., Reinhold, New York, 1958.

(63) Haydon, D. A., in "Recent Progress in Surface Science," p. 94, Danielli, Parkhurst, and Riddiford, eds., Vol. I, Academic, N. Y., 1964.

(64) Henniker, J. C., *Rev. Mod. Phys.* **21**, 322 (1949).

(65) Hiss, R., Dissertation, Heidelberg, 1913.

(66) Hoffman, W., Schoeneck, H., Wanniger, W., *Zeit. für Physik. Chemie*, Neue Folge II, 56 (1957).

(67) Jones, G., Ray, W. A., *J. Am. Chem. Soc.* **59**, 187 (1937).

(68) *Ibid.*, **63**, 288 (1941).

(69) Kamienski, B., *Electrochimica Acta* **1**, 272 (1959).

(70) Kitchener, J. A., *Nature* **182**, 1667 (1958).

(71) Kleinman, E., *Ann. Physik*, Ser. 4, **80**, 245 (1926).

(72) Knacke, O., Stranski, I. N., *Progr. in Metal Physics*, 181 (1956).

(73) Krynitsky, J. A., Garret, W. D., *J. Colloid Science* **18**, 893 (1963).

(74) Landolt-Börnstein, II Band, 3. Teil "Schmelzgleichgewichte und Grenzflächenerscheinungen," p. 421, 6th ed., 1956.

(75) Langmuir, I., *Science* **88**, 430 (1937); and *J. Chem. Phys.* **6**, 873 (1938).

(76) Loeb, L. B., "Static Electrification," Springer-Verlag, 1958.   See also "Progress In Dielectrics," Vol. 4, p. 249, J. B. Birks, ed., Academic, 1962.

(77) Low, P., "Advances in Agronomy," **13**, 269 (1961).

(78) Magat, M., *Journ. de Physique et le Radium*, Series 7 **6**, 179 (1935).

(79) Morgan, J. L. R., McAfee, A. McD., *J. Am. Chem. Soc.* **33**, 1275 (1911).

(80) Moser, H., *Ann. Physik* **82**, 993 (1927).

(81) Nemethy, G., Scheraga, H. A., *J. Chem. Phys.* **36**, 3382 (1962); *J. Chem. Phys.* **36**, 3401 (1962).

(82) Ono, S., Kondo, S., Handbuch der Physik, Vol. X, "Strucktur der Flüssigkeiten," p. 134, Flügge, ed., Springer Verlag, Berlin, 1960.

(83) Onsager, L., see Harned and Owen, *loc. cit.*, p. 541.

(84) Padday, J. F., Third Internat. Congr. of Surface Activity, Cologne, Vol. I, p. 233, Academic, New York, 1960.

(85) Pallasch, R., *Ann. Physik* **40**, 463 (1941).

(86) Partington, J. R., "An Advanced Treatise on Physical Chemistry," Vol. II, Longmans, Green and Co., London, 1951.

(87) Porwik, F., *Poznan. Towarz. Przyjaciol. Nauk. Wydzial. Mat. Pryzrod., Prace Komisji Mat. Przyrod.* **8**, 131 (1961).

(88) Posner, A. M., Alexander, A. E., *Trans. Faraday Soc.* **45**, 651 (1949).

(88A) Ree, T. S., Ree, T., Eyring, H., *J. Chem. Phys.* **41**, No. 2, 524–30 (1964).

(89) Schäfer, K., Masia, A. P., Jüntgen, H., *Zeit. fur Elektrochemie* **59**, 233 (1955).

(90) Schmidt, F., Steyer, H., *Ann. Physik* (4) **79**, 442 (1926).

(91) Smith, G. W., Sorg, L. V., *J. Phys. Chem.* **45**, 671 (1941), *J. Phys. Chem.* **48**, 168 (1944).

(92) Sparnay, M. J., Third Internat. Congr. of Surface Activity, Cologne, p. 232, Academic, New York, 1960, p. 232.

(93) Stephens, P. W., "Gas/Liquid and Liquid/Liquid Interfaces, A Bibliography," Vol. I and II, Joseph Crosfield and Sons, Ltd., Warrington, 1962.

(94) Stuke, B., *Zeit. für Elektrochemie* **63**, 140 (1959).

(95) Tammann, *Zeit. für anorg. und. allgemeine Chemie* **235**, 49 (1937).

(96) Taylor, J. E., *J. Chem. Educ.* **37**, 204 (1960).

(97) Teitelbaum, B. Y., Tritonov, N. A., Kachaturyan, V. R., (1947).   See Timmermans, J., "Physico-Chemical Constants of Binary Systems in Concentrated Solutions," Vol. 4, p. 45, Interscience, New York, 1960.

(98) Timmermans, J., "Physico-Chemical Constants of Binary Systems in Concentrated Solutions," Vol. 4, Interscience, New York, 1960.

(99) Timmermans, J., Bodson, H., *Compt. Rend.* **204**, 1804, 1937.

(100) Trapeznikov, A. A., Second International Congress of Surface Activity, Vol. I, pages 109 and 121, Academic, New York, 1957.

(101) Vaslow, F., *J. Phys. Chem.* **67**, 2773, 1963.

(102) Ward, A. F. H., Tordai, L., *Rec. trav. Chim.* **71**, 396 (1952).

(103) Wolf, C., *Poggendorf Annalen* **102**, 571 (1857) (*Ann. der Physik and Chemie* **178**).

(104) Wolf, K. L., "Physik und Chemie der Grenzflächen," p. 105, Springer Verlag, Berlin, 1957.

(105) Workman, E. J., Reynolds, S. E., *Phys. Rev.* **78**, 254 (1950).

# 4

# Adsorption and Thermodynamics at Liquid–Liquid Interfaces

SYDNEY ROSS    E. S. CHEN

# ADSORPTION AND THERMODYNAMICS AT THE
# LIQUID—LIQUID INTERFACE

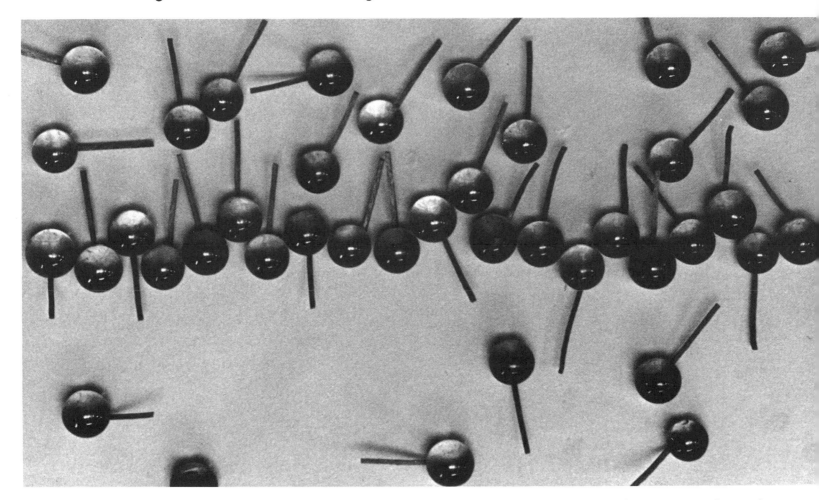

*Measurements of interfacial tensions can be used to obtain free energies of adsorption of a surface-active solute at the interface. This article shows how to perform the necessary calculations, and explains the meaning of the concepts that are introduced in the development of the procedure*

Adsorption from solution at the liquid/liquid interface is measured by means of the interfacial-tension isotherm—i.e., the variation at constant temperature of interfacial tension as a function of the concentration of a surface-active agent in one of the bulk-liquid phases. The agent may be distributed to a significant degree in both liquids, in which case its equilibrium concentration in one of the liquids must be measured independently. On the other hand, it may be so insoluble in one of the liquids that the equilibrium concentration in the solution phase can be calculated from the total quantity of solute originally added. By the term "surface-active agent" we mean any solute that reduces the interfacial tension, even though such solutes may be quite unlike the materials supplied commercially for that purpose. The latter agents exert a powerful effect at a low concentration, but for the purpose of scientific study this property is disadvantageous as it requires the measurement of extremely low concentrations of solute. Furthermore, the commercially available agents are never of sufficient purity, nor can they always be readily purified by available facilities. Finally, the powerful surface-active agents form micelles in the bulk-solution phase, and the presence of new molecular species makes the analysis of the observations more complex. All these disadvantages can be avoided by using solutes of low molecular weight, obtained in a pure state by vapor chromatography. Many such oil-soluble agents are available that are sufficiently surface active at an oil/water interface, but do not form micelles. The interfacial-tension isotherms that are then obtained are free from some of the more prominent defects that can make such data suspect. The present paper is devoted to methods of using interfacial-tension or surface-tension isotherms to derive thermodynamic functions pertaining to the solute, and of examining the question of whether such data can be used to obtain molecular dimensions and molecular interactions in the surface phase.

The subject of the thermodynamics of adsorption from solution at a liquid/liquid or vapor/liquid interface is vexed by a lack of agreement on the selection of a standard state for the interfacial or surface phase. Ward and Tordai (19) chose as standard states in both the bulk and surface phases a concentration of 1 molecule per cc. and then introduced a film thickness, $\delta$, for the surface phase, so that surface concentrations could be expressed in the same units as bulk concentrations. The value of $\delta$ varied with the solute, and was intended to represent the most probable length of the hydrocarbon chain plus 4.22 A. for the —COOH group. This length was assumed invariant with temperature.

Kemball and Rideal (11) used a standard state of 1 atmosphere for both surface and bulk phases and adopted a fixed and arbitrary film thickness of 6.00 A. to convert surface pressure into the same units as bulk pressure. Posner, Anderson, and Alexander (14) followed Ward and Tordai, with a value of $\delta$ based on the most probable length of the hydrocarbon chain plus 2.50 A. for the length of the —OH group. Jones, Ottewill, and Chater (10) elected to follow Kemball and Rideal. Other authors (9, 12) have been content merely to report experimental data, sometimes venturing so far as to calculate surface concentrations by means of the Gibbs adsorption theorem, without making any attempt to estimate the standard changes of the thermodynamic functions. Probably the unsettled character of this part of the subject is responsible for their caution.

The choice of a standard concentration is itself arbitrary, but the arbitrariness is tolerable since the state remains the same for all systems. But the introduction of a second arbitrary parameter, the value for film thickness, is one arbitrary parameter too many. The simi-

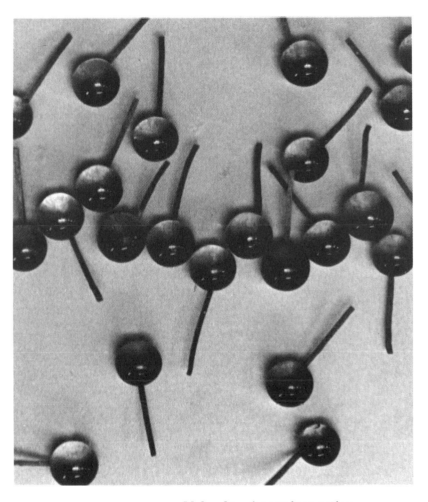

*Molecules of a surface-active agent orient themselves at the interface between a lipoid phase (above) and a water phase (below)*

larity of surface states is now destroyed, as $\delta = 6.00$ A. has a different meaning in terms of molar concentration when applied to different solutes. Varying the value of $\delta$ to suit the solute is an improvement, but the uncertainty of the proper value to use still remains, especially when one recalls that the estimated length of the solute molecule, which is the basis for the selected value of $\delta$, is not really relevant to the thickness of the surface phase. Thickness of surface phase is actually dependent on the position of the Gibbs surface that makes the excess surface concentration of the *solvent* equal zero.

The lack of uniformity among the investigators is not the most deplorable feature of this situation. More reprehensible is the introduction of such an uncertain parameter as film thickness, with its cognate assumptions that the adsorbed film is a monolayer and that the adsorbate molecules are oriented with the long axis normal to the interface. Those assumptions make uncertain any comparisons that one might wish to draw of standard free energy changes or standard entropy changes between different solutes or different interfaces. Since such comparisons are potentially the most valuable result that can be obtained from these laborious investigations, the problem of the standard state of the surface phase has acquired some importance. The plan to publish the revised International Critical Tables, which will include surface chemistry and physics, has made urgent the question of establishing a standard state that can be used for valid comparisons, and that will be applicable to any system for which appropriate data are available. In this paper we propose such a standard state and show how calculations can be made of the standard changes in the thermodynamic functions without introducing the parameter of film thickness, which has been the weakness of nearly all previous suggestions. At the same time, the standard state of the *bulk* phase should not be left to the caprice of authors. The units of concentration determine the standard state of the bulk phase; it may be 1 mole per liter of solution (molarity), 1 mole per 1000 grams of solvent (molality), or pure solute (mole fraction equal to unity). Standard free-energy changes calculated from surface-tension data are not comparable unless the same units of concentration are used as in the original measurements. The units of concentration are not interconvertible unless the density of each solution is reported, and this is seldom done in practice. For economy of mathematical expression, the mole fraction is the preferred unit. Only a few measurements, it is true, have actually been made in terms of mole fraction; but that need not affect our advocating this unit, for most of the previous work is likely to be repeated soon. The strong effect of impurities on surface and interfacial tensions makes purity of materials of paramount importance. The data now available are far from accurate because of insufficiencies in the isolation of pure materials. But chromatographic methods of separating substances now make possible hitherto-unattainable standards of purity. We may, therefore, expect to see much of the older data redetermined with materials of the requisite

quality. Let us be prepared, before this new work is well advanced, with standard states that are sufficiently logical to gain wide acceptance and avoid producing again the conflict and confusion that now prevail.

A lack of agreement about standard states is not the only weakness that requires correction in the usual way of treating the data of surface tension to obtain thermodynamic functions relating to adsorption. The measurements of surface tension *vs.* concentration cannot, with existing techniques, be carried out at such dilutions as are necessary to ensure that the surface film behave as an ideal two-dimensional gas. The treatment of data obtained at higher concentrations requires an extrapolation to infinite dilution, if ideal equations are to be used in calculating thermodynamic functions. None of the previous suggestions for performing this extrapolation is theoretically sound, and the second objective of this paper is to describe an improvement in the performance of this task.

### Concentration in the Interfacial Phase

The theory developed in this section is intended for ultimate application to a three-component system—oil, solute, and water. Hutchinson (9) pointed out in 1948 that although film behavior at oil/water and solid (protein)/water interfaces had an important bearing on biological phenomena, the field was relatively unexplored. The passing of 16 years has done little to dispel this neglect. The present contribution serves as the introduction to a series of researches to be devoted to soluble adsorbed films at the liquid/liquid interface. The treatment is sufficiently general, however, to admit of ready application to soluble films at the vapor/liquid interface.

Gibbs's adsorption theorem may be written

$$-\partial\gamma = \sum_i \Gamma_i \partial\mu_i \quad \text{(Constant } T) \qquad (1)$$

where $\Gamma$ represents concentration in the interfacial phase in moles/sq. cm.—i.e., $\Gamma_i = n_i/A$. The surface concentrations defined by $\Gamma_i$ are *total* surface concentrations. Equation 1 is often written, as for example by Gibbs, with $\Gamma_i$ defined as *excess* surface concentration. The relation between the two can be readily demonstrated: Suppose we have a system in which the solute has zero surface activity; then $\Gamma_i$ would not really differ from bulk concentration of component $i$, though expressed in different units. Let $\Gamma_i{}^b$ represent the surface concentrations under those conditions; then

$$-\partial\gamma = 0 = \sum_i \Gamma_i{}^b \partial\mu_i \qquad (1A)$$

Subtracting the above equation from Equation 1 gives

$$-\partial\gamma = \sum_i (\Gamma_i - \Gamma_i{}^b)\partial\mu_i \qquad (1B)$$

The term $(\Gamma_i - \Gamma_i{}^b)$ represents the *excess* surface concentration; Equations 1 and 1B have the same form with a different significance attached to the coefficient terms.

We shall use the subscripts 1, 2, and 3 to designate oil, solute, and water, respectively; and $L$ and $W$ to designate the oil (lipoid) and water phases. In applying Equation 1, two geometrical plane surfaces have to be placed to separate the interfacial phase from the bulk oil and water phases. More than one convention is possible in placing these surfaces because Equation 1 remains true no matter where the imaginary surfaces are drawn, although the individual values of $\Gamma_i$ are affected. A convenient and natural choice would be so to select the limits that they enclose the actual number of solute and solvent molecules in the film, which, at low concentrations, is likely to be no more than a monolayer. This convention corresponds to the $u$-convention of Hutchinson (9). The argument that follows is not, however, restricted by the assumption that the adsorbed film is monomolecular. Equation 1 would read for three components

$$-\partial\gamma = \Gamma_1\partial\mu_1 + \Gamma_2\partial\mu_2 + \Gamma_3\partial\mu_3 \qquad (2)$$

The Gibbs-Duhem equation applied to the oil phase ($L$) and to the water phase ($W$) gives us two more relations, which, if we can suppose the oil and water phases to have negligible mutual solubility, are as follows:

$$_LN_1\partial\mu_1 + {_L}N_2\partial\mu_2 = 0 \qquad (3)$$

$$_WN_2\partial\mu_2 + {_W}N_3\partial\mu_3 = 0 \qquad (4)$$

We can use Equations 3 and 4 to get the following:

$$\partial\mu_1 = -\left(\frac{_LN_2}{_LN_1}\right)\partial\mu_2 \qquad (5)$$

$$\partial\mu_3 = -\left(\frac{_WN_2}{_WN_3}\right)\partial\mu_2 \qquad (6)$$

Substituting Equations 5 and 6 in Equation 2 gives

$$-\partial\gamma = \left[\Gamma_2 - \left(\frac{_LN_2}{_LN_1}\right)\Gamma_1 - \left(\frac{_WN_2}{_WN_3}\right)\Gamma_3\right]\partial\mu_2 \qquad (7)$$

The whole coefficient of the term in $\partial\mu_2$ has the units of moles of component-2 per sq. cm.; it is, therefore, some kind of surface concentration of the solute, which it is convenient to designate by a separate symbol, $\Gamma_2{}^G$ (the Gibbs convention); or

$$\Gamma_2{}^G = \Gamma_2 - \left(\frac{_LN_2}{_LN_1}\right)\Gamma_1 - \left(\frac{_WN_2}{_WN_3}\right)\Gamma_3 \qquad (8)$$

Although variation in the conventions for fixing the plane boundary between the bulk and the surface phases causes variation in the separate values of $\Gamma_1$, $\Gamma_2$, and $\Gamma_3$, it cannot cause any variation in $\partial\gamma$. Therefore, the expression for $\Gamma_2{}^G$ given by Equation 8 is invariant regardless of how one regulates the convention. The invariant quantity given by Equation 8 is essentially the same as the quantity defined by Gibbs, denoted by him by the symbol $\Gamma_{2(1)}$, and usually called the "excess surface concentration." When both liquid phases contribute the same solute to the interface, the Gibbs excess concentration is the sum of the two excess concentrations from each immiscible phase.

A clearer understanding of the meaning of the Gibbs convention and the $u$-convention (or any other convention for defining $\Gamma_i$) can be gained by using small whole numbers to designate relative concentrations in the bulk and in the interfacial phases. Suppose the oil and aqueous phases are in equilibrium with the solute distributed in each phase, having a mole fraction of one

fifth and one seventh, respectively. Let the solute be positively adsorbed at the interface from each bulk phase according to the numbers in the diagram (Figure 1). The box on the left shows the $u$-convention in which the boundaries separating the interfacial phase are drawn immediately below the adsorbed layer, *which is not necessarily a monolayer.* The box on the right shows the Gibbs convention, with the boundaries of separation drawn so as to make the surface excess of solvent in each phase equal zero. To do so, the boundary must be raised by an additional one eighth of its thickness in the

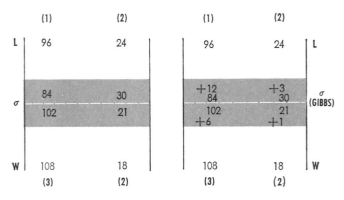

*Figure 1. Numerical representation of the Gibbs convention for "excess surface concentration" of solute at an oil/water interface, with the solute distributed between two bulk liquid phases and the interfacial phase. For these two cases:*

| U-CONVENTION | GIBBS CONVENTION |
|---|---|
| $\Gamma_1 = 84$ | $\Gamma_1{}^G = 0$; $\Gamma_3{}^G = 0$ |
| $\Gamma_2 = 30 + 21 = 51$ | $\Gamma_2{}^G$ in $L$-phase $= 33 - 24 = 9$ |
| $\Gamma_3 = 102$ | $\Gamma_2{}^G$ in $W$-phase $= 22 - 18 = 4$ |
| $\dfrac{_LN_2}{_LN_1} = \dfrac{1}{4}$; $\dfrac{_WN_2}{_WN_3} = \dfrac{1}{6}$ | Total $\Gamma_2{}^G \qquad\qquad = 13$ |

$$\text{Total } \Gamma_2{}^G = 51 - \frac{1}{4}(84) - \frac{1}{6}(102)$$
$$= 51 - 21 - 17 = 13$$

$L$-phase, and lowered by an additional one eighteenth of this thickness in the $W$-phase. This is done so that 12 additional molecular parts of solvent $L$ can be added to the $\sigma$-phase to bring its total up to 96, and so that 6 additional parts of solvent $W$ can be added to the $\sigma$-phase to bring its total up to 108. These conditions are the requirements that define the boundaries of the Gibbs layer. The number of solute molecules in the Gibbs layer has, meanwhile, been increased by 3 parts from the $L$-phase and 1 part from the $W$-phase. The total excess surface concentration of solute is $33 - 24 = 9$ parts with respect to the $L$-phase, plus $22 - 18 = 4$ parts with respect to the $W$-phase; or 13 parts in all. If we apply Equation 8, we get the same answer:

$$\Gamma_2{}^G = 51 - \frac{1}{4}(84) - \frac{1}{6}(102) = 13$$

No matter where the boundaries are drawn, the expression on the right-hand side of Equation 8 is invariant;

any increase in the $\Gamma_2$-term, which would arise by placing the boundaries of separation deeper in each of the bulk phases, is exactly offset by increases in the other two terms. Suppose, for example, we should decide to set the boundaries at the layer thickness demanded by the Gibbs convention in our numerical illustration. We should then have: $\Gamma_1 = 84 + 12 = 96$; $\Gamma_2 = 33 + 22 = 55$; $\Gamma_3 = 102 + 6 = 108$. Applying Equation 8,

$$\Gamma_2{}^G = 55 - \frac{1}{4}(96) - \frac{1}{6}(108) = 13$$

From this one can see that even if we use the same boundary of separation, the numerical values of $\Gamma_2$ and $\Gamma_2{}^G$ are not the same. Only at the limit $N_2 \rightarrow 0$ would it be correct to equate $\Gamma_2$ and $\Gamma_2{}^G$, where they both tend to zero.

Some authors represent the behavior of the soluble adsorbed film in terms of a relation between $\pi$ and area per mole of solute, thus making a close mathematical analogy between soluble films and insoluble adsorbed films on a liquid surface. Here, $\pi$ is the lowering of interfacial tension ($\pi = \gamma_0 - \gamma$). Two different kinds of area are possible depending on whether we define it as

$$A = 1/\Gamma_2{}^G \qquad (9)$$

or
$$\mathbf{A} = 1/\Gamma_2{}^u \qquad (10)$$

The former choice, Equation 9, is the simplest to use in practice, but it has a certain physical artificiality (to be discussed later) that creates an antipathy toward it in certain minds. It is the necessary choice, however, if the equation $d\pi = (1/A)d\mu_2$ is also to be used in the treatment. The latter choice, defined by $\mathbf{A}$, Equation 10, represents the actual area occupied per mole at the interface. Only one author, namely Hutchinson (9), has, as far as we know, ever taken the pains to work with this selection of $\mathbf{A}$. He has shown how it might be done and the requirements that must be met in the course of evaluating it. These requirements are:

(a) that the adsorbed film be monomolecular
(b) that the limiting areas per molecule of solvent and solute in the interface can be obtained from independent considerations—e.g., insoluble films or monolayers

These conditions are so special that the use of $\mathbf{A}$, in many respects a more attractive parameter than $A$, has not met with further acceptance.

### Standard State of the Interfacial Phase

The generally adopted standard state of the adsorbed film in studies of gas/solid adsorption is one originally suggested by de Boer (2). It is defined, by analogy with the standard state of a gas, in terms of a two-dimensional spreading pressure, $\pi^0$, where $\pi^0 = 0.338$ dyne/cm. The advantage of adopting the same standard state for the soluble adsorbed films at liquid/liquid and vapor/liquid interfaces is that values for the standard changes of the thermodynamic functions can then be compared directly for adsorption at different types of interface.

The thermodynamics of adsorption at the solid/liquid interface could also be brought to conform to this convention, when that subject has been sufficiently developed.

The source of the value $\pi^0 = 0.338$ dyne/cm. lies in de Boer's original definition of the standard two-dimensional spreading pressure: He defined it as the spreading pressure at which an ideal two-dimensional gas at 0° C. would have its molecules at the same average distance of separation as the molecules in an ideal three-dimensional gas at standard temperature and pressure. An ideal gas has a molar volume of 22,400 cc. and therefore has a molecular volume of $22,400/(6.02 \times 10^{23})$ cc. or $3.72 \times 10^{-20}$ cc.; the average distance of separation is the cube root of $3.72 \times 10^{-20}$ cc. or $33.4 \times 10^{-8}$ cm.; the average molecular area is $(33.4 \times 10^{-8})^2$ sq. cm. or $1114 \times 10^{-16}$ sq. cm. The standard spreading pressure, $\pi^0$, is then calculated from $\pi^0\sigma^0 = RT/N$, where $\sigma^0 = 1114 \times 10^{-16}$ sq. cm./molecule and $T = 273.1°$ K., from which $\pi^0 = 0.338$ dyne/cm. The value of $\pi^0$ is invariant with temperature, but $\sigma^0$ varies according to $\pi^0\sigma^0 = RT/N$, which gives

$$\sigma^0 = \frac{1.38 \times 10^{-16}}{0.338} T = (4.08 \times 10^{-16}) T$$

Although the ideal two-dimensional gas law was used in arriving at $\pi^0$, the value, once obtained, is completely arbitrary and implies no assumption that any actual adsorbed film is described by $\pi\sigma = RT/N$.

### Expressions for the Thermodynamic Functions

For convenience we shall now drop the anterior subscripts $L$ and $W$; the bulk phase may be considered as the liquid in which the equilibrium concentration of the solute is known.

The chemical potential of the solute in the bulk phase is given by

$$\mu_2 = \mu_2{}^0 + RT \ln \gamma_2 N_2 \qquad (11)$$

where $\mu_2{}^0$ is the chemical potential of the solute in its standard state, and $\gamma_2$ is the activity coefficient defined by the ideal dilute solution. The standard state of the solute is the hypothetical state in which $N_2 = 1$ and $\gamma_2 = 1$—i.e., the pure solute has the properties it would have in an infinitely dilute solution in the bulk phase.

We are free to select any convenient system of expressing *surface* concentration, always remembering that the selection once made establishes the units for the standard state of the interfacial phase. The most convenient to use is the Gibbs excess, $\Gamma_2{}^G$; the chemical potential of the solute in the interfacial phase is then

$$\mu_2{}^s = \mu_2{}^{0s} + RT \ln (\Gamma_2{}^G/\Gamma_2{}^{0G}) \qquad (12)$$

**AUTHOR** *Sydney Ross is Professor of Colloid Science, at Rensselaer Polytechnic Institute, Troy, N. Y. E. S. Chen is Surface Chemist with Watervliet Arsenal, Watervliet, N. Y. When this article was written, he held a graduate fellowship in colloid science at Rensselaer, sponsored by the Silicones Division of Union Carbide Corp.*

where the superscript $s$ refers to the interfacial phase. In Equation 12 the activity coefficient is omitted, although at high concentrations this can be a serious error, and activities rather than concentrations should be used. In the bulk-solution phase, $N_2$ denotes the concentration as the mole fraction of solute; in the interfacial phase, $\Gamma_2{}^G$ denotes the surface concentration in excess moles of solute per sq. cm. of interfacial area.

At equilibrium, the chemical potentials of the solute in the bulk solution and in the interfacial phase are equal:

$$\mu_2 = \mu_2{}^s \tag{13}$$

Previous writers, before applying Equation 13, perhaps from a mistaken impression that the two chemical potentials could not otherwise be equated, have taken pains to make sure that the concentrations in the bulk solution and in the interfacial solution are expressed in the same units. To do so, they have had to introduce the thickness of the interfacial film. But no advantage—indeed, a manifest disadvantage—attends this procedure. The value of $\mu_2$ is not affected by whatever mode of expressing concentration we choose to adopt (8), and for the interfacial phase, the most convenient concentration is expressed in moles/sq. cm.

Equating the chemical potentials defined by Equations 11 and 12 gives

$$\frac{\Gamma_2{}^G}{\Gamma_2{}^{0G}} = N_2 \exp[(\mu_2{}^0 - \mu_2{}^{0s})/RT] =$$
$$N_2 \exp(\Delta G^0/RT) \tag{14}$$

where $\Delta G^0$, the standard change of the Gibbs free energy for the desorption of 1 mole of solute from the interface, is

$$\Delta G^0 = \mu_2{}^0 - \mu_2{}^{0s} \tag{15}$$

At sufficiently low concentrations of solute, the experimental results are described by a linear dependence of $\gamma$ on concentration at constant temperature:

$$\pi = \gamma_0 - \gamma = mN_2 \tag{16}$$

or
$$\partial\pi = -\partial\gamma = m\partial N_2 \tag{17}$$

where $m$ is the slope of the isotherm.

From Equation 7, in the form

$$-\partial\gamma = \Gamma_2{}^G\partial\mu_2$$

by substitution in Equation 17, we get

$$\Gamma_2{}^G\partial\mu_2 = m\partial N_2 \tag{18}$$

If the solution is sufficiently dilute to show a linear $\pi$ vs. $N_2$ dependence, as described by Equation 16, indicative of an ideal solution in the interfacial phase, then it would also be permissible to treat the bulk solution as ideal; hence

$$\partial\mu_2 = RT\,\partial \ln N_2 \tag{19}$$

Combining Equations 18 and 19 gives

$$\Gamma_2{}^G = mN_2/RT \tag{20}$$

We wish to evaluate the ratio $\Gamma_2{}^G/\Gamma_2{}^{0G}$, which appears in Equation 14. When the interfacial solution is ideal we can use Equation 20 for this purpose, which gives

$$\Gamma_2{}^G/\Gamma_2{}^{0G} = N_2/N_2{}^{0G} \tag{21}$$

where $N_2{}^{0G}$ is the bulk concentration corresponding to the standard surface concentration designated $\Gamma_2{}^{0G}$. We can evaluate $N_2{}^{0G}$ by means of Equation 16 so that:

$$N_2{}^{0G} = \pi^0/m \tag{22}$$

Hence, Equation 14 becomes

$$\Delta G^0 = RT \ln (m/\pi^0) \tag{23}$$

The other thermodynamic functions for desorption can readily be evaluated from Equation 23. Differentiating with respect to $T$ gives

$$-\frac{\Delta G^0}{RT^2} + \frac{1}{RT}\frac{d\Delta G^0}{dT} = \frac{d \ln m}{dT}$$

which, since $d\Delta G^0/dT = -\Delta S^0$, becomes

$$-\Delta G^0 - T\Delta S^0 = -\Delta H^0 = RT^2 \frac{d \ln m}{dT} \tag{24}$$

Also

$$\Delta S^0 = (\Delta H^0 - \Delta G^0)/T \tag{25}$$

All these functions can therefore be obtained from the slopes of $\pi$ vs. $N_2$ isotherms at the limit $\pi \to 0$.

To this point we have developed the standard changes of the thermodynamic functions in terms of *mole fraction* as the unit of concentration. Our purpose in so doing is to encourage the use of that unit by future investigators. If we wish to consult the data that are currently available, however, we shall need to have expressions for a more commonly used unit, such as molarity. Let $c_2$ denote the concentration in moles of solute per liter of solution, and let **m** be the slope of the linear portion of the isotherm $\pi$ vs. $c_2$; then

$$\pi = \gamma_0 - \gamma = \mathbf{m}c_2 \tag{16A}$$

The corresponding equation for $\Delta\mathbf{G}^0$ is

$$\Delta\mathbf{G}^0 = RT \ln \frac{\mathbf{m}}{\pi_0} \tag{23A}$$

The standard free-energy change denoted by $\Delta\mathbf{G}^0$ is for the transfer of 1 mole of solute from the standard state of the interfacial film to the standard state of the bulk solution ($c_2 = 1$); $\Delta\mathbf{G}^0$ differs from $\Delta G^0$ in the choice of the standard state of the bulk solution, which is pure solute of the hypothetical sort already mentioned in the latter case.

### Equations for the Surface Tension Isotherm

The linear relation between surface or interfacial tension and concentration, which is the behavior by which we recognize the ideal interfacial solution, is to be observed only with dilute solutions; with solutes of pronounced surface activity, such as soaps or other detergents, the dilution required to get into the range of ideality of the interfacial solution is so extreme that such minute concentrations are rarely the subject of measurements. Solutes of low or moderate surface activity, however, can produce ideal solutions in the interfacial phase at equilibrium bulk concentrations that are several orders of magnitude greater. Most of the recorded data refer, however, to bulk concentrations that are too great for an ideal solution to exist at the interface. To evaluate the thermodynamic functions, the experimental value of the initial slope of the isotherm is required. Occasionally the data are sufficiently extensive to allow the initial slope to be measured with fair accuracy, but more often it has to be obtained by mathematical analysis.

An empirical formula that gives the relation between $\gamma$ and $c_2$ very satisfactorily was published by von Szyszkowski (*17*) in 1908. It is

$$\frac{\gamma_0 - \gamma}{\gamma_0} = \mathbf{b} \log \left( \frac{c_2}{\mathbf{c}} + 1 \right) \qquad (26)$$

where $\mathbf{b}$ and $\mathbf{c}$ are constants. Freundlich (*7*) quotes a selection of older data for aqueous solutions, as concentrated as 1 molar, that are well represented by Equation

## TABLE I. STANDARD MOLAR FREE ENERGIES OF DESORPTION

### FATTY ACIDS AT A WATER/VAPOR SURFACE

| Adsorbate | *t*, ° C. | *Freundlich (7)* $\Delta G^0$, kcal./mole | $\Delta G^0$, per $CH_2$, cal./mole | *Ward (19)* $\Delta G^0$ at 20°C., kcal./mole | $\Delta G^0$ per $CH_2$, cal./mole |
|---|---|---|---|---|---|
| Formic acid | 15 | 1.706 | | | |
| Acetic acid | 15 | 2.488 | 782 | | |
| Propionic acid | 15 | 3.174 | 686 | | |
| *n*-Butyric acid | 18.5 | 3.842 | 668 | 3.59 | |
| *n*-Valeric acid | 17.5 | 4.553 | 711 | 4.36 | 770 |
| *n*-Hexoic | 19 | 5.285 | 732 | 4.93 | 570 |
| *n*-Heptoic | 18 | 5.981 | 696 | 5.74 | 810 |
| *n*-Octoic | 18 | 6.959 | 978 | 6.63 | 890 |
| *n*-Nonoic | 18 | 7.416 | 457 | 7.34 | 710 |
| *n*-Decanoic | ... | ... | | 8.31 | 970 |
| | | | Average 714 | | Average 787 |

26. The initial slope as $c_2$ tends to zero can be evaluated by using the approximation $\log (1 + x) = x$ for small values of $x$; hence, for very dilute solutions

$$\gamma_0 - \gamma = \pi = \gamma_0 \mathbf{b} c_2 / \mathbf{c} = \mathbf{m} c_2 \qquad (27)$$

where

$$\mathbf{m} = \gamma_0 \mathbf{b} / \mathbf{c} \qquad (28)$$

Values of $\mathbf{b}$ and $\mathbf{c}$ for aqueous solutions of the fatty acids are reported by Freundlich (*7*), from which the standard molar free energies of desorption can be calculated by means of Equations 28 and 23A. The results are included in Table I.

More recently Ward (*19*) has published a set of values of $\mathbf{m}$ for aqueous solutions of the fatty acids, which data were critically selected from published literature on the subject. A correction, using the dissociation constant, for the degree of ionization of the acid was made, so that $\mathbf{m}$ could be based only in terms of the actual concentra-

tion of undissociated acid; the correction was more significant for the higher acids where the solutes were of low concentrations, entailing a higher degree of dissociation. The values of $\mathbf{m}$ and the values of $\Delta G^0$ calculated therefrom by Equation 23A are also reported in Table I for comparison with the earlier data and the indirect method of obtaining $\mathbf{m}$. The agreement is poor, and the increase in $\Delta G^0$ per —$CH_2$— added to the chain shows a rather wide variation, with a mean of about 750 cal./mole. The difficulty of obtaining a pure solute is probably the chief source of the discrepancies.

For strongly surface-active agents the method of obtaining the initial slope by direct measurement at low concentration is not practicable. For example, Ward and Tordai (*19*) report for the water/hexane interface that at concentrations of lauric acid in hexane as low as $10^{-4}$ molal, the linear portion of the $\gamma$ vs. $c_2$ curve was still not reached. For this reason, analytical equations that relate experimental measurements of $\gamma$ and $c_2$ in the range of the nonideal solution in the surface phase, and that can be extrapolated to infinite dilution, are of particular interest. Von Szyszkowski's equation is not the only such equation that has been suggested. A close analogy exists between the soluble adsorbed surface film and the insoluble monolayers on aqueous substrates that have been studied so intensively, first by Langmuir, then by Rideal, Adam, and others. The behavior of insoluble monolayers is described by two-dimensional equations of state of the form $\pi = f(\sigma, T)$, where $\pi$ is the two-dimensional spreading pressure and $\sigma$ is the molecular area. To find out whether soluble films can also be described by the same equations of state one must convert data of the form $\gamma$ vs. $N_2$ into the corresponding values of $\pi$ vs. $\sigma$. We have to rely on the Gibbs absorption theorem for this transformation. The insoluble monolayer on a water surface actually lowers the surface tension not only by virtue of its presence but also by its effect on the concentration and chemical potential of the water molecules that were originally present in the surface phase of pure water; nevertheless, because of its extreme insolubility in the bulk aqueous phase, only negligible error is introduced by considering $\pi$ as a function of the total surface concentration of the solute alone—i.e., $\Gamma_2{}^g \simeq \Gamma_2{}^u$. By analogy, if the lowering of surface tension created by a soluble surface-active agent is to be accounted for entirely in terms of solute molecules alone, the requisite form of the Gibbs theorem is

$$-\partial \gamma = \Gamma_2{}^g \partial \mu_2$$

from which we derive the analog-$\sigma$ as

$$\sigma = 1/N\Gamma_2{}^g \qquad (29)$$

Equation 29 represents the same convention, only in molecular rather than in molar terminology, as that mentioned earlier as Equation 9. The Gibbs convention is the basis of the definition and so deprives the "area per molecule" of its physical reality. We shall find ourselves obliged, nevertheless, to adopt this convention, not only because of the difficulties that would have to be overcome in order to gain a more physically realistic convention, such as that of Equation 10, but also because of our need to use the Gibbs convention for subsequent mathematical development. To convert the data of the surface tension isotherm into corresponding $\pi$-$\sigma$-$T$ isotherms is not of the greatest utility; more informative is to start with a suppositious two-dimensional equation of state and deduce therefrom an analytical expression for the surface tension isotherm. The mathematical difficulty of doing so is sufficiently great without its being complicated further by defining $\sigma$ otherwise than is done by Equation 29. We are, therefore, constrained to accept and develop that definition as a useful convention in its own right; we are not to consider it, as did Hutchinson, merely as an "approximation" to something more preferable—namely, the $u$-convention—as it is perfectly sound thermodynamically as stated.

As we have previously shown, the number of molecules of solute per sq. cm. represented by $\Gamma_2^G$ is less than the total number of molecules of solute per sq. cm. actually in the interfacial film. The representation of the behavior of the interfacial phase, therefore, by an equation of state $\pi = f(\sigma, T)$, while useful as a mathematical description of behavior, is rather artificial as a physical representation. Even when we postulate that the adsorbed film is confined to a monolayer, the area per solute molecule ($\sigma$) does not (and need not) directly refer to the *actual* condition of the surface film, and only does so at the limit of infinite dilution where $\Gamma_2^u = \Gamma_2^G$. The $\pi$ and $\sigma$ values that it relates are those that could be imagined if the molecules of solute, corresponding to $\Gamma_2^G$, were removed from the interfacial phase of the solution and allowed to spread as an insoluble monolayer on a substrate in which they did not dissolve; this imaginary substrate would have to retain all the other physical properties of the actual interface save the one of solvent ability. On this basis the molecular parameters and lateral interactions of the solute would have a metaphysical reality, not any less respectable than the activities and fugacities of solution thermodynamics. We are, nevertheless, willing to accept the artificiality, just as we accept the physical unreality of $\Gamma_2^G$, for its convenience, particularly as it provides a familiar mathematical analogy to a two-dimensional gas film.

Despite its artificial and apparently unreal basis, the behavior of soluble adsorbed films described in this way shows remarkable and unexpected agreement with that of insoluble monolayers determined by the film balance. Lauric acid is unique among the fatty acids in that it can be investigated by both methods, since it is sufficiently insoluble to allow its measurement by the film balance and sufficiently soluble for measurements of the variation of surface tension with concentration. Not only is an agreement thus obtained for lauric acid by both methods, but a continuous transition is observed in the behavior of fatty acids, which pass without a break as the experimental technique is changed, from insoluble films above $C_{12}$ to soluble films below $C_{12}$. According to Adam (1), this similarity "indicates that adsorbed soluble films and the insoluble films have a similar structure—

i.e., they are monomolecular." But, as we have seen, this is not a necessary conclusion.

The most revealing way to show the formal similarities in the behavior of insoluble and soluble films is by a two-dimensional Amagat diagram, in which the product $\pi\sigma$ is plotted *vs.* $\pi$. Both types of film show a linear relation on this plot at high values of $\pi$, which relation was described analytically by Schofield and Rideal (16) with the equation

$$\pi(\sigma - \beta) = ikT \qquad (30)$$

where $\beta$ is the two-dimensional correction term analogous to the conventional (three-dimensional) $b$ of the van der Waals equation, and $i$ is related to the forces of molecular interaction in the monolayer. Ward and Tordai (19) have tested the $\gamma$ *vs.* $c_2$ data for fatty acids in aqueous solution and found that these data could be well enough described by Equation 30. Values of $\beta$ and $i$ for these solutes agreed fairly closely with values for the corresponding constants derived from investigations of insoluble films of higher members of the same homologous series.

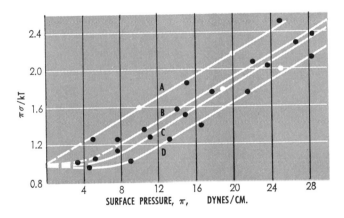

*Figure 2. The description of soluble adsorbed films by the nonideal gas–type of Gibbs monolayers, as revealed by two-dimensional Amagat diagrams (16)*

The transition of the experimental data from the range where it can be described by the Schofield-Rideal equation to its limit at infinite dilution where it can be described by the two-dimensional ideal-gas equation is demonstrated in Figure 2, which represents the data after suitable mathematical conversion for a series of water-soluble fatty acids at the water/air and water/benzene interfaces. Deviations from ideality are shown by plotting $\pi\sigma/kT$ *vs.* $\pi$. The initial nonideality at low values of $\pi$ is caused by intermolecular attraction; at higher values of $\pi$ the nonideality is the result of molecular area. The two factors contributing to the nonideality affect the $\pi\sigma$ product in opposite ways, the intermolecular attraction causing the product to decrease below $kT$ and the molecular area causing it to increase above $kT$. At the water/air interface both factors are operative, but at the water/oil interface the lateral intermolecular attraction may be so slight that the equation of state can reduce to

$$\pi(\sigma - \beta) = kT \qquad (31)$$

If the lateral interaction is indeed effectively eliminated, Equation 31, which is often referred to as the Volmer equation (3), gives a value for $\beta$ that is a genuine reflection of the effect of molecular area; but one cannot be certain that this special case applies—any small residual attractive or repulsive interaction would still permit the observations to be described by an equation of the Volmer type, even though "$\beta$" is now a complex function of $T$ containing both molecular-area and interaction corrections from ideality (2). We shall return later to consider the methods that have been used to obtain molecular dimensions from surface-tension data.

Two-dimensional equations of state, however well they can be brought to describe the behavior of a soluble adsorbed monolayer, do not convey any information about the adsorptive potential of a solute molecule with respect to the interface. The equation of state describes only the lateral behavior of the monolayer. The vertical interaction is merely implicit, inasmuch as it must exist if adsorption is to occur at all. Investigations that measure only $\pi$-$\sigma$-$T$ relations, such as measurements made with a film-balance on insoluble monolayers, are therefore unable to tell us anything about the strength of the adsorption forces between the adsorbate and the surface, however accurately they allow us to evaluate the molecular area and the lateral interactions within the monolayer. On the other hand, surface-tension measurements of $\gamma$ vs. $N_2$, or $\gamma$ vs. $p$, are affected by and reflect directly the vertical interaction, and so can be brought to yield information about adsorptive potentials. To bring this out we must not convert the original $\gamma$ vs. $N_2$ data into the derived $\pi$ vs. $\sigma$ variables; instead, we start with suggested two-dimensional equations of state and derive from them corresponding relations for $\gamma$ vs. $N_2$, which can then be compared with the measurements to see how well they serve as descriptions.

The first such nonideal equation of state that suggests itself on inspection of Figure 2 is Equation 31, the Volmer equation. Cassel and Formstecher (3) have shown that the Volmer equation can be combined with Gibbs's adsorption theorem and Equation 29 by solving Equation 31 for $\sigma$, followed by integration, to get

$$\ln (N_2/\pi) = (\beta\pi/kT) + I \qquad (32)$$

where $I$ is an integration constant. The test of Equation 32 is to plot $\ln (N_2/\pi)$ vs. $\pi$, which will yield a straight line with a positive slope if the equation should prove a valid description. At low values of $\pi$, $\ln (N_2/\pi) = I$, so that

$$m = (\partial\pi/\partial N_2)_T, (N_2 \to 0) = \exp (-I) \qquad (33)$$

The standard molar free energy of desorption is then obtained from the expression

$$\Delta G^0 = -RT(\ln \pi^0 + I) \qquad (34)$$

The adsorption of benzene, toluene, and $n$-heptane vapors by mercury was measured by Kemball and Rideal (11). The data ($\pi$ vs. $p$) were tested by Equation 32 in the form

$$\log (p/\pi) = (\beta/2.303kT)\pi + (I/2.303) \qquad (32A)$$

The data are adequately described by Equation 32A, and were therefore interpreted to mean that the adsorbed films are gaseous and obey the Volmer equation of state:

$$\pi(\sigma - \beta) = kT \qquad (31)$$

The authors verified the interpretation by plotting two-dimensional Amagat diagrams ($\pi\sigma$ vs. $\pi$) and demonstrating that the value of $\pi\sigma$ approaches $kT$ linearly as $\pi$ is decreased, although the authors mention that "there may be a tendency for the value of $\pi\sigma$ to dip below $kT$, as $\pi$ is decreased." The data were not obtained in sufficient detail and precision at low values of $\pi$ to determine this point definitively. The question at issue is whether the Volmer equation (Equation 31) or the Schofield-Rideal equation (Equation 30) provides the better description of the gaseous surface film. Our experience has been that the use of Equation 32 (or 32A), alone, does not adequately distinguish between those alternatives. The corresponding equation for the Schofield-Rideal equation of state is

$$\log [p/(\pi^i)] = (\beta/2.303\,kT)\pi + (C/2.303) \qquad (35)$$

**TABLE II.  STANDARD THERMODYNAMIC PROPERTIES**

| Substance | Temperature, °C. | Co-area ($\beta$), A.²/molecule | $\Delta G^0$, cal./mole | $\Delta H^0$, kcal./mole | $\Delta S^0$, e.u. |
|---|---|---|---|---|---|
| Benzene | 25 | 33.7 | 7497 | | |
| | 50 | 35.0 | 6747 | 16.27 | 29.5 |
| | 75 | 37.8 | 6063 | 15.71 | 27.8 |
| Toluene | 25 | 36.2 | 8608 | | |
| | 50 | 38.4 | 7533 | 21.5 | 43.2 |
| $n$-Heptane | 25 | 32.1 | 7801 | | |
| | 50 | 33.3 | 7332 | 13.4 | 18.8 |

Unless data are available in sufficient amount and degree of precision, both Equations 32A and 35 appear to be equally valid descriptions. Since Equation 35 is more general, it is to be preferred, although it is considerably more cumbersome because of its extra constant. The values of $\beta$ and $I$ in Equation 32A are simply not significant, unless, by testing the data by means of Equation 35, it can be shown that the $i$ of Equation 35 is actually equal to unity. If $i$ has any other value, the constants must be evaluated by means of Equation 35.

On the mercury substrate the value of $i$ is approximately equal to unity, which means that the lateral molecular interactions of adsorbed hydrocarbons have been effectively destroyed, presumably because of interaction with an induced electrical mirror image on the metal surface, thereby making similarly oriented, repulsing dipoles out of the adsorbate. The standard thermodynamic functions, derived from these data by means of Equations 34 and 25, for the standard states $\pi^0 = 0.338$ dyne/cm. and $p^0 = 760$ mm., are reported in Table II. The values of the constant $\beta$ are also included.

Equation 32A has become a favorite instrument of authors who attempt to interpret the data of surface tension of solutions. We have pointed out one hidden danger in its use, which, if taken into account, would demonstrate that in a number of situations it has been applied incorrectly. Another peculiarity of a different type sometimes occurs, as recently illustrated by results reported by Jones, Ottewill, and Chater (10) for the adsorption of insoluble vapors by a water surface. Applying Equation 32 to their data produced a straight line whose slope gave *a negative* value of $\beta$. The interpretation of a negative molecule area is inadmissible; consequently the theoretical basis of Equation 32 is thrown into doubt. But let us suppose that the two-dimensional equation of state has the form of an analog of the van der Waals equation, i.e.

$$\left(\pi + \frac{\alpha}{\sigma^2}\right)(\sigma - \beta) = kT \tag{36}$$

Writing Equation 36 in its expanded form

$$\pi\sigma = kT - \frac{\alpha}{\sigma} + \beta\pi + \frac{\alpha\beta}{\sigma^2}$$

Since both $\alpha$ and $\beta$ are small, the term $\alpha\beta/\sigma^2$ may be neglected, provided $\pi$ is not too large. Further, $\sigma$ may be replaced by $kT/\pi$ in the term $\alpha/\sigma$, so that

$$\pi\sigma = kT - \frac{\alpha\pi}{kT} + \beta\pi$$

$$= kT + \pi\left(\beta - \frac{\alpha}{kT}\right) \tag{37}$$

Solving Equation 37 for $\sigma$ and using the transformation of parameters made possible by the Gibbs equation, as mentioned above, give

$$\ln\frac{N_2}{\pi} = \left(\beta - \frac{\alpha}{kT}\right)\frac{\pi}{kT} + I \tag{38}$$

Equation 38 has the same form as Equation 32, save that the coefficient of $\pi$ can have either positive or negative values, depending on the predominance of the co-area term $\beta$ or of the attraction term, $\alpha$. In Kemball's experiments with adsorbed hydrocarbons on a mercury surface, the $\beta$-term predominates and the $\alpha$-term is almost nonexistent; Jones, Ottewill, and Chater's experiments, on the other hand, show that molecules of vapors adsorbed by a water surface exercise strong lateral attractions for one another.

The simplifying assumptions on which Equation 38 is based are no longer valid at higher values of $\pi$, so that the linear relation between $\ln(N_2/\pi)$ and $\pi$ holds only for a limited range of low values of $\pi$. To obtain a more extended description of the behavior of the surface film, we must work with the unmodified form of Equation 36. Undoubtedly this equation would have been introduced into this subject long before now if any convenient expression could have been derived from it for the surface tension isotherm relating $\pi$ and $N_2$. Unfortunately, only cumbersome expressions can be obtained. We have devised the following procedure, which yields the desired

results to a close approximation by a rather different route than usual.

The two-dimensional van der Waals equation, Equation 36, can be transformed, via the Gibbs adsorption theorem, into a relation between $N_2$ and $\theta$, where $\theta$ is the fraction of an adsorbed monolayer in equilibrium with the bulk concentration $N_2$. De Boer (2) has presented the argument justifying the use of the van der Waals co-area term $\beta$ as the limiting area per molecule in a close-packed monolayer; hence $\theta = \beta/\sigma$. Then:

$$N_2 = K\frac{\theta}{1-\theta}\exp\left[\frac{\theta}{1-\theta} - \frac{2\alpha\theta}{kT\beta}\right] \tag{39}$$

Taking logarithms of both sides and re-arranging give

$$\ln N_2 - \left(\ln\frac{\theta}{1-\theta} + \frac{\theta}{1-\theta}\right) =$$
$$\ln K - \left(\frac{2\alpha}{kT\beta}\right)\theta \tag{40}$$

or

$$W = \ln K - \left(\frac{2\alpha}{kT\beta}\right)\theta \tag{40A}$$

In the form of Equation 40, the two-dimensional van der Waals equation can be used to test experimental data, once $\theta$ is evaluated. The evaluation of $\theta$ is made from the surface tension isotherm by determining the slopes at different points and calculating $\Gamma_2{}^\sigma$ by the Gibbs adsorption theorem; thence $\sigma = 1/N\Gamma_2{}^\sigma$, and $\theta = \beta/\sigma$. The determination of $\beta$ to a close approximation can be made with the help of the empirical Schofield-Rideal equation

$$\pi(\sigma - \beta) = ikT \tag{30}$$

A plot of $\pi\sigma$ versus $\pi$ provides a ready method of obtaining $i$ and $\beta$ by Equation 30.

Instead of graphical differentiation to obtain the slopes $d\pi/dN_2$ at various values of $N_2$, the task can be performed analytically by using the Schofield-Rideal equation with one variable transformed by the Gibbs equation:

$$\ln\frac{N_2}{(\pi)^i} = \frac{\beta}{kT}\pi + C \tag{35}$$

Here the original data of $\pi$ and $N_2$ are used, with some gain in accuracy; a computer would make short work of the determination of the constants $i$, $\beta$, and $C$ in Equation 35. These constants can then be used for the calculation of $\sigma$:

$$\sigma = \frac{ikT}{\pi} + \beta \tag{41}$$

If this method is used, the values of $\sigma$ at low values of $\pi$, where Equation 30 is not a good description of the observations, are better obtained graphically; although at higher values of $\pi$ the graphical differentiation can be foregone by the use of Equation 41.

By plotting the variables $N_2$ and $\theta$ according to Equation 40, the correspondence of that equation to the data can be appreciated from the linearity of the plot; the constants $\alpha$ and $K$ are obtained from the slope and intercept. The constant $K$ is given by

$$K = \lim_{\theta \to 0} \frac{dN_2}{d\theta} \qquad (42)$$

The limiting slope, $m$, that we wish to obtain is found as follows:

$$m = \lim_{\theta \to 0} \frac{d\pi}{dN_2} = \lim_{\theta \to 0} \frac{d\pi}{d\theta} \bigg/ \lim_{\theta \to 0} \frac{dN_2}{d\theta} = \left(\frac{kT}{\beta}\right)\frac{1}{K} \qquad (43)$$

By using this method to find the limiting slope $m$ of the surface-tension isotherm, we avoid the incorrect (though customary) extrapolation illustrated in Figure 3, in which a smooth uninflected curve is drawn to the origin. The inflection may be small, particularly at temperatures above the Boyle temperature, and the error we are trying to eliminate is then negligible—but its possible existence should be recognized and taken into account in any work that claims to offer definitive values of the thermodynamic functions.

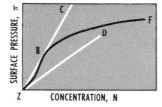 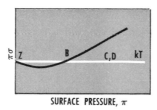

*Figure 3. Relation between the surface-tension isotherm (a) and the corresponding $\pi\sigma$ vs. $\pi$ diagram (b) for nonideal gas–type Gibbs monolayers*

The relation between the surface-tension isotherm and the two-dimensional Amagat diagram that corresponds to it is shown in Figure 3. In the first diagram a straight line through the origin of any slope whatever corresponds to the ideal gas law $\pi\sigma = kT$; hence the lines $ZD$ and $ZBC$ coincide in the second (Amagat) diagram. If the only available experimental data are those obtained in the region $BF$ of the surface tension isotherm, a graphical extrapolation, such as represented by the line $BZ$ to the origin, would not properly reflect the limiting slope $m$, and would lead to a more or less inaccurate estimation of the free energy of desorption by Equation 23. The surface-tension isotherm for low values of $\pi$ should be extrapolated according to the course of the isotherm corresponding to a nonideal gaseous film. The method we have outlined is a close approximation of that requirement, using the van der Waals equation as a guide. In doing so, of course, the artificial character of the monolayer of a soluble film should not be forgotten, though we have made such extensive use of the concept.

To illustrate the procedure, the data (4) for the interfacial tension at 20° C. at a dodecane/water interface as a function of the concentration of solute (n-octanol) in the oil phase are shown in Figure 4, the corresponding two-dimensional Amagat diagram is shown in Figure 5, and the test of the data by means

of Equation 40 is shown in Figure 6. The constants for the description of these data, and the standard free energy change on desorption are as follows:

$\alpha = 210 \times 10^{-30}$ ergs sq. cm. molecule$^{-2}$
$\beta = 31.3 \times 10^{-16}$ sq. cm. molecule$^{-1}$
$i = 0.712$
$\ln K = -6.24$
$\Delta G°$ at 20° C. = 5.76 kcal./mole

The value of $\beta$ is derived from the empirical Schofield-Rideal equation and is used unchanged in Equation 40. The standard free energy change on desorption refers to an initial state of the interfacial film of $\pi^0 = 0.338$ dyne/cm. and a final state of the oil solution of $N_2 = 1$ (idealized pure solute).

### Molecular Dimensions and Interactions from Surface-Tension Isotherms

The behavior of a two-dimensional nonideal gas requires both types of correction of ideality originally suggested by van der Waals which are embodied in the constants $\alpha$ and $\beta$. Numerous investigations have by now amply demonstrated that the $\alpha$-term is considerably reduced at an oil/water interface compared to a water/gas interface. The common procedure, in fact, is to describe the soluble adsorbed film at the oil/water interface without introducing any correction for lateral interaction. Our investigations of this interface have taught us that one can easily overlook small effects due to the existence of a residual lateral interaction. We have observed how experimental data, because of the lack of the necessary precision, can conform equally to a linear relation when plotted either as $\log N_2/\pi$ vs. $\pi$ or as $\log N_2/(\pi)^i$ vs. $\pi$, the former corresponding to a Volmer equation of state and the latter to a Schofield-Rideal equation of state. The same uncertainty occurs in plotting $1/\pi$ vs. $\sigma$, where the slope of the resulting straight line equals $1/(ikT)$, and so ought to be able to settle the question; but the inadequate precision of the experimental data, which is further reduced by the graphical exercise necessary to elicit values of $\sigma$, makes the determination of the slope a subjective matter—the persuasion that $i$ ought to equal unity has some influence in the weighting of points.

The two-dimensional Amagat diagram appears to be most sensitive to distinguish this question graphically; or a computer can be used to obtain values of $i$ determined from Equation 35.

When $i$ is found to equal unity, some reserve must still qualify the acceptance of the constant $\beta$ as a genuine measure of the molecular area. We have already shown (Equation 37) that, provided values of $\pi$ are not too large, a Volmer equation of state can still contain both $\alpha$- and $\beta$-terms such that the slope is affected by the presence of the $\alpha$-term.

One is probably on firmer ground, for the interpreting of $\beta$, if the $i$-term is not equal to unity, as the Schofield-Rideal equation is known to give an excellent empirical description of the $\pi$-$\sigma$ isotherm (15) at high values of $\pi$, and so is suitable for an analytic extrapolation to infinite

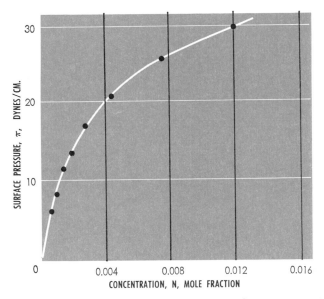

*Figure 4. The interfacial tension isotherm at 20.0° C. of n-octanol dissolved in dodecane at an oil/water interface where $\gamma_0 = 53.66$ dynes/cm.; $\pi$ = lowering of interfacial tension; $N_2$ = mole fraction of solute in dodecane*

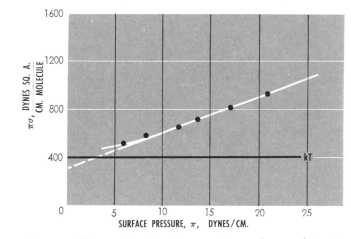

*Figure 5. The two-dimensional Amagat diagram ($\pi\sigma$ vs. $\pi$) for the data reported in Figure 4, showing their description as a nonideal gas–type of Gibbs monolayer*

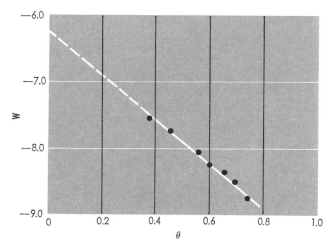

*Figure 6. The description of the nonideal gas–type of Gibbs monolayer shown in Figure 5 by means of an analog of the van der Waals equation applied to the surface film (two-dimensional)*

$\pi$, giving $\sigma = \beta$ as $\pi \to \infty$. In this respect the Schofield-Rideal equation is preferable even to the van der Waals equation, which never provides anywhere as good a description of the actual isotherm.

Another way that has been suggested to obtain molecular areas of solutes from surface-tension measurements is from the asymptotic saturation of the surface that is predicted by the Langmuir equation. The von Szyszkowski equation, Equation 26, can be used for this purpose, as it is actually equivalent to a Langmuir adsorption isotherm. This equivalence can be shown by evaluating $\Gamma_2^G$ from Equation 26 by means of the Gibbs adsorption theorem:

$$\frac{d\pi}{dc_2} = \frac{\mathbf{b}\gamma_0}{\mathbf{c} + c_2}$$

hence

$$\Gamma_2^G = \frac{(\mathbf{b}\gamma_0/RT)\, c_2}{\mathbf{c} + c_2} \tag{44}$$

As $c_2$ tends to infinity the value of $\Gamma_2^G$ tends to the limit $(\mathbf{b}\gamma_0/RT)$, which is therefore taken to represent the saturation of the surface by an adsorbed monolayer. We can also express this saturation in terms of the limiting molecular area $\sigma_L$, where

$$\sigma_L = kT/\mathbf{b}\gamma_0 \tag{45}$$

To this interpretation it may be objected that the Langmuir equation, as exemplified by Equation 44, is based on an improbable model (a nonmobile film) for an adsorbed soluble film at a liquid interface. This objection is met by the argument that the Langmuir equation could be considered only as an empirical equation that does, however, indicate, even at low surface concentrations, that the interfacial phase has a tendency to fill up to a certain saturation value. De Boer (2) has exposed the fallacy of this argument. He supposed the adsorbed film to be mobile and that it could be described by means of an equation of state that has corrections for nonideality, $\alpha$ and $\beta$, analogous to the $a$ and $b$ terms in the van der Waals equation. He then demonstrated that at low surface concentrations, the Langmuir equation would fit the observations for a limited range, giving by a long extrapolation an apparent saturation of the interface when the molecular area equals $\sigma_L$, defined by

$$\sigma_L = 2\beta - \frac{2\alpha}{RT} - \frac{(\beta - 2\alpha/RT)^2}{\sigma}$$

For sufficiently large values of $\sigma$ this becomes

$$\sigma_L = 2\beta - \frac{2\alpha}{RT}$$

The value of $\sigma_L$ that is obtained in this approximation, though it is a constant at constant temperature, depends on $\alpha$ and $\beta$ and is therefore not a correct measurement of the limiting molecular area. Even if the mutual attraction forces were negligible, $\sigma_L$ would have the value of $2\beta$. Although what seem to be reasonable values for limiting molecular areas for a number of solutes have been obtained by means of Equation 45 by Taubmann (*18*), the method should not be credited.

The application of the van der Waals equation to a monolayer of gas adsorbed on a solid substrate is now well known (*2*); applying it, however, to a soluble film on a liquid medium, which could be either the liquid/gas or the liquid/liquid interface, removes it much farther from its familiar use. The two-dimensional spreading pressure is the decrease of the interfacial tension and is therefore susceptible of mechanical measurement at the liquid interface; thermodynamically, however, it appears as the intensive variable for the work term $\pi d\sigma$, and is to that extent independent of any interpretation by a physical model. Intellectual difficulties appear when one tries to visualize adsorbed films at liquid surfaces in terms of a "solute gas." An analogous difficulty was at one time a source of confusion with respect to osmotic pressure, and a statement on that subject by Fitzgerald (1896) is worth repeating again for application in the present context (*6*):

"It is, no doubt, a most remarkable thing that osmotic pressure should be even roughly the same as what would be produced by the molecules of the body in solution if in the gaseous state; but to imply that the dynamical theory of the two is at all the same, or that the dynamical theory of a gas is in any sense an *explanation* of the law of osmotic pressures, is not at all in accordance with what is generally meant by the word 'explanation.' "

Following further the analogy of osmotic pressure for what we might learn, let us look at what has been done in that subject with various modifications of the van der Waals equation as a quantitative description of observed behavior. Out of about fifty suggested modifications, one in particular was found to express with fair accuracy the experimental relations between osmotic pressure and concentration (*5*):

$$(A/v + p - a/v^2)(v - b) = RT$$

In this equation $a/v^2$ is a factor intended to correct for a mutual attraction of the solute molecules, while the term $A/v$ is a correction for the attraction between solvent and solute. The volume of the solution that contains one mole of solute is represented by $v$. This equation holds good only over a limited range of values, and was not tested at different temperatures. The empirical constants could not be interpreted or predicted from the properties of the substances concerned. We may fear the same fate for our present application.

By considering the statistical thermodynamics of a two-component system, McMillan and Mayer (*13*) have shown that the osmotic pressure of a solution can be described by an equation analogous in form to that for the pressure of a nonideal gas; and undoubtedly a similar type of calculation could be made for the spreading pressure of a soluble adsorbed film, without introducing any kinetic model of a "pressure" exerted by the solute molecules in the interfacial film. On this basis, incidentally, the expression $\pi\sigma = kT$ for the description of the behavior of a very dilute adsorbed monolayer at a liquid surface is a thermodynamic requirement of the physical system.

To search for direct experimental verification of the expression (a very arduous undertaking indeed) is to test the validity of a thermodynamic derivation, which could probably be tested much more readily with paper and pencil by an expert on the subject; to call the dilute adsorbed film "a two-dimensional ideal gas" because of the similarity of its equation of state to that of an ideal gas is permissible only as a manner of speaking. One can still talk of nonideality and account for deviations from the behavior at the infinitely dilute surface concentration in terms of the magnitudes of solute and solvent molecules as well as the forces between them. In doing so, however, the two-dimensional van der Waals equation in its customary form, while it may yet furnish an adequate description of the observations, as in Figure 6, is not properly interpreted as reflecting the properties only of the solute. The constant $\alpha$ has lost its original significance and would require further analysis in terms of correction factors more rigorously defined to include both solute and solvent as liquids, before it could be used to elicit the potential of average force between solute molecules. An indication of the change of character of $\alpha$ is shown by its greatly increased variation with temperature compared with the usual $a$-term of a gas. The value of $\alpha$ quoted above for $n$-octanol in oil at the oil/water interface at 20° C. is reduced by 50% at 30° C. and by 50% of the remainder at 40° C. The values of $\beta$ were found (*4*) to decrease slightly with temperature; this variation, however, might be due to the lower surface concentrations that are now present at higher temperatures in the same range of measurement of $\pi$; which could result in too low an observed value for the limiting $\sigma$ as $\pi \rightarrow \infty$, as determined from the slope of such curves as those in Figure 2. In spite of these marked variations of the correction factors with temperature, the utility of an appropriately modified (i.e., semiempirical) van der Waals equation in predicting two-dimensional condensations and critical temperature phenomena of soluble adsorbed films is not affected; evidence for such phenomena is projected for investigation in our laboratory and may yet be forthcoming.

## LITERATURE CITED

(1) Adam, N. K., "Physics and Chemistry of Surfaces," Oxford, 1941.
(2) Boer, J. H. de, "The Dynamical Character of Adsorption," Clarendon Press, Oxford, 1953.
(3) Cassel, H., Formstecher, M., *Kolloid Z.* **61**, 18 (1932).
(4) Chen, E. S., Ph.D. thesis, Rensselaer Polytechnic Inst., 1965.
(5) Findlay, A., "Osmotic Pressure," 2nd edition, pp. 46–48, Longmans, Green, London, 1919.
(6) Fitzgerald, G. F., "Scientific Writings," pp. 364–5, Dublin Univ. Press, 1902.
(7) Freundlich, H., "Colloid and Capillary Chemistry," p. 65, Methuen, London, 1926.
(8) Glasstone, S., "Text-book of Physical Chemistry," pp. 674–5, Van Nostrand, New York, 1940.
(9) Hutchinson, E., *J. Colloid Sci.* **3**, 219, 235, 531 (1948).
(10) Jones, D. C., Ottewill, R. H., Chater, A. P. J., *Second Int. Congr. Surface Activity* **1**, 188 (1957).
(11) Kemball, C., Rideal, E. K., *Proc. Roy. Soc. (London)* **187A**, 53 (1946).
(12) McBain, J. W., *Advan. Colloid Science* **1**, 111–113 (1942), and references quoted.
(13) McMillan, W. G., Jr., Mayer, J. E., *J. Chem. Phys.* **13**, 276 (1945).
(14) Posner, A. M., Anderson, J. R., Alexander, A. E., *J. Colloid Sci.* **7**, 623 (1952).
(15) Ross, S., Secoy, C. H., *J. Phys. Colloid Chem.* **53**, 306 (1949).
(16) Schofield, R. K., Rideal, E. K., *Proc. Roy. Soc. (London)* **A109**, 57 (1925).
(17) Szyszkowski, B. von, *Z. Phys. Chem.* **64**, 385 (1908).
(18) Taubmann, A., *Acta Physicochim. U.R.S.S.* **5**, 356 (1936); *Idem. Compt. Rend. Acad. Sci. U.R.S.S.* **29**, 22, 103 (1940).
(19) Ward, A. F. H., Tordai, L., *Trans. Faraday Soc.* **42**, 399, 408, 413 (1946).

# 5

# Foams and Emulsions

# FOAMS AND EMULSIONS

## J. J. BIKERMAN

A descriptive survey of an immense body of knowledge, tailored to serve as an introduction to more specialized symposium papers

## PART I  FOAMS

Foams are dispersions of a relatively large volume of gas in a relatively small volume of liquid (1). When the volume of liquid is considerably greater than that of gas, the gas bubbles are, as a rule, spherical and their mutual interaction is weak; these systems are known as gas emulsions. In a true foam, the bubbles are so crowded that their shape is polyhedral; liquid is reduced to thin films separating the polyhedrons

Foams have a definite structure. Wherever three films come together, they form three angles of 120° each. The necessity of this arrangement is made clear in Figure 1, where A, B, and C are contiguous bubbles, and 1, 2, and 3 are the films separating them. Each film has a contractile tendency of $2\gamma$ per centimeter; $\gamma$ is the surface tension of the liquid and the factor 2 is due to the fact that each film has two liquid-gas interfaces. Three identical forces (in this instance, $2\gamma$ per cm.) can balance each other only if the three angles between them are identical—i.e., equal to 120° each. In a pentagonal dodecahedron—i.e., in the three-dimensional figure formed by 12 equilateral pentagons, the internal angles have the magnitude of 120°, and these figures almost completely fill the space. Thus, foam bubbles tend to have a shape similar to pentagonal dodecahedrons, if their volumes are equal. In the vast majority of foams, different bubbles have different volumes and, consequently, their shapes greatly deviate from the ideal.

### Formation

In common with other colloidal systems, foams can be produced by condensation or by dispersion. In the first case, the future gas phase initially is present as separate molecules which then gather together to form bubbles. Foam on beer is a typical example. Carbon dioxide produced by yeast first dissolves in the aqueous medium; when the pressure on the liquid is suddenly reduced (by uncorking the bottle), the solution becomes supersaturated and the excess of solute forms a dispersed gas phase. Many solid foams, which now are so widely used, are manufactured by condensation. The bubbles are derived from a deliberately added "blowing agent."

In the dispersion methods, the gas originally exists as a bulk phase. Small volumes of the latter are introduced into the liquid and become bubbles. The most easily controlled way of achieving this is to drive the gas through a capillary into the liquid; thus, each bubble forms singly at the tip of the capillary. In this manner, monodisperse foams (i.e., those consisting of bubbles of identical dimensions) can be obtained. Forcing the gas through a porous septum (plug) is a much quicker process but the foam produced is not monodisperse because many bubbles coalesce before breaking off the septum. Control over the properties of the foam is even poorer when the foam is produced by agitation, which may mean shaking a vessel partly filled with a liquid capable of foaming, or pouring such a liquid from one vessel into another, or causing turbulence with a propeller as in a commercial blender, or moving a perforated plate up and down in a cylinder holding liquid.

In all these methods, bubbles separated from each other by relatively thick liquid layers are initially produced, and transformation of these gas emulsions into true foams usually is achieved by gravitation. The bubbles rise in the liquid and accumulate near its top. In the process, each bubble has to traverse, at a reasonable speed, a distance of perhaps several centimeters but then must practically stop when a film only a few microns thick remains between it and the neighboring bubble. The reasons for this change of mind are the causes of foam stability, discussed later.

### Properties

Foams have some rigidity even if their films are completely liquid. This is so because the equilibrium structure outlined above corresponds to a minimum surface area and, consequently, a minimum surface energy, and every deformation increases this energy—i.e., requires

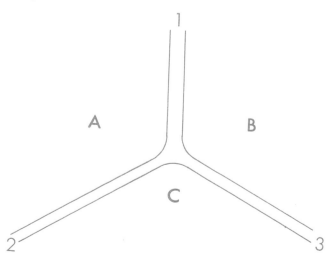

Figure 1. Three identical forces, as in the surface tension of three foam bubbles, are balanced only when the angles between them are each 120 degrees. Note also the angles in the solid foam above

external work. The degree of rigidity observed is particularly remarkable when the low density of foams is taken into consideration; an aqueous foam whose bubbles are about 1 cm. in diameter with films about $10^{-3}$ cm. thick has a density of about 0.003 g./cu. cm.

The combination of low density and marked rigidity is utilized, for instance, in fire-fighting foams. A foam blanket prevents contact between air and the combustible material in the same manner as does any other blanket, but the former may be 100 or more times as light as the latter. In addition, the main ingredient of a fire-fighting foam (i.e., water) is, generally speaking, readily available and not expensive. Solid foams are even more rigid than those of the gas-liquid type. In them, the films themselves are rigid, and this rigidity can be adjusted by varying the composition of the mix.

The area $A$ of the liquid-gas interface in a foam is very large—e.g., the aqueous foam mentioned above has a surface of about 2000 sq. cm. per gram. This property is utilized, for instance, in flotation. Under definite conditions, ore powder accumulates in the surface of an aqueous solution while valueless rocks sink in the liquid; if $A$ of the solution is small (e.g., 0.1 sq. cm./g.), only a small amount of ore can be separated by a given amount of liquid, but the same volume of solution when spread in foam films can serve for separating, say, a thousand-fold mass of ore. Presumably, processes analogous to flotation take place also in many instances of detergence. Here again foams offer a very extensive interface.

### Aging

Foams are fundamentally unstable systems. Three main processes occur in almost all foams: redistribution of bubble sizes, film thinning, and film rupture.

The first effect is caused by the dependence of the gas pressure in a bubble on the curvature of its walls. For simplicity's sake, consider a system of two bubbles only

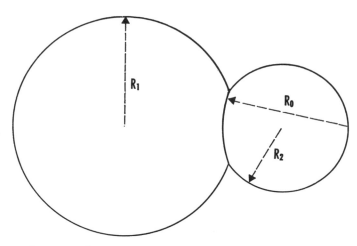

*Figure 2. Gas diffuses from the smaller to the larger bubble under the influence of pressure differential*

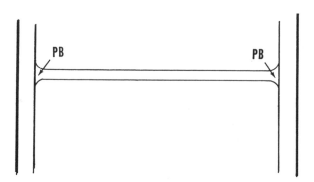

*Figure 3. A Plateau border (PB) in a horizontal single film, in which gravitation does not contribute to drainage*

(see Figure 2). Let the radius of curvature of the wall of the larger bubble be $R_1$, that of the smaller, $R_2$, and that of the partition (common to both) $R_0$. From Laplace's equation, the gas pressure in the first bubble is $P_a + 4\gamma/R_1$, if $P_a$ is the atmospheric pressure. The factor of $\gamma$ is 4 because the bubble has two gas-liquid interfaces, the internal and the external. In the small bubble, the gas is under pressure $P_a + 4\gamma/R_2$. To achieve mechanical equilibrium, the septum between the two bubbles must be concave toward the smaller bubble, and its radius of curvature be given by equation

$$\frac{4\gamma}{R_0} = \frac{4\gamma}{R_2} - \frac{4\gamma}{R_1} \qquad (1)$$

or $R_0 = R_1 R_2/(R_1 - R_2.)$

The mechanical equilibrium would be stable if the septum were completely impermeable to the gas in the bubbles. As no such impermeability exists, gas diffuses through the wall from the region of high into the region of low pressure. Thus, the smaller bubble (in which the gas pressure is greater) gets smaller, and the bigger bubble grows. If the difference between $R_1$ and $R_2$ is initially small, gas diffusion raises it. Thus polydispersity of foams tends to increase on aging.

The macroscopic effect of film thinning is foam drainage. If a vessel is filled with foam and left alone, after a time a layer of liquid usually appears at the bottom of the vessel and continues to grow until very little liquid remains in the foam films (or until the films burst). Gravitation is one of the two reasons for film thinning. If a vertical film of thickness $\delta$ and width $w$ may be treated as a slit filled with liquid between two plane parallel walls, then the volume of liquid flowing downward in unit time is $dV/dt = g\rho w\delta^3/12\eta$ ($g$ is acceleration due to gravity, $\rho$ the difference between the densities of the liquid and the air around the foam, and $\eta$ is the viscosity of the liquid). In reality, the film gets thinner when drainage takes place—i.e., $\delta$ decreases instead of being constant. Also the "walls" of the film usually are not solid, and their relative rigidity has a marked effect on the rate of drainage (5). Liquid drains also in the veins (in which three bubble walls meet), and the

volume passing through the veins may exceed that flowing in the walls, if $\delta$ is small.

The other reason for film thinning is suction by Plateau's borders. The wall between A and B in Figure 1 is sensibly plane, hence liquid filling the wall is under the same pressure as the gas in the two bubbles. However, the liquid-air interface near the junction of three bubbles is concave toward the air phase. Consequently the liquid there is under negative capillary pressure (see Equation 1), and the pressure difference drives liquid from the inside of the wall to this Plateau border. This pressure difference usually is much greater than that between the gas phases in two adjacent bubbles. Figure 3 shows a Plateau border (PB) in a horizontal single film, in which gravitation does not contribute to drainage.

**Film rupture**

Foam bubbles and foam films burst because the area (and, thus, surface energy) of the resulting drop or drops is smaller than that of the initial system. For instance, a bubble of 1-cm. radius and wall thickness of $10^{-5}$ cm. has surface area equal to approximately 25 sq. cm., and if it gives rise to just one droplet, the surface of the latter is about 0.2 cm.$^2$. The energy difference is so large that, when a film bursts, the liquid in it may acquire a speed of 1000 cm./sec. or 20 miles/hr.

Nevertheless, foams can persist for measurable time. Before the probable reasons for this persistence are outlined, the main methods of its measurement may be mentioned.

Single films, as illustrated in Figure 3, are produced and their lifetime $\tau$ is measured, or the time $\tau$ that a bubble which rises to the surface of the liquid spends there before bursting is determined. This $\tau$ is smaller

**AUTHOR** *J. J. Bikerman is now associated with Horizons, Inc., a Cleveland-based R&D organization with a strong interdisciplinary program. He was Supervisor, Adhesives Laboratory, at Massachusetts Institute of Technology when this article was prepared and has for many years been at the forefront of research in the physics and chemistry of surfaces, particularly in foams and emulsions.*

the greater the film or the bubble, and usually greatly depends on the humidity of the atmosphere, on convection currents, etc. It may be concluded, therefore, that bursting is caused not by processes inherent in the film but by external agents (such as dust).

Static measurements on multicellular foams are performed, for instance, by shaking a suitable liquid in a partly filled vessel and determining the volume of foam immediately after agitation and at definite time intervals afterwards. The results are influenced by the mode of agitation, by the volume ratio of liquid to gas, and so on.

For dynamic measurements on multicellular foams, gas is bubbled through a suitable liquid at a rate $V/t$ cu.cm./sec. ($V$ is gas volume, $t$ is time), and the steady-state volume $v$ of foam is read. The ratio $vt/V = \Sigma$ (2) is almost independent of $V/t$ and may be used as a measure of foaminess. $\Sigma$ is, for instance, about 6 sec. for 1% aqueous 1-butanol, about 140 sec. for a 0.04% solution of egg albumin at pH 4.8 (3), etc.

It is easy to understand why many protein solutions have very stable foams. Protein denatured at the solution-air interface forms a "skin" similar to that on hot milk. This "skin" may be classified as solid and, consequently, has no tendency to spontaneous rupture. Even when no visible skin is present, the surface layer of a solution may have a greater viscosity than the bulk; this surface viscosity (8) is the main cause of foaminess of, e.g., saponin solutions. When surface viscosity is absent (e.g., in aqueous alcohols), foaminess apparently is caused by the Marangoni effect—when the surface of a foam film is indented, as a preliminary to rupture, the underlying liquid is exposed; this liquid has a greater surface tension than the original surface and, consequently, tends to close the "wound." A striking manifestation of this effect is afforded by the observation (by Dupré) that solids (lead shot, etc.) and liquid drops (e.g., of mercury) can fall through a foam film without leaving any hole or causing rupture; however, when the film has drained for a long time, every projectile causes bursting.

A third cause of foam stability apparently exists in the films of colloidal electrolytes, such as soaps. These films consist of two layers of long-chain ions between which a solution containing an excess of counterions completes the sandwich. The electrostatic repulsion of the two equally charged walls prevents their mutual approach, the first step to bursting (1, p. 16; 4, 6).

### Chemistry of Foam

"Suitable liquids" have been repeatedly mentioned above. Clearly, none of the three causes of foam stability can be operative in pure liquids (as opposed to solutions). Also, saturated solutions do not foam. Thus a maximum of foaming capacity is observed in moderately concentrated solutions. When the solute strongly depresses $\gamma$, the concentration corresponding to this maximum usually is not far from that at which $-d\gamma/dc$ has the greatest value ($c$ is the concentration of the solution). When the solute has almost no effect on the $\gamma$ of the solvent and also does not form a viscous surface layer, the solution has no marked foaminess; many inorganic salts belong to this group.

Often, foam formation can be prevented and an existing foam destroyed by a second solute. The mechanism of this effect varies from case to case. For instance, the second solute may chemically react with the first, and the reaction product may be surface-inactive. Another mechanism, however, is more common—the second solute displaces the first from the surface but is a poor foamer itself. Thus a surface of moderate foaming capacity is substituted for one of greater ability to foam. The old observation of ether vapor causing collapse of beer foam presumably is an instance of this effect.

Because the surface layer of a solution capable of foaming has a composition different from that of the bulk, the composition of foam films also is different from the latter. Thus, mechanical separation of foam from the residual liquid permits a chemical separation. If there is only one solute, the foam may be enriched in it; this is accumulation in foam. If the liquid contains several compounds in mutual equilibrium, some of these compounds may be transported into foam preferentially to the other; thus, a shift of equilibrium in foam is observed. If there are several solutes, some may be concentrated in the foam while the others remain in the liquid; this is fractionation by foam. Examples of all three phenomena are known but the method is still little used. Some recent instances are: (a) accumulation of inorganic ions in froth; as these ions are mostly non-foamers, they are reacted with, e.g., a long chain detergent, and the resulting compounds are concentrated by foaming (9); and (b) fractionation of two stereoisomers of polyvinyl alcohol (7).

### LITERATURE CITED

(1) Bikerman, J. J., "Foams," Reinhold, New York, 1953.
(2) Bikerman, J. J., *Trans. Faraday Soc.* **34**, 634 (1938).
(3) Cumper, C. W. N., *Trans. Faraday Soc.* **49**, 1360 (1953).
(4) Deryagin, B. V., Titievskaya, A. S., *Koll. Zhur.* **15**, 416 (1953).
(5) Epstein, M. B., *et al.*, *J. Phys. Chem.* **60**, 1051 (1956).
(6) Ewers, W. E., Sutherland, K. L., *Austr. J. Sci. Res.* **A 5**, 697 (1952).
(7) Imai, K., Matsumoto, M., *Bull. Chem. Soc. Japan* **36**, 455 (1963).
(8) Ross, S., Butler, J. N., *J. Phys. Chem.* **60**, 1255 (1956).
(9) Sebba, F., "Ion Flotation," Elsevier, Amsterdam, 1962.

### ADDITIONAL READING

For additional information on foams:

Kishimoto, H., *Kolloid-Zeitschr.* **192**, 66 (1963).
Manegold, E., "Schaum," Strassenbau, Chemie u. Technik, Heidelberg, 1953.
Mysels, K., Shinoda, K., Frankel, S., "Soap Films," Pergamon, New York, 1959.
Ruyssen, R., *Boll. Chimico Farmac.* **101**, 105 (1962); *Chem. Weekblad* **60**, 109 (1964).
Vries, A. J. de, "Foam Stability," Rubber-Stichting, Delft, 1957.

## PART II   EMULSIONS

### Formation

Emulsions contain two liquid phases, one of which (the discrete, dispersed, or discontinuous phase) is distributed in the other (continuous phase) in the form of small droplets. When the concentration of these droplets is so high that they influence each other, they may cease to be spherical. In fact, an extremely concentrated emulsion has a structure analogous to that of a foam—thin films of the dispersion medium exist between deformed droplets of the discontinuous fluid.

From the point of view of formation, there are three classes of emulsions: critical emulsions, emulsions produced by condensation, emulsions produced by dispersion.

CRITICAL EMULSIONS. If two liquids, A and B, are partially miscible at room temperature and completely miscible above an "upper critical dissolution temperature" $T_1$, then warming a two-phase mixture of A and B to the vicinity of $T_1$ often causes appearance of critical opalescence due to formation of an emulsion. The interfacial tension $\gamma_i$ between the dispersed and the continuous phases and the difference $(\rho_1 - \rho_2)$ between their densities are the two most important causes of destruction of an emulsion. When, near $T_1$, the two liquids A-in-B and B-in-A have similar compositions, then $\gamma_1$ and $(\rho_1 - \rho_2)$ are small so that droplets (whatever the reason for their formation) may exist for a long time before they dissolve in the dispersion medium. These emulsions are reversible in the sense that an increase of temperature beyond $T_1$ causes their destruction (i.e., molecular mixing) but a new lowering of temperature to the vicinity of $T_1$ gives rise to an emulsion very similar to that observed initially.

A "lower critical dissolution temperature" $T_2$ exists for many pairs of compounds; this means that liquids C and D are miscible in all proportions below $T_2$ but form two mutually saturated phases at temperatures above $T_2$. In these systems also, critical emulsions exist near $T_2$.

EMULSIONS PRODUCED BY CONDENSATION. A supersaturated molecular solution of substance A in substance B is the starting system. When the supersaturation is, by whatever means, eliminated, the excess of A may gather to droplets and thus form an emulsion. Not many examples of this type are known.

EMULSIONS PRODUCED BY DISPERSION. This is by far the most common method. The starting system consists of two bulk liquid phases, and one of these has to be dispersed in the other.

Mechanical dispersion is based on the mechanism elucidated by the blind physicist Joseph Plateau a century ago. If a drop is extended to form a cylinder, this becomes unstable as soon as its length exceeds its circumference $(2\pi r)$ and two spherical drops form. If we succeed in extending the cylinder far beyond its stability limit, it will have the tendency to break down into many droplets, each approximately of the volume $4.5\pi r^3$. A prolate spheroid of revolution spontaneously affords two spherical drops when its major axis is approximately 3.9 times it minor axis.

These processes take place because, above a definite ratio of length $l$ to $r$, at least some indentations on the cylinder surface are such that capillary pressure near the bottom of the indentation is greater than that far from it. This pressure difference drives the liquid away from the indentation, which grows deeper and deeper until the cylinder is snapped in two. Another formulation of the effect is that rupture occurs spontaneously when the surface area of the system steadily decreases in going from a slight indentation to complete separation into two drops. A relative instability is observed also when the combined surface area of the final drops (whatever their relative volumes) is smaller than that of the original cylinder or spheroid. In short, rupture is accomplished because the interfacial energy $\gamma_i A_2$ of the separate spherical droplets is less than that of the initial elongated body, $\gamma_i A_1$, where $A_1$ and $A_2$ are the interfacial areas before and after break.

In practice, the elongation of drops needed to initiate Plateau's process is achieved, for instance, by squeezing a liquid through a narrow capillary (as in homogenizers), or by extending it into filaments (as in blenders). As long as external forces act on the filament (that is, as long as stirring continues), the filament may be quite stable, but as soon as stirring stops, a chaplet of droplets appears where the filament was visible. The advantage of interrupting the agitation is particularly clear in Briggs' method of preparing emulsions: A vessel containing two immiscible liquids is vigorously shaken, say, three or five times, left undisturbed for a few seconds, briefly shaken again, etc. An emulsion is obtained much sooner and after fewer shakes than when the agitation continues without interruption.

When two spherical droplets coalesce and form one spherical drop, the interfacial area, and consequently the interfacial energy, decreases. Thus coalescence is a spontaneous process, and all emulsions (except critical emulsions) would gradually give rise to two bulk phases if no third material were present to retard coalescence and thus stabilize emulsions. Materials having this function are called emulsifying agents. Usually they are commercial products which are mixtures of several compounds, but their main ingredients are proteins, or gum-like or soap-like substances. Examples of these three classes are gelatin as in many drug prescriptions and casein as in milk; acacia, tragacanth, gum arabic, etc.; and soaps and synthetic detergents. The number of recommended materials of this type is very large.

Emulsions may also be stabilized by powders. Mercury droplets on a dusty bench top provide a good example of this stabilization. The mechanism of this effect is relatively clear—when two droplets come in the vicinity of each other, the dust particles prevent one liquid from touching the other. There is no contact except that between liquid and dust and that between dust and dust, and hence no coalescence. Perhaps the action of many emulsifying agents is fundamentally analogous to that of solid particles, but the available data are not sufficient for a decision.

### O/W and W/O Emulsions—Phase Reversal

An emulsion contains at least two liquids. Very often, water is one of these. The other liquid, which is immiscible or poorly miscible with water, usually is designated as "oil." If this "oil" is the dispersed phase, an oil-in-water or O/W emulsion is present; when water forms the droplets, the emulsion is W/O type.

If a layer of water (or an aqueous solution) and a layer of oil are agitated together, in principle either an O/W or a W/O system may emerge. The result depends on at least four factors, namely the relative volumes of the two phases, their relative position, the concentration of the emulsifying agent, and the nature of the latter. Densely packed spheres all of the same size occupy approximately 74% of the total volume. If the combined volume of drops is greater—i.e., if the volume of the dispersed phase is >0.74 that of the emulsion, either smaller droplets must be present between the main drops, or these must be deformed, or both. Hence, there is a tendency of a two-phase liquid mixture (containing also an emulsifying agent) to form an O/W emulsion, when the volume of oil is smaller than that of water; and W/O when an excess of oil is present.

Nevertheless, it is possible to prepare emulsions containing 99% by volume of the discontinuous phase. Such systems, however, usually are not produced by shaking one volume of, say, an aqueous liquid with 99 volumes of oil but by gradual introduction of oil droplets in the aqueous phase.

If the walls of the vessel in which the two components are agitated together have been previously wetted with one of them, this liquid tends to be the external phase.

The nature and amount of the emulsifying agent are the main factors determining the kind of emulsion produced. Thus, emulsions of water in benzene have been obtained with large amounts of sodium stearate present under conditions which give rise to benzene-in-water emulsions when the amount of sodium stearate is small. Sodium soaps generally promote formation of O/W systems, while calcium and magnesium soaps favor the W/O type. The empirical rule that emulsifying agents soluble in a phase tend to make this the dispersion medium often is valid.

When a calcium salt is gradually added to an O/W emulsion stabilized with sodium stearate, calcium stearate forms. When the concentration of the latter is high enough, the O/W system is transformed into a W/O system. This is an example of phase reversal, also known as inversion of emulsion, a very important process which takes place, for instance, in the making of butter (W/O type) from cream (O/W type). In this case, however, the phase reversal is achieved by changing the volume ratio of oil to water from small to large. In many instances, the inversion is incomplete, and dual or multiple emulsions result. In these systems, minute droplets of, say, water are suspended in larger drops of, say, oil, and these drops in their turn are suspended in a continuous aqueous phase.

Often it is not immediately clear whether a given emulsion is of the O/W or of the W/O type. The following examination methods are commonly used:

—The emulsion droplets are viewed in a microscope and, by focusing upward, it is found whether the refractive index of the discrete phase is greater or smaller than that of the medium. If these indices are known for the two main ingredients, identification is not in doubt.

—The emulsion is diluted with, say, water. If water is the continuous phase, mixing proceeds smoothly. If no mixing immediately occurs, the continuous phase is made up of oil.

—The emulsion is divided in two parts. One part is sprinkled with a water-soluble dye, and the other with

Droplet size distribution is an important property of every emulsion. Usually, drop diameters can be measured or at least estimated by microscopic observation, although other methods also are used. In theory, these diameters may have almost any magnitude but the majority of the emulsions studied have diameters chiefly in the range 0.2 to 5 microns.
an oil-soluble pigment. If the first (second) powder dissolves, the dispersion medium is water (oil).

—The electric conductance of the emulsion is measured. Conductivity of O/W systems as a rule is greater than that of W/O systems.

## Properties

These limits are not due to chance. Droplets considerably smaller than, say, 0.2 micron must have a greater solubility in the continuous phase than larger drops. Thus, the former tend to disappear, and their substance enlarges the latter. Drops considerably greater than, say, 5 microns sediment or cream too rapidly. The linear rate $u$ of sedimentation or creaming is given approximately by the Stokes equation:

$$u = \frac{2}{9} g \frac{r^2}{\eta} (\rho_1 - \rho_2)$$

where $g$ is acceleration due to gravity and $\eta$ is viscosity of the medium. Let $\eta$ be 0.01 g./cm. sec. (as for water at 20° C.) and $(\rho_1 - \rho_2)$ be 0.1 g./cu.cm.; then the above equation gives $u = 2180\ r^2$ cm./sec., i.e., $u = 2 \times 10^{-5}$ cm./sec. for $r = 10^{-4}$ cm. and $u = 2 \times 10^{-3}$ cm./sec. for $r = 10^{-3}$ cm. The latter velocity is equal to that of 10 cm. in about 80 minutes. Thus, particles greater than 5 microns would form, in a vessel 10 cm. tall, a layer of cream in a few hours. Cow's milk has an $r$ of, usually, 1 to 2 microns.

Mechanical properties of emulsions differ from those of true solutions because deformation of an emulsion generally causes deviation of the droplets from the spherical shape—i.e., an increase in interfacial energy. Thus the work of deformation contains a term absent in one-phase liquids. If an emulsion contains $10^{10}$ droplets per cu. cm., of $r = 10^{-4}$ cm., the approximate interfacial area is 1200 sq. cm.[9]; if $\gamma_i = 40$ g./sq. sec.[2], the free interfacial energy is $5 \times 10^4$ ergs per cu. cm. of emulsion, a substantial quantity. A movement which doubles the surface area of the droplets by altering their shape needs additional energy of this magnitude. In connection with this effect, viscosity of emulsions (especially when their concentration is high) depends on the rate of shear (also known as velocity gradient).

Because the refractive index of the oil phase almost always is different from that of the aqueous phase, practically all emulsions are turbid. Light scattering is often used for calculating droplet dimensions.

Both mechanical and optical constants of an emulsion are influenced by those of the emulsifying agent. Even greater often is the effect of these agents on the electric properties of the system. Very many emulsifying agents (e.g., proteins and soaps) give ions to the aqueous (and perhaps also to the oil) phase. Hence, the electrical conductivity $\kappa$ of an emulsion frequently depends above all on the nature and concentration of the surface-active substance present. For instance, if this is a protein, $\kappa$ may be a minimum at the isoelectric point.

Emulsion droplets move in a uniform electrostatic field (i.e., manifest electrophoresis). When the insoluble ion of the emulsifying agent is positive (i.e., a cationic detergent is used), the direction of the movement is toward the cathode. With anionic detergent, droplets move to the anode. At the isoelectric point of the protein, no movement is observed.

In practice, other properties of emulsions are more likely to be important than those mentioned above. An emulsion of an "oil" in water presents a smaller fire hazard, a smaller probability of poisoning, and an advantage in price, as compared with a solution of this "oil" in an organic solvent. An advantage of a more special kind is utilized in emulsion polymerization. Polymerization of a large volume of liquid may result in a temperature increase in the central part of this volume so great that charring, gas evolution, and other unwanted processes take place. If monomer is suspended in the aqueous phase as discrete droplets, each droplet is cooled by the surrounding water, its temperature does not rise unduly, and no decomposition occurs.

### Stability and Breakdown

The rate of creaming or sedimentation of an emulsion increases with the value of $(\rho_1 - \rho_2)$. This behavior may make the emulsion unsuitable for a particular application but, from the scientific point of view, gives no indication of stability or instability. The stratification may be striking but each of the emulsions stacked up, one on top of the other, is still an emulsion, and the total number of droplets is identical with that before creaming.

Breaking of an emulsion occurs when many droplets coalesce and, finally, give rise to a bulk phase. This is an effect which, in theory, is independent of sedimentation. However, in a cream, where the concentration of droplets is high, the probability of collisions and perhaps coalescence is also high. The main driving force of coalescence originates, as far as is known, from the energy of the oil-water interfaces. If $10^{10}$ drops referred to above flow together to one drop, the decrease in interfacial energy is about $5 \times 10^4$ ergs. This quantity may be compared with the work of creaming. If $10^{10}$ drops of $\rho_2 = 0.9$ rise 10 cm. in water ($\rho_1 = 1.0$), the work of gravitation is (for $r = 10^{-4}$ cm.) about 40 ergs, i.e., less than 0.1% of the energy gained during coalescence.

The driving force of breaking is smaller when $\gamma_i$ is less. Consequently, emulsions of A in B or of B in A are easy to prepare, show little tendency to coalescence, and often can be readily restored after coalescence, if the interfacial tension between A and B is small (less than, say, 5 g./sq. sec.). In this region of $\gamma_i$ values, natural convection may be strong enough to cause emulsification which, thus, appears to be spontaneous. Emulsions of this type are not industrially important.

If $\gamma_i$ is high (e.g., 50 g./sq. sec.), coalescence can be prevented only by preventing liquid-to-liquid contact, as in powder-stabilized systems. A possibility is to have all droplets electrically charged (all positive or all negative), the charge being more or less uniformly distributed over the surface of each sphere. Mutual approach of two drops is then resisted by their electrostatic repulsion or, more correctly, by the mutual repulsion of their electric double layers. Emulsions which belong to this class have been repeatedly prepared in laboratories and have considerable theoretical importance, but the role of the repulsion in industrial emulsions is still debated. The mechanism of the stabilization by emulsifying agents also is not known with certainty.

If breakdown of an emulsion is wanted, the procedure to be used depends on the cause of stability. If a small value of $\gamma_i$ is this cause, one should attempt to raise the interfacial tension. Suppose, for instance, that the two main ingredients of the emulsion (A and B) are mutually insoluble and have a great $\gamma_i$, and that the emulsion is relatively stable because a third substance (C), which lowers $\gamma_i$, has been added. Remove C by, for instance, vaporization, and the emulsion will break.

Droplets stabilized by their electric charge can be discharged by a suitable electrolyte. Thus, oil drops, positively charged because they contain more tetraalkylammonium ions than chloride ions, may be made nearly neutral by adding, say, sodium picrate to the aqueous phase. It has been claimed in older publications that rapid coalescence of emulsions of this class sets in when the electrokinetic potential (or $\zeta$ potential) of the droplets decreases below the "critical" potential of about 0.025–0.030 volt.

Common emulsions break when their emulsifying agent is destroyed or made ineffective. An elegant method of achieving this goal is to add to the emulsion micro-organisms which feed on the emulsifying agent (belonging, for instance, to proteins) without attacking the "oil." Reagents which by a chemical reaction break or transform the stabilizing material may be used instead of micro-organisms. When substances which, in larger concentrations, cause phase reversal are used in smaller amounts, often coalescence results. Thus, addition of a calcium salt to an O/W emulsion stabilized with a sodium soap may cause coalescence as long as the ratio Ca/Na is neither too small nor too large. When the concentration of Na$^+$ is just right for an O/W, and the concentration of Ca$^{+2}$ is just right for a W/O system, the mixture is "confused," "does not know" what type of emulsion to produce, and gives rise to two bulk phases. An analogous "confusion" occurs when, say, a W/O emulsion is diluted with water so that the ratio is favorable to formation of an O/W system.

### ADDITIONAL READING

Becher, P., "Emulsions," Reinhold, New York, 1957.
Bikerman, J. J., "Surface Chemistry," 2nd ed., Academic Press, New York, 1958.
Blair, C. M., *Chem. & Ind.*, 1960 p. 538.
Sumner, G. S., *Paint Technol.* **24**, No. 266, 14 (1960).
Voyutskii, S. S., *Uspekhi Khimii* **30**, 1237 (1961); *Russ. Chem. Rev.* **30**, 556 (1961).

# 6

# Surface Active Agents Their Behavior and Industrial Use

# Surface Active Agents–Their Behavior

E. G. SCHWARZ     W. G. REID

*For producing foams or preventing foams — theoretical and empirical approaches to industrial use of surfactants are collected and explained.*

The physical properties exhibited by surface active materials in aqueous solution, viz., surface tension, interfacial tension, critical micelle concentration, micelle aggregation number, contact angle, spreading coefficient, etc., depend on the composition and structure of the surfactant molecule as a whole and also in part—i.e., on the composition and structure of the surfactant hydrophobe and hydrophile. Hartley considered the possession of hydrophobic and hydrophilic tendencies and their asymmetrical distribution so fundamental a property of surface active agents that he coined the word "amphipathy" for it (*10*). This article considers how molecular composition affects the fundamental properties that define surface activity, and tries to relate the importance of both the theoretical approach and the empirical approach to the progress of surfactant technology.

## Surface Tension

Surfactant molecules are adsorbed at an aqueous surface because the attraction between water-water dipoles is much greater than that resulting from hydrophobe-water plus hydrophile-water attractions. The surfactant hydrophobe is "squeezed" out of solution. If we keep the same hydrophile, such as a polyalkylene oxide, and compare fluorocarbon, silicone and hydrocarbon hydrophobes, the ultimate aqueous surface tensions obtained will depend on the surface energy (van der Waals' attractions) of the hydrophobes themselves.

Fluorocarbons, silicones, and hydrocarbons possess different cohesive forces (van der Waals' attractions) because of the relative deformability (polarizability) of the valence electron clouds around C—C—F, Si—C—H and C—C—H bonds (*5*). This difference is reflected in the surface tensions and solubility parameters (both measures of the cohesive forces) of these materials. Comparing liquids containing about the same number of atoms, the order of decreasing cohesive force is hydrocarbon > dimethylsilicone > fluorocarbon (Table II).

In the light of our own experience, the surface tension attainable with a particular type of surfactant in aqueous solution is never less than the surface tension of the parent hydrophobe. Any surface tension greater than this value would be ascribed to the absence of a complete monolayer of surfactant at the water-air interface. Thus the order of decreasing aqueous surface tension for surfactants having about the same water solubility would be hydrocarbon > dimethylsilicone > fluorocarbon. This is shown by aqueous surface tension data (Table III), in which, as far as possible, comparisons were made between agents having the same or similar hydrophiles and approximately the same water solubilities for both nonionic and ionic surfactants.

Nonionic surfactants are materials that do not ionize in aqueous solution; water solubility is imparted by hydrogen-bonding groups such as ether, oxygen, and hydroxyl. Such surfactants usually have a "cloud point," or temperature at which they become insoluble in aqueous solution. As the temperature of an aqueous solution of surfactant is increased, hydrogen bonds between surfactant hydrophile and water are disrupted, thereby causing insolubility.

Ionic surfactants are those materials that form ions in aqueous solution. The names anionic and cationic refer to the charge on the surfactant hydrophobe.

## Interfacial Tension

Surfactants that appreciably lower the surface tension of water will usually lower the interfacial tension between water and organic liquids. The extent of the lowering of interfacial tension will depend in a complex way upon the solubility of the surfactant in both the aqueous and organic phases. This will be a function not only of the surfactant hydrophile-lipophile balance (HLB) (*1, 8*), but also of the nature of the hydrophobe and hydrophile. In general, a low solubility of the surfactant in both phases will promote interfacial activity.

The effects of several types of surfactants on the mineral oil/water interfacial tension (52.0 dynes/cm.) and a dimethylsilicone/water interfacial tension (32.8 dynes/cm.) are listed in Table IV.

# and Industrial Use

The oil/aqueous solution interfacial tensions attained with silicone and hydrocarbon surfactants were generally lower than the corresponding interfacial tensions resulting from the fluorocarbon surfactants. This might be due to too low a solubility of the fluorocarbon portion of the surfactant in the oil phase, so that the surfactant cannot ideally orient at the water/oil interface and thus gives low interfacial tensions.

Becher (2) believes that his data indicate that high interfacial tensions occur when surfactants are not ideally oriented because of perturbing effects of either the surfactant hydrophobe or hydrophile. Applying Becher's theory, Figure 1 shows the possible orientations of a surfactant at the oil/water interface.

Figure 1, A and C corresponds to high interfacial tension. In 1A, this arises from the perturbing effect of the hydrophobe on the water structure. This would describe fluorocarbon surfactants at the mineral oil/water interface, since the fluorocarbon hydrophobe would not be very soluble in mineral oil. As for Figure 1C, the high interfacial tension arises from the perturbing effect due to presence of the hydrophile in the oil phase. This occurs when a surfactant is quite soluble in the oil.

Figure 1B represents the ideal position (perturbations at a minimum) and corresponds to the case of silicone and hydrocarbon surfactants at the mineral oil/water and silicone/water interface discussed above.

## Micellization and Aggregation Number

A surfactant molecule can escape from the bulk aqueous solution by being adsorbed at the water/air interface and also by forming clusters of molecules, called micelles, in the bulk solution. (A surfactant molecule can also be adsorbed on the container walls.) In micellization the surfactant hydrophobe is again "squeezed" out of the water and the cluster of hydrophobes is shielded from the water by the outer layer of hydrophiles. These processes are represented by:

$$\text{surfactant} \underset{}{\overset{K_1}{\rightleftharpoons}} \quad \text{surfactant} \underset{}{\overset{K_2}{\rightleftharpoons}} \quad \text{surfactant}$$
$$\text{in micelles} \qquad \text{in bulk solution} \qquad \text{at the surface}$$

The equilibrium constants $K_1$ and $K_2$ are dependent on surfactant composition, structure, and activity.

The number of molecules per micelle, called the aggregation number, will be largely dependent on the structure of the surfactant molecule and nature of the surfactant hydrophobe and hydrophile. Organic sur-

### TABLE I. SOURCE OF MATERIALS

| Surfactant | Company | Structure |
|---|---|---|
| FC-170 | 3M Company | Not disclosed |
| FC-128 | " | " |
| FC-134 | " | " |
| L-77 | Union Carbide Corp., Silicones Division | Dimethylsilicone–poly-alkylene oxide |
| L-79 | " " | Dimethylsilicone cationic |
| Y-4723 | " " | Dimethylsilicone–poly-alkyleneoxide |
| Y-4724 | " " | " " |
| Y-4725 | " " | Dimethylsilicone-anionic |
| Y-4726 | " " | Dimethylsilicone–poly-alkylene oxide |
| Triton X-100 | Rohm and Haas Co. | $C_8H_{17}(C_6H_4)O-(C_2H_4O)_{9.5}H$ |
| TMN-6 | Union Carbide Corp., Chemicals Division | $C_{12}H_{25}O(C_2H_4O)_6H$ |
| TMN-3 | " " | $C_{12}H_{25}O(C_2H_4O)_3H$ |
| Aerosol OT | American Cyanamid Co. | $C_8H_{17}OOCCH_2CH-(COOC_8H_{17})SO_3Na$ |
| Na lauryl sulfate | E. I. duPont de Nemours & Co. | $C_{12}H_{25}OSO_3Na$ |
| Aliquat 204 | General Mills | $(C_{12}H_{25})_2(CH_3)_2-N^+Cl^-$ |

### TABLE II.

| Hydrophobe | No. of Atoms | Surface Tension, 25° C., Dynes/Cm. | Solubility Parameter = $\left(\dfrac{\Delta E}{V}\right)^{1/2}$ (Cal./Ml.)$^{1/2}$ |
|---|---|---|---|
| $CH_3(CH_2)_6CH_3$ | 26 | 21.8 | 7.6 |
| $(CH_3)_3CCH_2CH-(CH_3)_2$ | 26 | 18.3 | 6.9 |
| $(CH_3)_3SiOSi(CH_3)_3$ | 27 | 15.7 | 6.0 |
| $CF_3(CF_2)_6CF$ | 26 | 13.6 | 5.7 |
| $CH_3(CH_2)_{10}CH_3$ | 38 | 25.0 | 7.8 |
| $(CH_3)_3SiOSi(CH_3)_2-OSi(CH_3)_3$ | 37 | 16.9 | 5.5 |
| $CF_3(CF_2)_{10}CF_3$ | 38 | m.p. 74.5° C. | $\Delta H_v$ not available |

*Solubility parameters are calculated from the heat of vaporization and molar volume at 25° C., which is the most accurate method (16).*

factants usually have aggregation numbers ranging from about 20 to 150. Our measurements, which utilized a vapor phase osmometer, have shown that dimethylsilicone surfactants have aggregation numbers less than five. These small numbers could be attributed to the presence of hydrophilic oxygen groups along the dimethylsilicone chain (small hydrophiles within the hydrophobe). In order to allow contact of these oxygen groups with water, only small micelles could form, with the methyl groups forming the micelle core. Zisman has shown that polydimethyl siloxane molecules are adsorbed at an aqueous surface with the oxygen

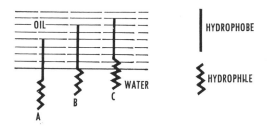

*Figure 1. Possible orientations of a surface active agent at an oil/water interface*

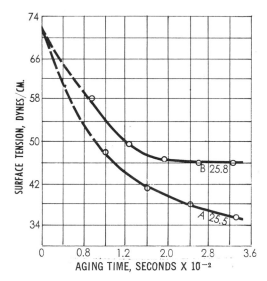

*Figure 2. The dynamic surface tension of silicone-oxyalkylene copolymers in 1% aqueous solution. (Ross and Chen, 1960)*

atoms attracted to the water because of the semi-ionic nature of the Si-O bond (7).

Silicone surfactant micelles solubilize liquids insoluble in water, but to a lesser extent than do hydrocarbon surfactant micelles.

Fluorocarbon surfactants probably form micelles also, since the same driving force that causes surfactant molecules to be adsorbed at the surface of an aqueous solution is involved in the phenomenon of micellization. Our literature survey revealed no studies of micellization by fluorocarbon surfactants.

### Wetting

The ability of a liquid to spread on a solid is measured by the spreading coefficient:

$$S = \gamma_s - (\gamma_l + \gamma_{s/l}) \qquad (1)$$

$\gamma_s$ = free energy of the solid surface
$\gamma_l$ = free energy of the liquid surface
$\gamma_{s/l}$ = free energy of the solid/liquid interface.

If the spreading coefficient is positive, a liquid should wet-out a solid—i.e., spread to a thin film.

Materials like polyethylene and polytetrafluoroethylene have low surface energies ($\gamma_s$) and are thus harder to wet than more polar materials such as glass or steel. There are no direct means of measuring the surface energy of a solid, but an estimate can be obtained by measuring the contact angles of a homologous series of liquids—e.g., alkanes—on the solid. Plotting the surface tension of the spreading liquid, $\gamma_l$, vs. contact angle on the solid gives a straight line. Extrapolating the line to zero contact angle, representing the wetting-out of the solid by a liquid, gives the surface tension of liquid needed to just wet-out the solid. Examination of the forces involved in this spreading shows that:

$\gamma_l \cos \theta = \gamma_s - \gamma_{s/l}$, where $\theta$ is the contact angle   (2)
Thus when $\theta = 0$, $\gamma_l = \gamma_s - \gamma_{s/l}$.

At zero contact angle (wetting-out), if it is assumed that $\gamma_{s/l}$ is small, then $\gamma_l \cong \gamma_s$. Surface tension, $\gamma_l$, of a liquid that just wets-out the solid has been termed the critical surface tension of the solid, $\gamma_c$, by Zisman (17). Although Zisman's critical surface tension theory generally applies to the spreading of pure, non-hydrogen bonding liquids on low surface energy solids, he has extended the theory to aqueous surfactant solutions on low energy solids (3).

Fluorocarbon, silicone, and hydrocarbon surfactants lower the surface tension of water, thereby increasing the ability of water to spread. A comparison of the aforementioned surfactants was made by measuring the spreading of 0.02 ml. of 1.0 wt. %, and 0.10 wt. % aqueous solutions of these surfactants on clean, smooth polyethylene. The per cent increase in diameter of a spread droplet over that of water alone was measured. Table V shows that even though all aqueous solutions of the surfactants tested have surface tensions lower than the critical surface tension of wetting ($\gamma_c$) of polyethylene (31d ynes/cm.) (15) only one material, L-77, allowed water to wet-out the polyethylene.

The inability of some of these agents to wet-out when the theory above predicts that they should wet-out could be accounted for by higher interfacial energy, $\gamma_{s/l}$, than the small value that was assumed, or another phenomenon might occur. Zisman (9, 18) describes a situation where the wetting agent alters the surface to be wet by being adsorbed with the hydrophobe outermost so that the critical surface tension of wetting of the new surface is less than that of the spreading liquid itself. Such liquids were described as "autophobic." For example, we have shown how a 1 wt. % solution of L-77, a silicone-oxyalkylene copolymer, wets-out clean, smooth polyethylene. If an identical polyethylene specimen is deliberately coated with a film of dimethylsilicone oil, the L-77 solution will not wet-out.

### Foam Stabilization

Pure liquids do not foam. To form a foam and maintain it a liquid must contain a surface active agent.

### TABLE III. AQUEOUS SURFACE TENSIONS

| Surfactant Type | Trade Name | Cloud Point, ° C. | Aqueous Surface Tension, Dynes/Cm., 25° C. | | | |
|---|---|---|---|---|---|---|
| | | | Conc. = 1.0% | 0.1% | 0.01% | 0.001% |
| NONIONIC: Hydrophobe | | | | | | |
| Fluorocarbon | FC-170 | 60 | 18.5 | 18.5 | 20.0 | 25.0 |
| Dimethylsilicone | Y-4723 | 54 | 20.8 | 21.2 | 22.6 | 27.2 |
| Hydrocarbon | Triton X-100 | 65 | 30.4 | 30.0 | 31.1 | 46.2 |
| Dimethylsilicone | Y-4724 | 40 | 21.3 | 21.2 | 22.7 | 43.0 |
| Hydrocarbon | TMN-6 | 34 | 26.1 | 26.1 | 38.3 | 51.5 |
| Dimethylsilicone | L-77 | <0 | 20.4 | 20.5 | 21.3 | 38.8 |
| Hydrocarbon | TMN-3 | <0 | 26.1 | 26.4 | 28.3 | ... |
| ANIONIC: Hydrophobe | | | | | | |
| Fluorocarbon | FC-128 | ... | 14.3 | 14.7 | 19.0 | 34.2 |
| Dimethylsilicone | Y-4725 | ... | 20.1 | 21.6 | 37.3 | ... |
| Hydrocarbon | Aerosol OT | ... | 26.2 | 29.2 | 43.4 | 54.9 |
| Hydrocarbon | Na Lauryl Sulfate | ... | 32.7 | 31.9 | 44.5 | ... |
| CATIONIC: Hydrophobe | | | | | | |
| Fluorocarbon | FC-134 | ... | 15.0 | 16.2 | 17.3 | 23.8 |
| Dimethylsilicone | L-79 | ... | 20.3 | 21.6 | 26.6 | 45.3 |
| Hydrocarbon | Aliquat 204 | ... | 26.0 | 27.0 | 29.0 | ... |

### TABLE IV. INTERFACIAL TENSIONS

| Surfactant Type | Trade Name | Cloud Point ° C. | $H_2O$/Oil Interfacial Tensions, 1.0 Wt. %; Surfactant, 25° C. | |
|---|---|---|---|---|
| | | | Mineral Oil–$H_2O$ (52.0 Dynes/Cm.) | $(Me_3SiO)_2SiMe_2$–$H_2O$ (32.8 Dynes/Cm.) |
| NONIONIC: Hydrophobe | | | | |
| Fluorocarbon | FC-170 | 60 | 9.6 | 7.7 |
| Dimethylsilicone | Y-4726 | 54 | 3.5 | 2.3 |
| Hydrocarbon | Triton X-100 | 65 | 2.4 | 3.2 |
| ANIONIC: Hydrophobe | | | | |
| Fluorocarbon | FC-128 | .. | 10.1 | 5.4 |
| Dimethylsilicone | Y-4725 | .. | 2.9 | 0.0 |
| Hydrocarbon | Aerosol OT | .. | 2.3 | 1.0 |
| CATIONIC: Hydrophobe | | | | |
| Fluorocarbon | FC-134 | .. | 6.2 | 6.8 |
| Dimethylsilicone | L-79 | .. | 2.2 | 0.3 |
| Hydrocarbon | Aliquat 204 | .. | 1.2 | 1.0 |

### TABLE V. WETTING OF POLYETHYLENE

| Surfactant | Aqueous Surface Tension, 25° C. | | % Increase in Diameter[a] of Spread Droplet after 3 Minutes, 25° C. | |
|---|---|---|---|---|
| | 1.0 Wt. % | 0.1 Wt. % Surfactant | 1.0 Wt. % | 0.1 Wt. % Surfactant |
| FLUOROCARBON | | | | |
| FC-170 | 18.5 | 18.5 | 180 | 96 |
| FC-128 | 14.3 | 14.7 | 162 | 22 |
| SILICONE | | | | |
| L-77 | 20.4 | 20.5 | >300 (wets) | >300 (wets) |
| L-79 | 20.3 | 21.6 | 220 | 42 |
| HYDROCARBON | | | | |
| Tergitol TMN-3 | 26.1 | 26.4 | 110 | 36 |
| Aerosol OT | 26.2 | 29.2 | 146 | 6 |

[a] Greater than 300% considered to be superior wetting.

The fact that foams that are easily formed are not necessarily stable—i.e., resistant to collapse—indicates that more than one mechanism must be at work. There is no such thing as a universal foam stabilizer for all systems, but in each one the surface active agents must do the following.

**Lower the surface tension of the system.** Since surface tension is really an energy term describing the differential work, $dW$, required to increase surface area differentially, $dA$—i.e., $dW = \gamma \, dA$—a low value means that less work is required to expand a liquid film.

**Produce film elasticity under dynamic conditions.** A thinning spot on a bubble wall is a potential seat of film rupture and the surfactant must operate to make the liquid draw toward that spot and restore its original thickness. Suppose some stress or stretching to which the bubble was subjected accidentally had caused an increase in its surface area and a resulting transient depletion in the surface concentration of the surfactant. A higher surface tension would then be produced at that spot and the restoring process would be caused by the migration of appreciable quantities of fluid directed along the surface in response to the pull of the localized high tension that had suddenly appeared. This explanation is associated with the name of Marangoni (11). Experimentally, it can be shown that dynamic surface tension—i.e., the rate at which a newly formed surface reaches its static or equilibrium surface tension—is a key factor in stabilization early in the life of the foam (13). Generally, to produce a stable foam a newly formed surface must not reach equilibrium value too rapidly.

Dynamic surface tension is a quantitative expression of how surface tension varies with age of a new surface.

Figure 2 shows dynamic surface tension measurements of two different silicone-polyoxyalkylene block copolymers in 1% aqueous solutions. Surface tension vs. time curves were determined with the Rayleigh vibrating jet tensiometer (12, 13). Curve A represents a copolymer rich in concentration of dimethylsilicone; B, one of normal concentration. A gives marginal performance as a stabilizer of urethane foam. The average slope of Curve A is greater, indicating a more rapid attainment of equilibrium surface tension, allowing less time for the Marangoni effect to come into play. While we have not proved the relation between surfactant efficacy in a complex system like urethane foam and dynamic surface tension in a model (aqueous) system, the effect is consistent with current theories of foam stabilization and shows how critical is the composition of surfactant in this application. Ross and Haak (13) have given a calculation of the Marangoni effect:

"An estimate of the magnitudes involved is instructive: Schulman and Teorell (14) measured rates of flow of monomolecular films of oleic acid on water; the monolayer carried with it a quantity of subsurface water approximately 30 microns deep, and moved with a speed of 2 to 5 cm./sec. The surface layer would, therefore, move to cover a distance of 1 mm. in 20 to 50 msec., during which time the surface tension of a newly produced surface of 0.4% sodium oleate, for example,

would not yet have reached static surface tension equilibrium. If the extension of the surface were much greater, however, the diffusion to the surface would have reached equilibrium before the lateral movement of the surface layer had had time to cover the new surface. This calculation, at least, confirms the general experience that soap films cannot be stretched indefinitely without losing resilience."

**Produce surface plasticity.** Longer-lived liquid foams are made possible by this property, which can be considered as caused by a particular alignment of surface active molecules in the adsorbed surface layer.

For practical purposes there are two types of foams: (1) those that start out as liquids and, undergoing no change in composition, remain that way, supported by the gas that generated them; (2) those that by some change in their composition become capable of supporting themselves—i.e., a "solid" foam.

Type 1 depends upon surface plasticity for its longevity; eventually, however, drainage causes the bubble wall (or lamella) to thin to the point where coalescence occurs and the foam collapses.

Type 2 is illustrated by cellular plastics. Here the

**TABLE VI. SURFACE TENSION OF POLYETHER TRIOL 3000 MOLECULAR WEIGHT**

| Surfactant (1.0 Wt. %) | Surface Tension at 25° C., Dynes/Cm. |
|---|---|
| None | 32.0 |
| Nonyl phenol polyoxyethylene copolymer | 32.0 |
| Sulfonated fatty ester | 31.2 |
| Dimethylsilicone | 26.5 |
| Dimethylsilicone polyoxyalkylene copolymer[a] | 25.6 |
| Fluorocarbon polyoxyalkylene copolymer | 24.0 |

[a] A type that stabilizes polyurethane foam.

foam must be stabilized for a relatively short, but critical time period, until changes occur in the foaming material that permit it to support itself. An example of solid foams is polyurethane foam. The success of the current manufacturing process is due in large part to a unique type of surface active agent.

Polyurethane foams are reaction products of tolylene diisocyanate (TDI) with polyether triols (polyol) and with water. The TDI simultaneously reacts with the polyol forming a three-dimensional polyurethane, and with the water to form $CO_2$ and a diamine. This reacts with more TDI to provide additional crosslinking through the formation of disubstituted ureas. The $CO_2$ is usually supplemented with a fluorocarbon blowing agent, vaporized by the exothermic reactions.

The mixture of the unreacted components, including catalysts and the surface active agent, has low viscosity, which makes for an unstable foam. Several reactions then occur simultaneously, foam temperature increases, and there is a delicate balance between gas generation and polymerization. For example, if $CO_2$ is generated too rapidly relative to polymerization, bubbles can coalesce leading to "splits" and collapse. If polymerization occurs too quickly, high densities result.

A third phenomenon must occur in flexible foams. The cells must open enough be to interconnecting when the foam reaches the top of its rise. The polymerizing liquid system starts out at low viscosity which increases as foaming progresses, passes through a viscoelastic solid stage, and finally becomes an elastomer. As in all liquid foams, drainage occurs and the bubble walls become thinner. The fragility of the wall and the rate of polymerization must therefore be balanced, so that the cells become interconnecting but do not coalesce further before the foam has become elastomeric.

The particular surface active agents that are useful for urethane foams are organosilicone block copolymers, which are reaction products of dimethyl silicones and polyoxyalkylene glycols. The requirement of low surface tension to make conditions thermodynamically favorable for bubble formation has already been discussed. Conventional profoamers do not reduce the surface tension of organic liquids such as urethanes, since the surface tensions of these liquids are relatively low to begin with. As an illustration, Table VI gives surface tension measurements made of a polyoxypropylene triol, one of the major ingredients of a urethane foam, used as a solvent for various surfactants.

Note that the organic surface active agents, common foam stabilizers for aqueous systems, are without effect in this system. It is significant that while a dimethyl-silicone and a fluorocarbon material bracket the surface tension produced by the dimethylsilicone–polyoxyalkylene copolymer they do not stabilize urethane foam, indicating that surface tension lowering is a necessary—but not a sufficient—requirement for foam stabilization.

### Antifoaming

Many process industries suffer serious problems from unwanted foams. As mentioned earlier, a surface-active agent must be present to permit the formation and persistence of foams.

Foam is difficult, if not impossible, to handle, and antifoamers are often added. Any distinction between the terms "antifoaming" and "defoaming" is one of semantics. The requirements for an antifoam are:

—limited solubility
—low surface tension
—low interfacial tension with the foaming liquid

These requirements add up to saying that an antifoam must have a positive and large spreading coefficient. Spreading coefficient here is analogous to Equation 1, with changes for the system involved:

$$S = \gamma_f - (\gamma_a + \gamma_{f/a}) \qquad (3)$$

$S$ = spreading coefficient, antifoam on the liquid
$\gamma_f$ = surface tension of the foaming liquid
$\gamma_a$ = surface tension of the antifoam
$\gamma_{f/a}$ = interfacial tension, foaming liquid/antifoam

Spreading rapidly on the surface of a liquid film, the antifoam drags away the original liquid and replaces it with a liquid (itself) incapable of sustaining a film.

Surface active agents such as polyoxyalkylene glycols and their derivatives exhibit inverse water solubility with temperature and can function as antifoaming agents above their cloud point and as profoamers below. What happens to such agents in aqueous systems as temperature varies is summarized qualitatively as:

| decreasing temp. | cloud point | increasing temp. |
|---|---|---|
| ← | ═══ | → |
| greater solubility (hydrophilic) | | greater insolubility (hydrophobic) |
| $S \leq 0$ | | $S > 0$ |
| profoaming | | antifoaming |

Changes of composition have similar effects. Decreasing the concentration of the hydrophilic portion of the molecule (low hydrophile-lipophile balance—HLB) (1, 8) lowers the cloud point.

$$\text{HLB} = 20 \quad \xleftarrow{\text{inc.}} \xrightarrow[]{\text{HLB} \quad \text{dec.}} \quad \text{HLB} = 1$$

$$\text{(hydrophilic)} \xleftarrow[]{\text{inc.} \quad \text{cloud point} \quad \text{dec.}} \xrightarrow{} \text{(hydrophobic)}$$

As a typical industrial application we can cite a foaming problem that occurred recently in the continuous dying of a synthetic fabric. The combined effects of conventional wetting agents used in the dye solution (which were profoamers), high temperature, and aeration by the fabric being drawn through the bath produced intolerable volumes of foam. Furthermore the froth prevented uniform dye contact with the fabric. Several antifoam agents of the dimethyl silicone type were found to maintain foam at a tolerable level, but were found to plate out on the fabric and because of their low incompatibility with organic systems interfered with subsequent treatments. Since the bath operated at approximately 90° C., a silicone polyoxyalkylene copolymer with a cloud point of about 55° C. was able to prevent foam formation by the mechanism described above. Since this surfaceactive agent was partially organic in nature it did not interfere with subsequent treatment of the fabric.

### LITERATURE CITED

(1) Atlas Chemical Industries, Inc., "The Atlas HLB System" (1962).
(2) Becher, P., J. Colloid Sci. 18, 672 (1963).
(3) Bernett, M. K., Zisman, W. A., J. Phys. Chem. 63, 1241, 1911 (1959).
(4) Bikerman, J. J., "Foams: Theory and Industrial Practice," Reinhold, 1946.
(5) Bondi, A., J. Phys. and Coll. Chem. 55, 1355 (1951).
(6) Burrell, H., Interchemical Review 14, No. 1, p. 8 (1955).
(7) Fox, H. W., Taylor, P. W., Zisman, W. A., IND. & ENG. CHEM. 39, No. 11, 1408 (1947).
(8) Griffin, W. C., J. Soc. Cosmetic Chemists 1, 311, (1949).
(9) Hare, E. F., Zisman, W. A., J. Phys. Chem. 59, 335 (1955).
(10) Hartley, G. S., Prog. Rept. Chem. Fats Lipids 3, 20 (1955).
(11) Kitchener, J. A., Cooper, C. F., Quarterly Reviews, Vol. 13, 83 (1959).
(12) Ross, S., Chen, E. S., Unpublished data (1960).
(13) Ross, S., Haak, R. M., J. Phys. Chem., 62, 1260 (1958).
(14) Schulman, J. H., Teorell, T., Trans. Faraday Soc. 34, 1337 (1938).
(15) Shafrin, E. G., Zisman, W. A., J. Phys. Chem. 64, 552 (1960).
(16) Small, P. A., J. Appl. Chem. 3, 71 (1953).
(17) Zisman, W. A., Advan. Chemistry Ser. 43, 12 (1964).
(18) Ibid., p. 23.

AUTHOR E. G. Schwarz is Product Development Engineer with the Silicones Div. of Union Carbide Corp., Tonawanda, N. Y. W. G. Reid is Research Chemist with the same division.

# 7

# Colloidal Dispersions, Electrokinetic Effects, and the Concept of Zeta Potential

# Colloidal Dispersions
# Electrokinetic Effects
# and the concept of
# ZETA POTENTIAL

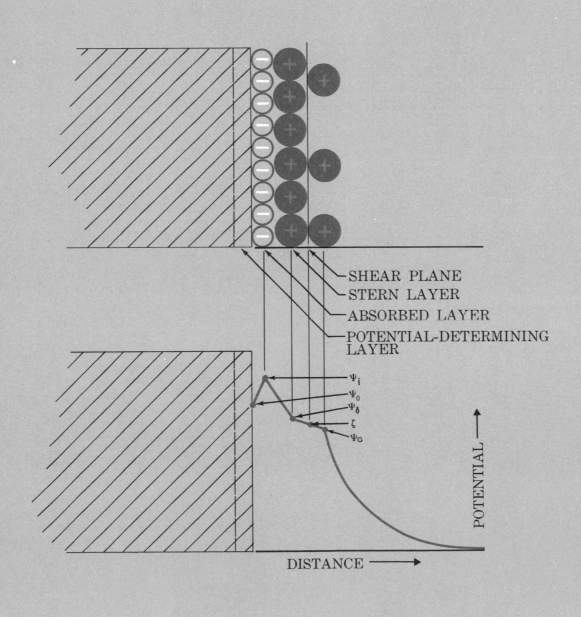

PAUL SENNETT     J. P. OLIVIER

*The colloid chemistry of*

*lyophobic systems is, in fact,*

*the surface chemistry of the*

*dispersed phase, and*

*colloidal dispersions*

*can be understood*

*on this basis. We are*

*concerned with reviewing*

*the electrical aspect of*

*liquid / solid interfaces,*

*and its relation to the*

*stability and behavior*

*of lyophobic colloids*

*Figure 1. A model of the electric double layer*

In present day industrial technology it is common to deal with dispersions of a solid in a liquid, or with emulsions of two immiscible liquids. Although a system is said to be a dispersion when it consists of a homogeneous continuous phase that contains a discontinuous second phase, a dispersion may exist in three distinct conditions depending upon the degree of subdivision of the discontinuous phase. For example, during the hydraulic transport of a coarsely ground limestone through a pipeline, we are able to determine the technologically important physical properties of the system from the bulk properties of the separate phases and by application of appropriate laws of mechanics and hydraulics; chemical composition of the phases, as such, is unimportant. If, however, the same limestone–water mixture is subjected to grinding to reduce the particles to submicron size, the system takes on characteristics unpredicted by the laws that previously applied; it may behave as a semisolid paste or as a free-flowing liquid, depending upon the presence of trace amounts of certain dissolved electrolytes that have no discernible effect on the original mixture. Further reduction of particle size to atomic dimensions, say by dissolving with hydrochloric acid, will yield a system with a third type of behavior—that characteristic of liquid phases.

The coarse particles in water might be called a gross dispersion, if the term mixture is regarded as inadequate; the system of fine particles is termed a colloidal dispersion, or more specifically, a sol or suspension; the third system consists of a molecular or ionic dispersion, although strictly speaking it is a one-phase system. It is the systems characterized by a degree of subdivision intermediate between gross and molecular that are of special interest to many because of their unique properties; it is the study of such systems that has led to development of the discipline of colloid science.

Colloidal systems have been the subject of rather intensive investigation for more than a century (the colloidal condition was recognized by Selmi as early as 1845). But not until the past few decades has anything like an adequate basis for theoretical development been available. Even today, nomenclature of the subject tends to reflect its long history as an observational science. Some terms reflect inaccurate hypotheses or experimental limitations; their meanings are sometimes misunderstood. For instance, we might refer to a particular substance as a colloid, but should realize that a colloidal state of matter, as distinguished from the crystalline state, does not exist as was once thought. Properly, the term "colloid" should be used with reference to a whole colloidal system.

Historically, two major classes of colloidal systems have been recognized; these are lyophilic and lyophobic colloids. Gelatin, starch, gums, some synthetic polymers, and similar materials that show such a marked affinity for water or other appropriate solvent that they form spontaneously a colloidal sol when mixed are classed as lyophilic colloids. Liquid dispersions of small solid or liquid particles produced by mechanical or chemical means are termed lyophobic colloids.

Because these terms imply an interaction with the solvent that may not actually exist, some workers prefer the terms "reversible" and "irreversible" colloids in place of lyophilic and lyophobic, respectively.

Lyophilic colloids, according to present day knowledge, are essentially true solutions and perhaps are better described as macromolecular colloids; the class also includes association colloids such as micellar solutions of surface active agents.

The primary property of lyophobic colloids that sets them apart is their great sensitivity to electrolytes; addition of small amounts of soluble salts to such dispersions will generally cause the particles to clump together, or flocculate. Lyophilic colloids, being true solutions, are insensitive to electrolytes and do not flocculate in the same sense, although they may be precipitated by high salt concentrations.

The classical, and to a great extent current, definition of the colloidal state is in terms of size alone; the lower limit is generally taken to be in the neighborhood of 10 to 50 A., and the upper size limit, in the older literature, as 0.1–0.2 micron. The lower size limit at which we differentiate between a colloidal particle and a dissolved molecule is understandably vague, but the upper size limit is annoyingly arbitrary in that it was chosen because it represented the smallest particles visible with the light microscope. More recent authors have considered the colloidal range to extend to the region of 1-micron size but, again, this is an artificial limit corresponding roughly to the maximum size of particle that will stay in suspension for a reasonable time.

Dispersions of particles smaller than 1 micron are commonly considered sols, whereas those in which the particles are larger than 1 micron are considered suspensions. While the terms sol and suspension are useful to convey an idea of particle size, it is undesirable to thus separate suspensions (and most emulsions) from colloid science because of their degree of subdivision, as is frequently implied. Emulsions and suspensions may exhibit colloid properties and can be so treated.

How, then, should we define the colloidal size range? So that our definition will apply to systems having certain characteristics in common, it must distinguish colloidal dispersions from true solutions on the one hand, and from boulders in a lake on the other. We do this indirectly by defining a colloidal dispersion as one in which the discontinuous phase is subdivided into units that are large compared with simple molecules, but small enough so that interfacial forces, as well as inertial forces, are significant in governing system properties.

Some of the properties commonly associated with colloids, such as Brownian motion, diffusion rates, and light scattering phenomena, are direct functions of particle size. But the behavior of the system, as regards its stability or rheology for instance, is a function of the nature, as well as extent, of the particle/fluid interface. The above definition is therefore an operative one based on the macroscopic properties of a dispersion; it perhaps reflects the bias of the authors, because in practical situations, usually the bulk properties must be controlled.

The properties of colloidal dispersions, therefore, may be changed in two ways: by effecting a change in particle size distribution and hence interfacial area through crystal growth, by comminution, or by fractionation into differing size ranges; and by changing the nature of the interface by adding electrolytes or surface-active agents.

The extent of interface between a dispersed particle of given shape and the surrounding continuous phase is proportional to $d^2$, where $d$ is a characteristic linear dimension of the particle; the inertia or mass of the particle increases with $d^3$. As a result, the ratio of interfacial to inertial forces varies with $d^{-1}$—hence the rapid appearance of colloid properties as a dispersion is made finer. This relation is shown in Figure 2. The diagram illustrates that particle shape is a large factor in any such relationship. The value of $d$ below which interfacial effects become significant may be said to represent the upper colloidal size limit.

But more than size and shape must be considered with regard to inertial forces: the effective mass of the dispersed particles will also be determined by their density relative to the dispersing medium. If the density difference is small, then interfacial forces can be important up to large particle sizes. For example, if we attempt to mix clean polystyrene beads of about 1-mm. diameter with pure water, the beads tend to cling together and float to the surface in spite of their slightly higher density. The surface of the plastic resists being wet by the water, and the effective mass of the particles plus attached air is not great enough to overcome this resistance.

The extent of interface in a given dispersion is often a fixed quantity; any changes in the bulk properties of the system must then be brought about by changing the character of the interfacial region. In the example quoted above, the addition of a trace of an appropriate surfactant to the water allows the plastic to be completely wetted, and the beads will deflocculate and sink. As another example, a moist, crumbly mass of kaolin clay may be transformed into a free-flowing liquid by the addition of a fraction of a per cent of an alkali polyphosphate and resolidified by a trace of calcium

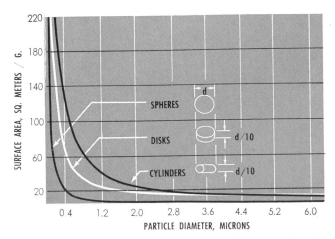

*Figure 2. Variation of surface area with particle size. Note that 1-micron spheres, 4-micron disks; and 7-micron cylinders should be equally colloidal according to our definition*

chloride. Observations such as these illustrate that interfacial forces do indeed control the behavior of even coarse colloidal dispersions, and that these forces are very susceptible to alteration.

The colloid chemistry of lyophobic systems is, therefore, the surface chemistry of the dispersed phase. The size of colloidal particles is an incidental quantity except insofar as it affects the degree to which surface forces are manifested. Although this point of view was adopted by Freundlich by 1909 (34), the historical emphasis on particle size persisted. Only in relatively recent years has colloid science, in its broader aspect of surface chemistry, received widespread application.

### Historical Development

The phenomena referred to collectively as electrokinetic effects pertain to the liquid flow that occurs along a solid/liquid interface as a result of an applied potential gradient, and conversely to the potential developed when a liquid is made to flow along an interface. Reuss (82), in 1808, observed that when a potential difference was maintained across a porous plug of wet clay or sand separating two portions of water, a flow of water occurred from one side of the diaphragm to the other. This phenomenon, now called electroosmosis, is almost always observed when an e.m.f. is applied to electrodes located on opposite sides of a porous diaphragm immersed in water or other liquid. If the liquid flow is not restricted, it will continue as long as a potential difference is maintained; if the flow is restricted, a pressure will build up until it is sufficient to cause a back-flow through the diaphragm that exactly balances the electroosmotic flow.

Quantitative measurements of electroosmosis were first made by Wiedemann (108) about 1850 to determine the relation between pressure, flow, and applied potential. Equilibrium pressure was found to be proportional to applied voltage and independent of dimensions of the diaphragm for a given system; mass flow rate with no pressure-drop was proportional to the current applied, and was also independent of diaphragm dimensions.

About 10 years later, Quinke (78) reasoned that because a porous object essentially consists of a mass of fine capillaries, electroosmosis should occur in a single capillary tube; this was indeed the case. Quinke also discovered that when a liquid was forced to flow through a capillary tube or porous diaphragm, a potential difference was created; this is the converse of electroosmosis, and the e.m.f. developed is called the streaming potential. He further showed that the liquid flow in electroosmosis is not necessarily in the same direction as the current flow. These facts led to the hypothesis that the observed effects were caused by the presence of electrically charged layers of opposite sign at the solid/liquid boundary. An applied voltage would therefore cause a relative displacement of the charged layers; the liquid, being free to move, thus flowed in a direction dependent on the sign of the charge it carried.

This hypothesis also explained the streaming potential as the result of a charge displacement caused by the forced flow of liquid along the solid surface.

A third manifestation of the electrokinetic effect was investigated in 1880 by Dorn (21), who noted that when suspended particles are forced to move through a liquid in response to gravitation, a potential gradient is generated in the direction of movement. This phenomenon, variously called the Dorn effect, sedimentation potential, centrifugation potential, or migration potential, can also be qualitatively explained by this hypothesis.

The development of the theory of the electric double layer dates from 1879 and the work of Helmholtz (47), who postulated that formation of such a layer was of general occurrence at a phase boundary. He related mathematically the velocity of electroosmotic flow to charge separation in the double layer; the flow was shown to depend on an "electrokinetic potential" that corresponded to the potential drop across the layer of charge contained in the moving liquid.

At about this time, Schulze (89, 90) showed that certain colloidal sols (the lyophobic colloids) were rendered unstable and flocculated by the addition of electrolytes, and that multivalent ions had a disproportionate effect in this regard. In 1892, Linder and Picton (60) made the important observation that the particles in a colloidal sol migrate under the influence of an electric field, indicating that they are electrically charged with respect to the dispersion medium. Determination of the sign of the particle charge from the direction of its movement now made it clear that the flocculating effect of electrolytes was determined by the valency of the ion of opposite charge to the sol. This generalization is now called the Schulze-Hardy rule.

Hardy (45) and Burton (14) demonstrated that the stability of lyophobic sols is closely related to their mobility in an electric field; thus, the dependence of colloid stability on the degree of particle charge was established. Migration of particles in colloidal suspension in response to an applied electric field was first called cataphoresis, but the more general term electrophoresis is now preferred.

The assumption that the particle charge was created by the presence of an electric double layer, as proposed to account for electroosmotic flow and streaming potential, received further support from the extensive investigations of Perrin (73). He showed that the effectiveness of electrolytes in decreasing electroosmotic flow depended on the valency of the ion of opposite charge to the surface; hence the effect is completely analogous to the Schulze-Hardy rule.

By the beginning of the twentieth century, results of the investigations of Schulze, Linder, Picton, and others had aroused great interest in electrokinetic phenomena, for these methods seemed to provide a way of investigating the structure and properties of the electric double layer. Stability of colloidal sols could now be qualitatively explained in terms of a coulombic repulsion, but the origin of the surface charge and its quantitative relation to the concentration and valency of dissolved ions were yet to be explained before the problem of stability could be attacked in detail.

The experimental methods currently used for determining electrokinetic zeta potential are summarized in Table I. These are described later in this article.

### Theory of Electrokinetic Effects

Since the initial work of Helmholtz, theoretical interpretation of electrokinetic effects in terms of double-layer structure has received more detailed consideration from many investigators; results show that a rigorously quantitative treatment presents many difficulties not yet completely overcome. Useful approximations to exact expression of the relationships may be derived, however, as the basic factors are easily visualized.

Consider, for example, a solid in contact with an aqueous electrolyte solution. According to the double-layer hypothesis, the solid (by mechanisms to be considered later) will acquire a certain charge density localized in the plane of its surface; thus, a difference in

### TABLE I. METHODS OF DETERMINING ELECTRO-KINETIC POTENTIAL

| NAME OF PROCEDURE | PROPERTY MEASURED | MOBILE PHASE | EXAMPLE |
|---|---|---|---|
| Electrophoresis | Particle mobility | Particle | Microelectrophoresis |
| | | | Moving boundary |
| | | | Electrophoretic transfer |
| Sedimentation potential | Potential | Liquid | Sedimentation potential |
| Streaming potential | | | Streaming potential |
| Electroosmosis | Pressure | None | Electroosmosis |
| | Velocity | Liquid | |

electrical potential between the surface and the bulk solution will be produced. Because the system as a whole is electrically neutral, the surface charge must be exactly balanced by an opposite excess charge in the liquid phase. Because of coulombic attraction the counterions will tend to concentrate in the vicinity of the solid surface, while ions of similar charge are repelled.

If no other force were operating, the potential drop across the double layer from the solid surface through the layer of counterions would be sharp. However, the ions in solution are subject to diffusional forces arising from the thermal agitation of the molecules constituting the liquid; thus the abrupt concentration gradient that would otherwise exist is dissipated to some extent. Our model of the double layer therefore involves an immobile surface-charge layer and a diffuse layer of counterions distributed in the adjacent solution according to some equilibrium function; this results in a more or less gradual decrease in potential with increasing distance from the surface.

A theoretical treatment of the structure of the double layer relating the distribution of the dissolved ions and the potential gradient near the surface to the composition of the aqueous phase was first performed by Gouy (41, 42), and independently by Chapman (15). These detailed considerations, and the modifications proposed by Stern (95) and Grahame (44) need not be introduced.

### Electroosmotic Flow.

To account for electrokinetic phenomena, it is only necessary to assume that the diffuse region of the double layer (the Gouy layer) is at least in part mobile—i.e., free to move with the liquid phase. We will say, therefore, that a shear plane may exist in the diffuse double layer at some unknown distance from the solid surface. When an external electric field is applied tangentially to a fixed surface, the mobile portion of the diffuse double layer will flow because of the forces acting on the excess ionic charge contained within it. A constant flow rate will be reached when the force exerted by the external field on the counterions (hence, on the liquid as a whole) is exactly balanced by the frictional forces arising from the viscosity of the liquid. We shall show, following Kruyt (57), that a quantitative relation between the electroosmotic velocity of flow, the double-layer potential at the shear plane, and the applied external field may be derived without further consideration of the double-layer structure.

The double layer must satisfy Poisson's equation

$$\nabla^2 \psi = -4\pi\rho/D \tag{1}$$

where $\nabla^2$ is the Laplace operator, $\psi$ is the double-layer potential at a point located a distance $x$ from the surface, $\rho$ is the net space charge per unit volume at the same point, and $D$ is the dielectric constant of the medium. We assume that the liquid undergoes laminar flow, that its viscosity $\eta$ and dielectric constant $D$ are uniform throughout the mobile part of the double layer, and that the thickness of the double layer is small compared to the radius of curvature of the surface.

When an external field of strength $E$ is applied, each volume element in a layer of liquid of thickness $dx$ at a distance $x$ from the surface will experience a force:

$$F_1 = E\rho dx \tag{2}$$

At the steady state, the viscous drag on the liquid layer will be contributed by adjacent layers that are moving at a different velocity. The side of the layer at a distance $x$ from the surface will be retarded by a force given by

$$f_x = -\eta \, (dv/dx)_x \tag{3}$$

where $v$ is the liquid velocity; the side at a distance $x + dx$ from the surface will be accelerated by a force

$$f_{x+dx} = \eta \, (dv/dx)_{x+dx} \tag{4}$$

The net frictional force on the layer in question is:

$$F_2 = \eta \, (dv/dx)_{x+dx} - \eta \, (dv/dx)_x \tag{5}$$

At steady state, the total force on the layer is zero:

$$E\rho dx = \eta \, (d^2v/dx^2)dx \tag{6}$$

By substituting in Equation 6 the value of $\rho$ given by Equation 1, and by recognizing that for a plane surface

$$\nabla^2 \psi = (d^2\psi/dx^2) \tag{7}$$

we obtain

$$-\frac{ED}{4\pi} \frac{d^2\psi}{dx^2} = \eta \frac{d^2v}{dx^2} \tag{8}$$

This must be integrated over the whole liquid from the shear plane to infinity. The first integration yields

$$-\frac{ED}{4\pi} \frac{d\psi}{dx} = \eta \frac{dv}{dx} + C$$

and $C$ is zero from the boundary condition that

$$(d\psi/dx)_{x=\infty} = 0; \quad (dv/dx)_{x=\infty} = 0$$

The second integration yields

$$-(ED/4\pi) \, \psi = \eta v + C'$$

From the conditions that at $x = \infty$, $\psi = 0$ and $v = v_e$ (the electroosmotic velocity), and at the shear plane, $v = 0$ and $\psi = \zeta$, we obtain the classical expression

$$v_e = DE\zeta/4\pi\eta \qquad (9)$$

Within the framework of our assumptions, therefore, electroosmotic flow caused by a given applied voltage gradient should indeed be determined by the potential at the boundary between the fixed and mobile parts of the double layer, as had been indicated by Helmholtz. In many textbooks we find the relation expressed by Equation 9 derived on the basis of a parallel plate capacitor model of the double layer and we might be misled to assume that this model constitutes an approximation in the derivation; the derivation given here shows that the same result is obtained on the basis of a diffuse double layer of unspecified form with the capacitor model representing the limiting case of zero diffusion. Consequently the zeta potential, as determined by experimental measurements, can by itself tell us nothing about the structure of the double layer. On the other hand, the zeta potential represents a real physical quantity accessible to experimental determination (at least to a first approximation), and therefore any theoretical consideration of the structure of the double layer and its relation to soluble electrolytes must account for its magnitude and variation.

The electroosmotic velocity given by Equation 9 is not the quantity ordinarily determined experimentally; usually, volume rate of liquid flow, or equilibrium counterpressure developed by the liquid, is determined as a function of the applied field. In all the expressions given for electrokinetic effects, c.g.s. units are implied. The practical unit of voltage must be divided by a factor of 300 to obtain potential in e.s.u—for example, the right side of Equation 9 must be divided by $9 \times 10^4$ if $E$ and $\zeta$ are expressed in practical units (volts per centimeter and volts, respectively).

If we consider the case of electroosmotic flow in a capillary of uniform cross sectional area $A$, then, using Equation 9, the expression for volume flow rate is:

$$V_e = Av_e = ADE\zeta/4\pi\eta \qquad (10)$$

This equation is an approximation in that it assumes that all the liquid moves with the velocity $v_e$, whereas the mobile part of the double layer near the shear plane moves more slowly than $v_e$. Equation 10 may only be applied, therefore, when the thickness of the double layer is much smaller than the capillary diameter. This condition holds for capillaries larger than 1-micron diameter.

We may eliminate the area $A$ by use of Ohm's law

$$E = i/A\lambda \qquad (11)$$

where $\lambda$ is the specific conductance of the liquid and $i$ is the current passing through the capillary. Substitution of Equation 11 in Equation 10 gives

$$V_e = D\zeta i/4\pi\eta\lambda \qquad (12)$$

which is useful because $i$ and $\lambda$ are easily measured.

We must now consider whether Equation 12 is applicable to the electroosmotic flow in porous plugs. A rigorous treatment of the question has been given by Von Smoluchowski (106), and the following might be called a more intuitive version of his reasoning.

Assuming that a porous plug can be represented by a parallel combination of capillaries, each of nonuniform cross section, we may proceed in the following way. First, we examine a single capillary of insulating material with a nonuniform cross section. At any arbitrary location $x$ on the capillary axis, the rate of liquid flow across the whole cross-sectional area $A_x$ is:

$$(V_e)_x = A_x E_x D\zeta/4\pi\eta$$

where $E_x$ is the local electric field (which is everywhere parallel to the insulating walls). At another location a distance $dx$ from the first, we have

$$(V_e)_{x+dx} = (A_{x+dx}E_{x+dx}D\zeta)/4\pi\eta$$

If the liquid is incompressible, we have the requirement

$$dV_e/dx = 0$$

Hence, for Equation 12 to be applicable at any point:

$$d(AE)/dx = 0$$

This latter condition is met, for it is the requirement that Ohm's law (Equation 11) applies to the system at every point—i.e., the electric current also flows as if it were an incompressible liquid. Therefore, Equation 12 is valid for a capillary of arbitary and nonuniform cross-sectional area. It also applies to any parallel combination of such capillaries, as the total volume rate of flow and the total applied current are given by summing the respective contributions of each capillary; the condition that the pore diameter be large compared to the double-layer thickness must, as with Equation 10, be observed.

**Electroosmotic Pressure.** When the electroosmotic effect is measured in terms of the counterpressure required to obtain zero rate of flow through the capillary or porous plug for a given applied field, the zeta potential may be calculated by realizing that the electroosmotic pressure $P_e$ must cause a reverse flow of liquid in the capillary or porous plug exactly equal to the volume transported by electroosmosis.

With a capillary of uniform circular cross section, the backflow is given by Poiseuille's equation.

$$V_e = \pi P_e r^4/8\eta l \qquad (13)$$

Equating Equations 12 and 13, we obtain

$$P_e = (2D\zeta li)/(\lambda\pi^2 r^4) \qquad (14)$$

where $r$ is the radius and $l$ the length of the capillary. Or, by making use of Equation 11:

$$P_e = (2DlE\zeta)/\pi r^2 \qquad (15)$$

The product $El$ corresponds to the total applied potential.

With a porous plug, the counterflow is not directly given by Equation 13, but it may be expressed by

$$V = K\,PA/\eta L \qquad (16)$$

where $A$ is the area and $L$ the length of the diaphragm, and the constant $K$ is determined experimentally by measuring flow rate as a function of pressure with no applied field. By use of Equations 12 and 16 we find

$$P_e = (D\zeta Li)/(4\pi\lambda_p KA) \qquad (17)$$

where $\lambda_p$ is now the specific conductance of the liquid-filled diaphragm. The quantity $L/\lambda_p A$ is therefore the electrical resistance across the plug and hence

$$P_e = DE\zeta/4\pi K \qquad (18)$$

where $\mathbf{E}$ is now the total applied potential.

The expressions derived above for the electroosmotic

effect state that flow rate will be proportional to applied current, and counterpressure proportional to applied voltage, but both are independent of capillary or diaphragm dimensions; this agrees with the experimental findings of Wiedemann (108), referred to above.

**Streaming Potential.** The streaming potential $E_s$ is the voltage difference developed between the ends of a capillary tube or porous diaphragm through which liquid is forced to flow by an applied pressure difference $P$. An expression relating $E_s$ to $P$ and the zeta potential may be derived for laminar flow through a circular capillary of uniform diameter, where the diameter is much greater than the thickness of the double layer.

Liquid flow through the capillary carries with it the mobile part of the double layer and its contained charge. A potential difference in the direction of liquid flow is thus established and a reverse flow of electricity through the liquid will occur. At the steady state, the charge transported by the moving double layer per unit time will be balanced by the current conducted through the liquid. Equilibrium potential difference is therefore:

$$E_s = il/\lambda \pi r^2 \qquad (19)$$

where $r$ is the capillary radius; $l$, its length; $\lambda$, specific conductance of the liquid; and $i$, the electric current.

Velocity of flow in the double layer is not constant; it varies from zero at the shear plane to a maximum value at the capillary axis. The liquid velocity at a distance $x$ from the shear plane (measured along a radius) is:

$$v_x = P(2rx - x^2)/4\eta l \qquad (20)$$

The volume of liquid with a velocity $v_x$ is represented by a hollow cylinder of radius $(r - x)$ and thickness $dx$; volume rate of flow in this cylindrical layer will be

$$2\pi(r - x)v_x dx = dV = \frac{2\pi P}{4\eta l} (2rx - x^2)(r - x)dx \qquad (21)$$

and the rate of charge transport will be

$$i = \int_0^r \rho dV \qquad (22)$$

Substituting Equation 1 and Equation 21 in Equation 22, and assuming $x$ is negligible with respect to $r$, we obtain

$$i = \frac{PDr^2}{4\eta l} \int_0^r x \frac{d^2\psi}{dx^2} dx \qquad (23)$$

If Equation 23 is solved by partial integration and if boundary conditions are applied such that at $x = 0$, $\psi = \zeta$; and at $x = r$, $\psi = 0$, $d\psi/dx = 0$, then

$$i = (PDr^2\zeta)/4\pi\eta\lambda \qquad (24)$$

Using Equation 19 and rearranging terms, we obtain the final expression for streaming potential:

$$E_s = PE\zeta/4\pi\eta\lambda \qquad (25)$$

A more general derivation of Equation 25 shows that it is also applicable to a porous plug (57, page 204).

**Electrophoresis.** The phenomenon of electrophoresis is essentially the converse of electroosmosis in that the solid is not fixed in position as part of a diaphragm, but is free to move; the suspending liquid as a whole is stationary. In either case, forces acting on the double layer as a result of an applied potential gradient produce a relative movement; therefore, the electrophoretic velocity is given by the same expression.

$$v_E = DE\zeta/4\pi\eta \qquad (26)$$

As with electroosmosis, shape and size of the particles have no effect on the resulting velocity, provided that the double layer is thin compared to the dimensions of the particle. Unfortunately, this condition is not so easily met for finely divided colloidal dispersions such as sols, and the problem of the appropriate correction factors for Equation 26 is still not completely solved.

**Corrections for Deviations from Theory.** In the preceding analyses, assumptions have been made that affect the validity of the derived expressions to varying degrees, and under certain circumstances, can destroy their usefulness even as first-order approximations.

The assumption of laminar flow in the liquid represents a condition that is easily met in practice; deviations would be likely only in streaming potential measurements at such high pressures that turbulent flow occurs.

Constancy of the viscosity coefficient $\eta$ and the dielectric constant $D$ are assumed because experimental and theoretical information concerning their variation is lacking at the present time. Further work in this area might well show that the concept of a shear plane separating mobile and immobile parts of the double layer represents an approximation to a region of more or less rapidly changing viscosity near the solid surface caused by the high concentration of ions of like charge. If such a relation could be developed, the equation for electrophoretic velocity would require solution of

$$v_E = \frac{E}{4\pi} \int_0^\psi \frac{D}{\eta} d\psi \qquad (27)$$

Equation 9, basic to all electrokinetic phenomena, is derived for a mathematically plane surface (Equation 7), a condition seldom encountered; little error is introduced in many practical situations, however, because the thickness of the double layer, seldom exceeding $10^{-5}$ cm. and usually closer to $10^{-6}$ to $10^{-7}$ cm., is small compared to the capillary or particle dimensions. In electrophoresis of the smallest sol particles, the assumption of a plane surface must be discarded and account taken of the curvature of the double layer.

The expression for electroosmotic flow (Equation 10) also requires that the double-layer thickness be negligible compared to pore dimensions. It assumes that flow in the double layer occurs at the same velocity as in the bulk liquid, whereas it actually is somewhat slower. For fine capillaries—e.g., 1-micron diameter—and dilute electrolytes ($\cong 10^{-5}N$) where the double-layer thickness is of the order of $10^{-5}$ cm., Equation 10 would lead to values of $\zeta$ about 10% too low. To correct the equation, we need an analytical expression for double-layer potential as a function of distance from the surface.

Implicit in the derivation of Equations 12 and 25, which describe electroosmosis and streaming potential, respectively, is the requirement that the electrical resistance of the systems be determined by $\lambda$, the specific conductance of the liquid phase; this ignores the contribution of surface conductance to the current flow. The specific conductance of the surface is greater than that of the bulk liquid because of the higher concentration of ions in the double layer; conductance along the surface may be of the same order of magnitude as through the bulk liquid in the case of dilute solutions. In Equations 11 and 19, λ should be replaced by the total specific conductance:

$$\lambda_T = \lambda + (2\lambda_s/r) \qquad (28)$$

where $\lambda_s$ is the specific surface conductance and $r$ is the capillary radius. This correction can only be made in the case of uniform capillaries (57, page 206). As no valid correction for surface conductance applicable to porous plugs is presently available, accurate values of zeta potential from experiments on porous plugs can only be obtained if the surface conductance is negligible.

Conditions for the application of Equation 26, both in electroosmosis and in electrophoresis, are that the double layer be thin compared to particle dimensions (electrophoretic retardation effect), and that the surface (and bulk solid) conductance be so small that the external

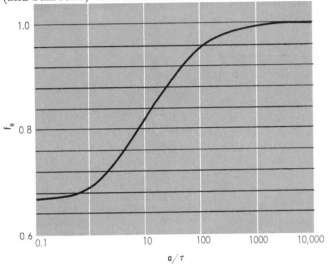

*Figure 3. Correction factor for ratio of particle radius to double-layer thickness, for spherical particles*

applied field is not disturbed (relaxation effect). Surface conductance reduces electrophoretic velocity by distorting the electric force-field. An approximate correction has been worked out for this effect (48).

Henry (48) has also solved the electrophoretic equations for any ratio of the particle size to double-layer thickness. His solutions are limited, however, to spheres and cylinders. His derived equation has the form

$$v_E = f_H (DE\zeta/4\pi\eta) \qquad (29)$$

The retardation factor $f_H$ is a function of $a/\tau$, where $a$ is the particle radius and $\tau$ is the double-layer thickness. For spherical particles, $f_H$ varies from $^2/_3$ to 1 (Figure 3). The thickness of the double layer is given by

$$\tau = \left(\frac{DkT}{8\pi e^2 \sum n\nu^2}\right)^{1/2} \qquad (30)$$

where $e$ is the electronic charge and $n$ is the concentration of ions of valency $\nu$ in the bulk liquid. Equation 29 is strictly valid only for $\zeta \leq 25$ mv.

Calculation of the relaxation correction poses a difficult mathematical and theoretical problem, and a satisfactory solution has not been reached. Overbeek's calculations (57, page 211) indicate that the relaxation effect may be small in the case of 1–1 electrolytes for all values of $a/\tau$; for values of $a/\tau$ greater than $10^2$, both the retardation and relaxation corrections are small, and

Equation 26 can be used directly. When $a/\tau$ has values in the range 0.1 to 100 and multivalent electrolytes are involved, both corrections may be large; the zeta potential then calculated can be seriously in error.

### Ion Distribution in the Double Layer

The above discussion shows that electrokinetic phenomena can be described accurately by merely assuming the presence of a double layer of charge at the solid/-liquid interface, provided that the double layer occupies a negligible portion of the system in question. When this condition does not prevail, further analysis will require a specific description of the double-layer structure—i.e., an expression for potential in the double layer as a function of distance from the solid surface. Such a situation will arise in any theoretical consideration of the stability of colloidal dispersions. In order to flocculate, colloidal particles must approach each other, collide, and adhere; during this process, the distance between the particles will decrease to values not only comparable to, but less than the double-layer thickness.

The formation of a double layer requires that the solid surface be charged. We can recognize three mechanisms by which this potential is developed:

—The crystal lattice of the solid may contain a net positive or negative charge arising from interior defects or lattice substitutions; the net charge is therefore compensated by an equivalent ionic charge at the surface. In contact with water, the compensating ions dissociate to form the counterions of the double layer. This type of double-layer formation, while generally uncommon, is important in describing the behavior of certain ion exchanging minerals, such as the zeolites, and clay minerals, such as montmorillonite (103). Solids that contain ionizable groups at their surface, such as sulfonated organic polymers, may also be considered as belonging to this class, which is characterized by a surface charge density that is a fixed quantity independent of the concentration of ions in the surrounding liquid.

—In the case of sparingly soluble ionic solids dispersed in water, an equilibrium exists between the ions making up the surface of the crystal and these same constituent ions in solution, where their concentrations are determined by the solubility product for the material. The potential of the solid will thus be fully determined by a thermodynamic (adsorption) equilibrium, in accord with a Nernst equation. Using colloidal AgI as an example we have:

$$\psi_0(\text{AgI}) = A + (RT/F) \ln C_{\text{Ag}^+}$$

or

$$\psi_0(\text{AgI}) = B - (RT/F) \ln C_{\text{I}^-} \qquad (31)$$

where $A$ and $B$ are constants, $\psi_0$ is the potential of the solid surface with respect to the bulk liquid, $F$ is the Faraday charge, and $C$ is the concentration (activity) of the particular ion in solution. Thus, if excess silver ions are added to the solution, $\psi_0$ will become more positive; addition of excess iodide ions will make $\psi_0$ more negative. At some point the potential will be zero, and the concentration of silver or iodide ions at this point is called the zero point of charge concentration. In general, we may express the potential of the solid by

$$\psi_0 = (RT/\nu F) \ln (C/C_0) \qquad (32)$$

where $\nu$ is the valency and $C_0$ is the zero point of charge concentration; $C_0$ does not necessarily correspond to the equivalence point, because one of the ions is usually more strongly adsorbed by the solid than the other. If it is the anion that is selectively adsorbed, then the solid will acquire a negative potential with respect to the solution at the equivalence point. The value of $C_0$ can be accurately determined by electrokinetic experiments as it corresponds to zero movement, and no corrections need be applied. The potential-determining ions for a given solid are usually apparent from its chemical composition. For most metallic oxides and hydroxides, $H^+$ and $OH^-$ ions are potential-determining. Solids of this class are characterized by having the potential at the solid surface fixed by the concentration of potential-determining ions and independent of the presence of other indifferent electrolytes; that the surface charge, however, will be increased by the addition of indifferent electrolytes will be shown later.

—A third mechanism by which the surface charge may originate or be affected is the adsorption of specific ions from the solution. Specific ions may be strongly adsorbed, or chemisorbed, by formation of a surface complex or compound—for example, the tri(poly)phosphate anion complex with aluminum sites on the kaolinite surface (63). Adsorption may also be aided by hydrogen bond formation or by the London dispersion (van der Waals) forces, particularly in the case of large organic molecules or ions. The adsorption mechanism is seldom responsible for the entire surface charge or potential of a solid surface (except for potential-determining ions); it is frequently a complicating factor in the other mechanisms. In some cases, the extent of adsorption, or even the adsorption isotherm of specific ions on the solid surface, may be determined from analytical measurement (57, page 161).

In general, those ions that increase the potential of the solid surface by their presence are effective as "peptizing," "stabilizing," or "deflocculating" agents for the system. The term "dispersing agent," although commonly used in industry, should be avoided, for a colloidal sol or suspension does not necessarily cease to be a dispersion when it is flocculated.

The formation of an electric double layer is easily imagined in the case of a charged surface in contact with an aqueous electrolyte solution; the ions in the solution will respond to the field of force near the interface by taking up new positions until a distribution is reached that represents an equilibrium between thermal and electrostatic forces. The analysis of the distribution, while it resembles the Debye-Huckel theory of strong electrolytes (20), was carried out about a decade earlier by Gouy (41, 42) and independently by Chapman (15).

**Gouy-Chapman Model.** Analysis of the double layer according to the model of Gouy and Chapman involves several assumptions. The charge on the solid surface is considered to be uniformly distributed; the ions making up the diffuse layer are considered as point charges; and the solvent is a structureless medium whose only influence is through its dielectric constant.

A basic requirement of the space charge in the double layer is that Poisson's equation be satisfied (Equation 1). The distribution of ions in the potential field is given by a Boltzmann relation analogous to the barometric formula.

$$n_i = n_{i0} \exp\left(-\nu_i e\psi/kT\right) \tag{33}$$

where $n_i$ is the concentration and $\nu_i$ the valency (including sign) of ions of kind $i$ at a point where the potential is $\psi$, $n_{i0}$ is the bulk concentration, $e$ is the electron charge, and $k$ is the Boltzmann constant.

The space charge density $\rho$ is the net sum of the positive and negative ion concentrations.

$$\rho = \sum \nu_i e n_i \tag{34}$$

Equations 1, 33, and 34 give the differential equation

$$\nabla^2 \psi = -\frac{4\pi}{D} \sum \nu_i e n_{i0} \exp\left(-\frac{\nu_i e\psi}{kT}\right) \tag{35}$$

that describes the variation of $\psi$ with location in the double layer. For simplicity, the surface is assumed to be a plane, and Equation 35 integrates to give

$$\frac{d\psi}{dx} = -\left(\frac{8\pi nkT}{D}\right)^{1/2}\left[\exp\left(\frac{\nu e\psi}{kT}\right) - \exp\left(-\frac{\nu e\psi}{kT}\right)\right] \tag{36}$$

where $\nu$ is now the valency of the ion of charge opposite to that of the surface and $n$ is its bulk concentration. A second integration gives the final expression

$$\kappa x = \ln \frac{\left[\exp\left(\frac{\nu e\psi}{2kT}\right) + 1\right]\left[\exp\left(\frac{\nu e\psi_0}{2kT}\right) - 1\right]}{\left[\exp\left(\frac{\nu e\psi}{2kT}\right) - 1\right]\left[\exp\left(\frac{\nu e\psi_0}{2kT}\right) + 1\right]} \tag{37}$$

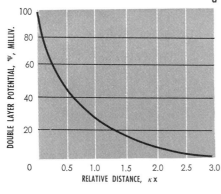
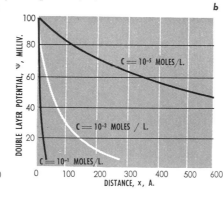
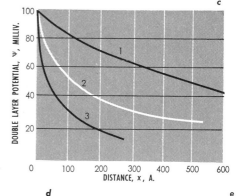
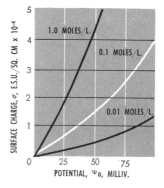
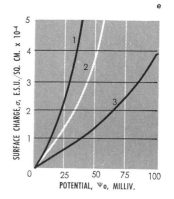

*Figure 4a. A representation of Equation 37 for monovalent counterions and an arbitrary $\psi_0$ of 100 mv. At a distance x equal to the double-layer thickness, $\kappa x = 1$, $\psi$ has decreased to roughly less than a third its maximum value. Figure 4b. Effect of monovalent electrolyte concentration, for $\psi_0 = 100$ mv. (Equation 37). Added electrolyte compresses the double layer, so that $\psi$ approaches zero more rapidly; the degree of compression is linear with $(n)^{1/2}$. Figure 4c. The marked effect of counterion valency is shown where $\psi_0$ is 100 mv., electrolyte concentration is $10^{-5}$ moles/liter. Value of $\nu$ is indicated on the lines (Equation 37). Figures 4d and 4e. It is shown that the surface charge is proportional to $(n)^{1/2}$ for a given value of $\psi_0$, and that $\psi_0$ is inversely proportional to $\nu$ at a given charge density (Equation 41). Figure 4d is for monovalent electrolyte concentrations. Figure 4d is for 0.1 mole/liter electrolyte, with values of $\nu$ indicated*

where
$$\kappa = (8\pi v^2 e^2 n / DkT)^{1/2} \qquad (38)$$

The function $\kappa$ is the reciprocal of the double-layer thickness (Equation 30).

A relation between the surface charge density $\sigma$ and $\psi_0$ can be obtained from Equation 36, for the electroneutrality of the system requires that

$$\sigma = - \int_0^\infty \rho dx \qquad (39)$$

Using Equation 1 we can integrate the above expression

$$\sigma = \frac{D}{4\pi} \int_0^\infty \frac{d^2\psi}{dx^2} dx = -\frac{D}{4\pi} \left( \frac{d\psi}{dx} \right)_{x=0} \qquad (40)$$

and insertion of Equation 36 gives

$$\sigma = \sqrt{\frac{DnkT}{2}} \left[ \exp\left( \frac{ve\psi_0}{2kT} \right) - \exp\left( -\frac{ve\psi_0}{2kT} \right) \right] \qquad (41)$$

For surfaces of fixed potential, Equation 37 describes how $\psi$ decreases from its initial value $\psi_0$ with increasing distance from the surface at any given concentration of indifferent electrolyte. For surfaces of constant charge, however, $\psi_0$ will depend on electrolyte concentration (Equation 41); once it is determined, Equation 37 will apply.

The effect of electrolyte concentration and valency on the value of $\psi$ as a function of $x$ or $\sigma$ is shown in Figure 4.

In spite of the assumptions made, the Gouy-Chapman analysis of the double layer has been useful in developing an understanding of colloid stability. But in the study of electrocapillary effects, this model leads to a double-layer capacity that is much too high—i.e., the surface charge density $\sigma$ given by Equation 41 is too large at high electrolyte concentrations or high potentials. The reason for this is made clear if we consider the situation at a surface having a potential of 200 mv. in a $0.1N$ monovalent electrolyte solution. By Equation 33 the electrolyte concentration near the surface should be $300N$, which is impossibly high. Because we know that $\psi_0$ can be even greater than 200 mv., the difficulty must lie in the assumption of point charges; one way around this difficulty was developed by Stern (95).

**Stern Theory.** Stern recognized that the error caused by neglect of the finite ionic size was important only in the immediate vicinity of the surface; in fact, the first layer of ions at the surface is usually sufficient to decrease the potential to values low enough so that the Gouy-Chapman model becomes reasonable. Stern proposed that the counterions could be considered as divided between a diffuse layer of point charges and an immobile surface layer of thickness $\delta$ able to contain a certain maximum number of counterions per square centimeter. A Langmuir-type adsorption equilibrium is assumed between the ions in solution and those in the Stern layer, where the adsorption energy is divided into electrical and van der Waals contributions. The electric potential at the Stern layer is indicated by $\psi_\delta$, and the van der Waals energy by $\phi$. The adsorbed charge per unit area is then given by

$$\sigma_s = \frac{n\sigma_m}{n + A \exp\left( -\frac{ve\psi_\delta}{kT} + \phi \right)} \qquad (42)$$

where $\sigma_m$ is the charge corresponding to a monolayer of counterions and $A$ is a frequency factor (57, page 133). Total charge density at the surface is then

$$\sigma = \sigma_s + \sigma_G \qquad (43)$$

where $\sigma_G$ is the charge density corresponding to the Gouy model when $\psi_0$ is replaced by $\psi_\delta$. The total surface charge is also given by

$$\sigma = (D'/4\pi\delta) (\psi_0 - \psi_\delta) \qquad (44)$$

if we assume that the Stern layer comprises a molecular condenser with a dielectric constant $D'$. The complete expression for the Stern model of the double layer is

$$\frac{D'}{4\pi\delta} (\psi_0 - \psi_\delta) = \frac{n\sigma_m}{n + A \exp\left( -\frac{ve\psi_\delta}{kT} + \phi \right)} +$$
$$\left( \frac{DnkT}{2\pi} \right)^{1/2} \left[ \exp\left( \frac{ve\psi_\delta}{2kT} \right) - \exp\left( -\frac{ve\psi_\delta}{2kT} \right) \right] \qquad (45)$$

If we have an estimate of $D'$, $\delta$, and $\sigma_m$, the double layer can be described for surfaces governed by Equation 32 for $\psi_0$. Investigations of double-layer capacity in electrocapillary effects (44) show that $D'$ has a value in the range 3–6 and that $\delta$ is of the order of $5 \times 10^{-8}$ cm.; $\sigma_m$ can be estimated from hydrated ionic radii. For surfaces of constant charge, the left side of Equation 45 becomes a constant—i.e., $\psi_0$ and $\psi_\delta$ decrease equally for a given change in concentration.

The Stern model, while still a crude picture of what we may imagine to be a complex situation, does display most of the properties of the double layer that have been inferred from experimental observations of double-layer capacity. This model also helps to explain the origin of the zeta potential calculated from electrokinetic effects.

In the theory of the electrokinetic effects, we introduced the concept of a shear plane located at some distance from the surface, but did not at that point indicate the reason. For a large class of surfaces, an absolute value of $\psi_0$ can be obtained with Equation 32. Because $\psi_0$ changes by 57 mv. per decade of concentration change, and because 6 or 8 decades are not unreasonable for a material such as AgI, $\psi_0$ may have values up to several hundred millivolts. The corresponding values of $\zeta$, however, are much smaller (57, page 231); therefore, the shear plane must be located at a distance $x$ corresponding to $\psi = \zeta$. The concept of a shear plane in the Gouy layer is somewhat of a contradiction of the model, however. The Stern theory provides a model in which a shear plane is already conceptually present. It is probable that $\zeta$ corresponds more or less closely to $\psi_\delta$; a rigorous test of such a correlation is difficult, for it is difficult to obtain good electrokinetic data on reproducible surfaces under conditions such that $\zeta$ may be calculated with reasonable certainty.

An extension of the Stern model has been proposed by Grahame (44). Although both anions and cations can be adsorbed by forces other than electrical—i.e., chemical or van der Waals—anions are the less strongly hydrated; Grahame therefore postulates that the nonelectrical forces are chiefly operative for anions, which become adsorbed with loss of their hydration shells. By this model, the Stern layer is in turn divided into two parts: a relatively thin surface layer (of variable occupancy) of strongly adsorbed anions whose centers of charge lie in a plane (inner Helmholtz plane) at a distance $x_i$ from the surface, followed by a Stern layer (outer Helmholtz plane) of hydrated counterions whose centers of charge lie in a plane at a distance $\delta$ from the surface and whose concentration is given by the Stern theory (Equation 42). The Gouy-Chapman model is then used for values of $x$ greater than $\delta$.

As thus defined, however, it would appear that when the Stern layer is highly occupied, the distance of closest approach of ions in the Gouy layer to the Stern plane should be greater than $\delta$ because the ions are not actually point charges; it would seem reasonable that the Gouy layer limit would be more accurately located at a distance $\delta + d_c$, where $d_c$ is the diameter of the hydrated cation.

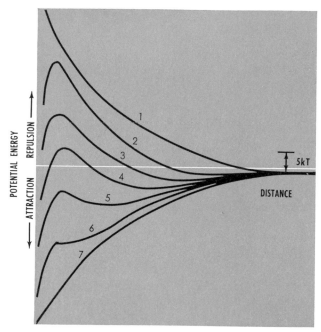

*Figure 5. Net potential energy of interaction between colloidal particles. Curve 7—the attraction that exists in the absence of any repulsion. This corresponds to a high electrolyte concentration and rapid flocculation as described by Equation 47. Curves 6 to 1—show, in that order, the effect of decreasing electrolyte concentration that leads to increasing double-layer thickness, and hence, longer range repulsing forces. Curve 3—the barrier of about 15 kT would impart considerable stability to the dispersion. Curve 4—slow flocculation would take place. Curve 5—flocculation would be rapid*

Taking the effective anion diameter as $d_a$ and the cation diameter as $d_c$, we have (for $\psi_0$ negative)

$$x_t = d_a/2; \quad \delta = d_a + d_c/2$$
$$x_{sp} = d_a + d_c; \quad x_G = d_a + 3d_c/2 \tag{46}$$

where $x_{sp}$ is the location of the shear plane and $x_G$ locates the closest approach of diffuse ions.

Grahame's model is illustrated schematically in Figure 1, where the relative distances are in accord with Equation 46. The quantitative expression of the relationships involved depends on adsorption equilibria that are not well understood at present. One feature of the model is the activation energy required for chemisorption of ions of the same sign as the surface; another

is the possibility of eliciting an expression for the zeta potential, as the location of the shear plane seems reasonable and consistent with the model.

Of the various double-layer treatments that have been postulated, that of Bolt (9) is particularly interesting in that a variation of the dielectric constant with $\psi$ is taken into account, as well as the effect of ionic size, polarization, and interaction. The results indicate that the original Gouy-Chapman expressions are valid for estimating particle-particle repulsion in the theory of stability, but not valid for the treatment of ion exchange equilibria.

### Stability of Colloidal Dispersions

The term stability, when applied to colloidal dispersions, is a relative term intended to express the resistance of the dispersion to change. The usual meaning is stability with respect to time, but the term could also refer to tolerance of added solutes, heat, freezing, vibration, dilution, etc. We will restrict ourselves here to reviewing briefly the theoretical aspects of the stability of dispersions toward flocculation with respect to time; we will not consider such changes as sedimentation or crystal growth through aging.

When we refer to a colloidal dispersion as deflocculated, or peptized, we imply a system in which the forces of repulsion acting to keep the particles separated exceed the forces of attraction that would cause particles to adhere on contact; in a flocculated system, the attractive forces predominate. The condition of the dispersion is not determined by a simple balance of forces, however. If this were the case, then a dispersion would either be perfectly stable or unstable, flocculating almost instantly; this is contrary to all observations.

The time for which sols are stable, or inversely, the flocculation rates of sols, is known to cover a wide range of values from years to fractions of a second. The observed range of flocculation rates indicates that even when the flocculated condition is the lowest energy state of the system (which thermodynamically is always the case) an energy barrier can exist that prevents particle to particle adhesion on contact, and that contacts can be frequent. The rate of flocculation will therefore depend on the collision frequency of the sol particles and their energy with respect to the energy barrier. Colloidal particles undergo Brownian motion and thereby diffuse and collide; they are in kinetic-thermal equilibrium with the suspending fluid. In the absence of an energy barrier, the flocculation rate will be determined solely by the collision frequency. The theory of rapid flocculation was developed by Von Smoluchowski in 1919 (57, page 278) and leads to the expression

$$N/N_0 = [1 + (t/T)]^{-1} \tag{47}$$

where $N/N_0$ is the fraction of particles remaining per unit volume after time $t$. The term $T$ is the time required for the number of particles to decrease to half the original number. Groups of adhering particles are counted as units in this expression.

The problem of slow flocculation, in which an energy barrier prevents the close approach of particles, has been summarized by Overbeek (57); by the model of diffusion in a field of force, it is possible to show how the coagulation, or flocculation, rate is decreased by the barrier. Because colloidal particles diffuse slowly and their motion is random, the problem cannot be treated in the same way as a chemical reaction involving an energy barrier. It becomes necessary to know the total shape of the potential energy curve, rather than just its height.

Verwey and Overbeek (105) in 1948 published their now famous treatise on the interaction of sol particles having an electric double layer. Starting with a consideration of the free energy of the double layer, Verwey and Overbeek show how, on the close approach of two surfaces, the overlapping double layers interact to increase the free energy of the system, thus leading to a potential energy of repulsion. With the Gouy description of the the double layer, it was possible to relate the energy of repulsion between particles as a function of their separation to the ionic makeup of the solution. The picture of the interaction was completed by a consideration of the London dispersion forces as applied to particles of colloidal size, which as an approximation

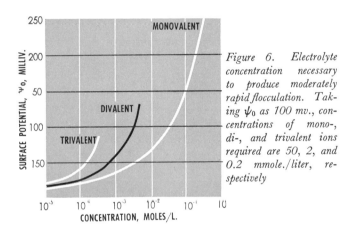

*Figure 6. Electrolyte concentration necessary to produce moderately rapid flocculation. Taking $\psi_0$ as 100 mv., concentrations of mono-, di-, and trivalent ions required are 50, 2, and 0.2 mmole./liter, respectively*

leads to an attraction varying with $d^{-2}$ for small distances, and with $d^{-4}$ at larger separations.

Figure 5 shows schematically the net potential energy of interaction obtained by adding the two effects. Stability and flocculation of the dispersion are demonstrated by these curves, as explained in the caption.

Another feature of the curves obtained by Verwey and Overbeek is the secondary minimum occurring at relatively great distance of separation ($\cong 200$A.); in curve 4, this minimum is deep enough to trap a sizable fraction of the particles. This type of flocculation is reversible, as the particles can occasionally diffuse apart. Flocculation in the secondary minimum is shown by calculation (57, page 324) to be most probable for relatively large anisometric particles, and can account for the formation of tactoids and Schiller layers in sols of rodlike or platelike particles.

As well as accounting for the observed flocculation rates of sols at various electrolyte concentrations, the theory of Verwey and Overbeek quantitatively describes the Schulze-Hardy rule. This is illustrated in Figure 6 for particles with a platelike shape under moderately rapid flocculation conditions. The area to

the left of the curves defines the region of stability; this agrees with observations.

### Measurement of Electrokinetic Effects

The methods for the determination of zeta potential all use the phenomena resulting from the impression of a potential or pressure gradient across the system being studied. For instance, small charged particles suspended in a system will move under the influence of an applied potential gradient; from the measurement of the resulting velocity of motion, the zeta potential may be calculated with the appropriate formula. If the particles can be held stationary, the liquid becomes the easily observed mobile phase and its flow rate can be measured and converted to zeta potential. If both liquid and particulate material are held fixed, the pressure developed may be used to calculate zeta.

Table I summarizes the presently used experimental methods for determining zeta potential that will be described in greater detail. For detailed descriptions of the various apparatus used, the references in the following sections should be consulted.

**Electroosmosis.** The apparatus for electroosmosis (Figure 7) requires that the material whose zeta potential is being determined can be formed into a capillary or a porous plug so as to constitute a system of capillaries. The porous plug is placed between two measuring electrodes connected to a high impedence voltmeter. When a potential gradient is established *via* the working electrodes, the electrolyte flows. If the system is kept closed, the rate of movement of the electrolyte can conveniently be observed by measuring the movement of a small bubble in the capillary and converting this to flow rate. If, during the impression of a voltage, the upper stopcocks are left open and no short-circuiting path is provided by a capillary, the electrolyte will rise in one of the tubes to an equilibrium level. The potential gradient is determined from the voltage across the measuring electrodes and their spacing.

When the rate of movement of the bubble is measured, the zeta potential may be calculated by Equation 12; when the pressure developed (as measured by the height of liquid rise) is measured, Equation 18 is used.

Electroosmosis has been used in the study of aqueous dispersions of kaolinite at various pH levels (4), of quartz in KCl solutions (84), of calcite in solutions of various salts (23, 43), and of bentonite in aqueous solutions of several salts (69).

**Streaming Potential.** The apparatus for determining streaming potential (Figure 8) is similar to that used for electroosmosis. Again, it must be possible to form the material into a capillary or a porous plug, held between two electrodes

To measure the streaming potential it is only necessary to measure the potential developed when the electrolyte is forced through the porous plug by a constant pressure. From the voltage developed, the zeta potential may be calculated by Equation 25, provided that the measuring circuit draws no current from the system.

The streaming potential setup is well suited to the determination of the zeta potential of materials such as glass that can be formed into capillaries. It is also easily applied to coarse mineral particles such as those frequently treated by froth flotation processes (35).

Streaming potential determination for substances in aqueous electrolytes include: quartz in dodecylammonium acetate solutions (36); $Al_2O_3$, $SnO_2$, $Fe_2O_3$, and $TiO_2$ in various electrolytes (55); corundum in solutions of surface active agents (37, 38); stainless steel in acids (59); corundum in various electrolytes (65); rutile at different pH levels with surface active agents (43); gypsum in solutions of several salts (10); barium sulfate in various electrolytes (10–13, 88); and scheelite in solutions of salts and surface active agents (70).

**Electrophoresis.** The electrophoretic separation and identification of proteins and other lyophilic colloids having an isoelectric point are a familiar and useful analytical tool in biochemistry. However, methods applicable to lyophobic systems will be emphasized here.

There are two well known methods of electrophoresis that are applied to dispersions: they involve the measurement of particle velocity either individually, by observing the particles directly with a microscope, or collectively, by measuring the velocity of a mass of particles by following the movement of a sharp concentration gradient. A third method, used by the authors and recently patented, has been termed the mass-transport method.

The measurement of the velocity of individual particles in a potential gradient is usually carried out in an apparatus such as that shown schematically in Figure 9. This apparatus consists essentially of a microscope with a calibrated reticule for the observation of the individual particles; a thin transparent cell, equipped with platinum measuring electrodes, that contains the colloidal suspension under study; zinc–zinc sulfate reversible working electrodes connected with a constant voltage supply; and a system of tubing and stopcocks for filling and cleaning the cell and electrode compartments. The platinum electrodes are used only for measuring the potential drop across the cell in which the particles are being observed; the potential gradient is developed by applying a voltage to the zinc electrodes further removed from the cell area. Platinum is not a suitable working electrode material because gas formation and polarization at the electrodes give rise to an uncontrollable variation in potential drop. Zinc or copper electrodes are generally used with aqueous systems; they must, however, be sufficiently removed from the measuring area so that ions from the electrode chambers do not have time to move to the measuring area during the experiment. Extremely small quantities of divalent ions have a marked effect on the particle mobility.

The cell itself must be transparent and thin and is frequently of rectangular cross section (1, 22, 68). A long, cylindrical cell has also been used by many workers (49, 83, 86, 97, 98) and is used in a currently available commercial instrument (112); the thin flat cell of rectangular cross section is also available commercially (99).

No matter what the cell geometry, the electrical double layer at the cell wall itself imparts a motion to the whole suspension in the cell. The suspension moves rapidly in one direction near the wall, more slowly further from the wall, and in the opposite direction at the center of the cell. At some point in the cell there is no net motion applied to the suspension as the result of the zeta potential of the cell wall–liquid interface. It is at this point that the observed velocity of the particles in the system is equal to their electrophoretic velocity. Calculations have shown that this stationary level is located at a distance equal to 21.2% of the total cell thickness from the top (or bottom) of a wide flat cell, and at a distance equal to 14.8% of the diameter from the wall of a cylindrical cell (57, page 219).

In use, the cell is filled with the suspension under study and a known potential is applied. With an objective lens that gives a small depth of focus, the microscope is focused at the stationary level and the time for a particle to move a known distance is measured with a stopwatch. When particles of several kinds are present (each kind having its own characteristic mobility), a number of particles may be measured so that the distribution of mobility may be obtained. The results are reported as mobility cm./sec. (v./cm.) or converted to zeta potential by Equation 26.

This technique can be applied only to dilute suspensions so that the individual particles may be distinguished. The particles must also be small enough or have a density close enough to that of the suspending medium so that they will neither rise nor fall out of the stationary level under the influence of gravity while they are observed. The particles do, of course, have to be large enough to be easily seen in the microscope. An ultramicroscope or dark-field illumination may be used to extend the range of the method to finer particles.

The microscopic determination of electrophoretic mobility has been applied successfully to such diverse aqueous systems as kaolinite (34, 50, 97, 98, 104), xylene emulsions (68), proteins adsorbed on quartz particles (1), colloidal particles present in water supplies (83), cellulose and carbon black treated with various surface active agents (22), bacteria at different levels of pH (54), and normal and sickle human red blood cells (89).

In many cases, even when the particles are too small to be readily seen by use of the ultramicroscope, the migration rate of a mass of particles under the influence of a potential gradient may be measured by the moving boundary method. It is necessary in this method to form a sharp interface between a colloidal suspension and the colloid-free dispersing medium. Some of the early work on electrophoretic migration performed by Burton (14) on metal sols was carried out by this method. A simplified drawing of a moving boundary electrophoresis apparatus is shown in Figure 10.

The apparatus for moving boundary electrophoresis in its simplest form consists of a U-tube fitted with electrodes at the top of each arm of the U. Colloidal dispersion is added to the bottom of the U.

An apparatus used extensively by Tiselius (100) for the study of proteins is a more elaborate modification of the simple U-tube. In the Tiselius apparatus the cell arms

# MEASUREMENTS OF ELECTROKINETIC EFFECTS

ELECTROOSMOSIS

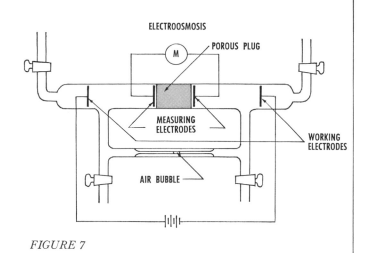

*FIGURE 7*

STREAMING POTENTIAL

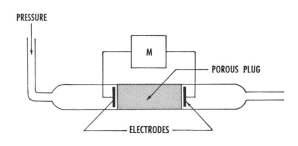

*FIGURE 8*

MICROELECTROPHORESIS

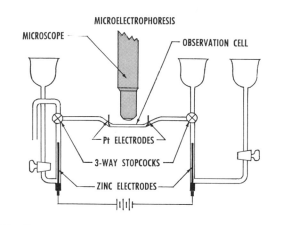

*FIGURE 9*

MOVING BOUNDRY ELECTROPHORESIS

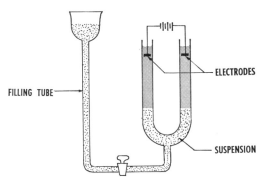

*FIGURE 10*

ELECTROPHORETIC TRANSFER

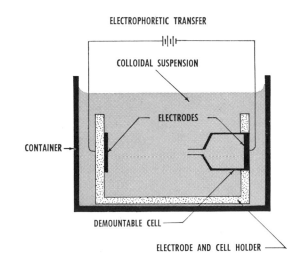

*FIGURE 11*

SEDIMENTATION POTENTIAL

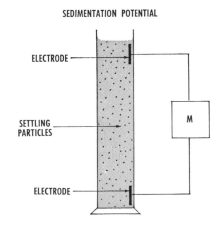

*FIGURE 12*

are of rectangular rather than circular cross section so that the visibility of the boundary is much improved. The boundary surface is established by sliding together the previously filled upper and lower portions of the cell; the upper portion contains the colloid-free supernatant liquid, while the lower portion contains the colloidal suspension. The boundary formed in this way is well defined. The Tiselius design also has reversible electrodes in a relatively large compartment well removed from the boundary; in this way, the colloidal dispersion is not contaminated by electrode reaction products, even in prolonged experiments. With lyophilic colloids such as proteins the Schlieren method of viewing the boundary may be used (57, page 216).

The zeta potential may be calculated from the observed mobility by Equation 26 if its limitations are observed.

The moving boundary method is suitable for almost any colloidal sol provided that a boundary can be formed that can be seen directly or observed by the use of techniques such as the Schlieren method. It is necessary to have a supernatant liquid of the same composition as the liquid in which the particles are suspended, and this can usually be obtained by the centrifugation of some of the colloidal suspension with the same composition as is placed in the bottom of the U-tube. Density of the particles must be close to that of the suspending liquid because gravitational forces must be negligible.

In addition to the initial work of Burton (14) and the later work of Tiselius (100), this technique has been used on other substances by various investigators. The systems studied include the effect of several electrolytes on platinum, gold, silver, bismuth, lead, iron, and selenium sols (14, 107); the effect of electrolytes on latex emulsions (64); and the effect of various electrolytes on arsenic trisulfide and ferric oxide sols (107). All these materials can be prepared as extremely fine particles and hence are amenable to study by this method.

A device for measuring electrophoretic velocity has been developed by the authors and is shown in Figure 11. It consists of a container filled with the suspension under study in which is immersed a bracket that supports two electrodes placed opposite each other. One electrode, shown on the left in the diagram, is completely accessible to the solution, while the electrode shown on the right is placed at the closed end of a cell that has a restricted tubular opening directly between the two electrodes. The electrode in the cell must be reversible; Ag–AgCl and zinc have both been used successfully. To measure mobility with this device, the cell and container are filled with the suspension to be studied. When a potential difference is impressed between the two electrodes, particles having an electric charge will migrate either into or out of the cell (depending on the sign of the cell electrode). After a short time there will be a change in composition of the cell contents because of the migration of the particles; the change may be determined by analysis, and from this concentration change the mobility and zeta potential of the particles can be calculated. Because kaolin has a specific gravity of about 2.58, the concentration change may be detected

by weighing the cell before and after the impression of the voltage gradient. In this case, the mobility may be calculated from the weight change by

$$v_E = \frac{\Delta W}{t} \frac{\rho_s}{\rho_s - 1} \left[ \frac{1}{AME} + \frac{1}{\rho_s A} \right] \qquad (48)$$

where the voltage gradient $E$ is given by the current.

$$E = \frac{i}{\lambda A} \qquad (49)$$

In the above equation, $\Delta W/t$ is the change in cell weight per second, $v_E$ is the electrophoretic mobility, $M$ is the colloid concentration in grams per cc., $A$ is the area of the cell opening, $\rho_s$ is the density of the colloid, and $\lambda$ is the specific conductance of the suspension.

This apparatus, which we call the electrophoretic mass-transport cell, is similar in principle to the Hittorf method for determining the transference number of ions. Indeed, the Hittorf method or modifications thereof could be used to measure the zeta potential of systems that are amenable to moving boundary methods. It appears, however, to be little used.

In the measurement of the mobility of kaolin clays dispersed in water, the major difficulty preventing the use of the moving boundary or microelectrophoresis technique is gravity settling of the larger clay particles.

Kaolin clays such as those of the Georgia deposits consist of small hexagonal platelets or loosely bound stacks of platelets. The kaolin particles generally have a wide size distribution, ranging from 0.2-micron diameter platelets which may be only 0.01 micron thick or less, up to large stacks of platelets 5 or 10 microns in diameter and 30 or more microns thick. By the older definition of colloids in terms of particle size, most of a material such as this would not be so classified; however, these clays do exhibit typical colloidal behavior (such as deflocculation and flocculation) so that the zeta potential of clay systems can give considerable information about the nature of the clay surface and thus help to explain the rheology of concentrated kaolin suspensions.

The device shown in Figure 11 is especially valuable for studying kaolin–water systems or other systems containing particles large enough to preclude the use of the microelectrophoretic or moving boundary methods. With this device, the time of application of the voltage gradient is short (only a few minutes at most); therefore, most of the larger particles will still be in suspension at the end of the experiment. Although some of the larger particles may have settled out from the area between the two electrodes directly in front of the cell opening, corresponding size particles from a level of solution above the cell opening have settled into this area. Hence, little change in composition of suspension caused by particle settling can occur. A further unique property of this device is that electrophoretic mobility at a high

**AUTHOR** *J. P. Olivier is Assistant Research Director, Freeport Kaolin Co., Gordon, Ga. Paul Sennett is Senior Chemist, with the same company.*

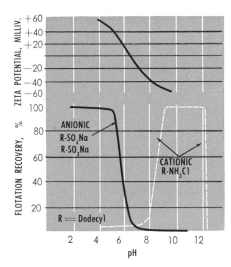

*Figure 13. Flotation recovery of goethite, using anionic and cationic collectors. Note that zeta potential goes from a high positive value at low pH, through zero at a pH of 6.7, to a high negative value. All values determined in 0.0001M NaCl*

colloid concentration may be measured. The instrument has been used to measure clay mobilities in aqueous suspensions containing up to 70% by weight of kaolin.

**Sedimentation and Centrifugation Potential.** The e.m.f. produced by particles falling through a suspending medium $E_D$ (Dorn effect) may be used to calculate the zeta potential if the particles are of uniform size.

$$E_D = \frac{D\zeta}{3\eta\lambda} r^3(\rho - \rho')ng \qquad (50)$$

where $r$ is the particle radius, $(\rho - \rho')$ is the difference in specific gravity, $n$ is the concentration, and $g$ is the gravitational acceleration.

Where particles move by gravity through a liquid, the experimental setup shown in Figure 12 may be used for the measurement of zeta potential. Particles may also be made to move through the liquid by centrifugation (53, 87) or by ultrasonic vibration (19, 85).

Neither the sedimentation potential, centrifugation potential, nor the potential developed by ultrasonic vibration has been used extensively. Sedimentation potential has been used for measurement of the zeta potential of borosilicate glass, fused silica, silicon, fused alumina, and carborundum in KCl and $BaCl_2$ solutions (72); for quartz in KCl solutions (84); and for glass in solutions of several salts (80). Centrifugation potential has been used in the study of AgI and $As_2S_3$ sols in KI and $KNO_3$ solutions (53, 87). The ultrasonic vibration technique has been used with quartz (85).

**Other Methods.** Work by Elton (29, 30) showed that if particles in a narrow size range were allowed to sediment in an ionic solution, they would settle more slowly than they would in a nonionic solvent of the same viscosity. This he attributed to a viscous drag brought about by the shearing of the electrical double layer. From measurements of the retardation of settling he was able to calculate zeta potentials in reasonable agreement with values determined by other methods. The method was applied to quartz, borosilicate glass, carborundum, and silica in aqueous KCl solutions (24, 25, 31, 32).

When a capillary containing an electrolyte is vibrated mechanically, an a.c. voltage is generated between its two ends. This phenomenon, extensively studied by Ueda, Tsuji, and Watanabe (102) and termed the "U effect" is related to the zeta potential and was used by them to measure an a.c. streaming potential of a glass capillary containing a KCl solution.

### Effects in Practical Systems

Although not always taken into account, the nature of the electrical double layer has an important influence on many practical systems. Although in many cases the technique used for its measurement gives rise to some doubts that the number obtained is valid, the zeta potential is an important characteristic property of the double layer. A review of the literature shows that many workers have made extensive investigations of the relation of zeta potential to the properties of various systems. The following paragraphs illustrate some of these.

**Flotation.** The sign and magnitude of surface charge influence profoundly the adsorption characteristics of mineral surfaces. Because the whole practice of froth flotation depends on the nature of solid-liquid and solid-liquid-gas interfaces, it is not surprising that zeta potential measurements relate to the flotation behavior of many mineral substances.

Figure 13 from the work of Iwasaki, Cooke, and Colombo (52) illustrates the close correlation of zeta potential with flotation behavior. In the flotation of oxide minerals where the collector must be adsorbed by the surface, anionic collectors should be effective on positive surfaces, and cationic collectors on negative surfaces. That this is indeed the case is shown in the bottom half of the figure where flotation recovery for a cationic collector and for two anionic collectors is plotted as a function of pH. At the zero point of charge, little collector is adsorbed and flotation recovery is nil. Above a pH of 12 the flotation efficiency falls off abruptly because of the low concentration of quaternary ammonium ions available at high hydroxide ion concentrations.

Other studies have shown similar behavior for rutile (43), corundum (66), hematite (51), and quartz (36, 38, 52). A discussion of the relationship between flotation and zeta potential is given by Aplan and Fuerstenau (3) and by deBruyn and Agar (18).

**Clarification and Filtration.** In light of the previous discussion of the influence of zeta potential on colloid stability, it is perhaps surprising that more practical research effort has not been expended on the influence of various electrolytes on the stability of colloids in water supplies and similar dilute colloidal suspensions.

In the purification of municipal water and in the cleaning up of industrial wastes, it is usually necessary to remove solids from dilute suspensions. To this end, flocculating agents such as aluminum sulfate are frequently used before a filtration, decantation, or centrifugation procedure. The effect of the trivalent aluminum is to lower markedly the zeta potential, even at low aluminum ion concentration (as noted in the discussion of the Schulze-Hardy rule); the lowering of the potential al-

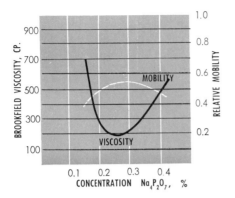

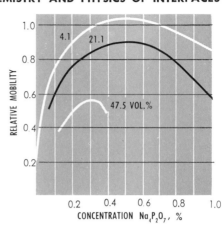

*Figure 14. Mobility and viscosity of a 47.5 volume % kaolinite suspension with addition of deflocculant. Apparently, some degree of correlation exists*

*Figure 15. Mobility of kaolinite as a function of flocculant addition for several kaolinite concentrations, as measured by mass transport electrophoresis*

lows the fine particles to gather into aggregates which are more easily removed by one of the above processes. In many cases, such as in sewage and paper mill effluents, there is appreciable lyophilic material present. Because these lyophilic colloids coat lyophobic particles, the problem of economic clarification is complicated.

In the wet processing of kaolin clays, it is necessary first to make a stable dispersion at fairly low solids so that the naturally occurring mineral may be classified by centrifugal techniques into fractions of various particle size distribution (*2*). As a final step in the processing, the clay must be filtered out of the dispersion so that it can be dried economically. The filtration rate of the deflocculated particles is extremely slow, so the clay-water dispersion is treated with sufficient acid to lower the zeta potential and flocculation occurs.

To obtain the maximum filtration rate, the zeta potential must be lowered to zero; under plant operating conditions, however, the clay still has a negative charge although it is well flocculated. Oakes and Burcik show a nearly linear relation of filtration rate to zeta potential reduction in a sample of Wyoming bentonite (*69*).

**Relationship between Mobility and Viscosity.** Einstein (*28*) derived an equation that relates the viscosity of a suspension of uncharged spherical particles to that of the suspending medium itself. The equation takes the form

$$\eta = \eta_0(1 + 2.5\phi)$$

where $\eta$ is the viscosity of the suspension, $\eta_0$ is the viscosity of the dispersion medium, and $\phi$ is the volume fraction occupied by the spherical particles. The equation is valid under the conditions for which it was derived

Deviations might come about through

—nonspherical particles
—high colloid concentration, which gives rise to particle interference
—forces of attraction and repulsion caused by an electrical double layer on the particles

Insofar as this latter effect is reflected by the zeta potential determined from mobility measurement, the zeta potential might correlate with the flow behavior of colloids.

One of the few substances studied as to the relation of zeta potential to viscosity is kaolin clay. In terms of a

study of the influence of the double layer on viscosity, the choice is a poor one because it represents a highly complicated system; nonetheless, it is of important commerical interest.

Van Wazer and Besmertnuk (*104*) concluded from microelectrophoresis measurements that although low viscosity deflocculated slurries consisted of particles having a high zeta potential, other forces were the primary factor in determining consistency. Street, however, found a good correlation between viscosity at low rates of shear and zeta potential when low colloid content slurries were used (*96, 97*).

The authors have used the electrophoretic mass-transport cell for determining the mobility of a fine-particle kaolin clay as a function of the amount of deflocculant tetrasodium pyrophosphate added; Brookfield viscosity was also determined. The results obtained (Figure 14) show that some relationship exists between zeta potential and viscosity. Certainly no better correlation should be expected for at least three reasons:

—Clay slurries are not Newtonian; therefore, no single number describes the rheological behavior

—Kaolin particles may have a charge on the face surfaces different from that on the edge; thus nature of the floc may change as well as degree of flocculation.

—The measurements were made on a 47.5 volume % slurry, so that particle-particle interference would be expected.

The mobility of kaolinite as measured by mass-transport electrophoresis is a function of concentration, as the data plotted in Figure 15 show. In addition to particle-particle interference at higher particle concentrations, an electroosmotic effect is likely to occur when the mass-transport method is applied to highly concentrated kaolinite suspensions. The kaolinite particles are platelets about 0.2 micron thick; at 50 volume %, the space between platelets is not large compared to the double-layer thickness, and the flow is retarded.

**Soil Structure.** Soils used for agricultural purposes contain an appreciable fraction of colloidal material. This material consists of both lyophobic and lyophilic colloids, but in any case its state of flocculation profoundly influences the soil structure. The soil must be kept in a flocculated state in order that it be porous.

Calcium ion is an excellent flocculant. Organic polyelectrolytes are also effective in maintaining a flocculated soil by forming bridges between particles.

A classic example (79) of the influence of the state of flocculation on the structure of soil occurs when good agricultural land is flooded by sea water. The calcium of the naturally occurring clay minerals exchanges for the sodium of the sea water. The sodium-exchanged soil is also flocculated, but continued leaching by rainwater removes sufficient sodium so that the soil becomes deflocculated and packs into a hard mass not suitable for good plant growth. This condition can be avoided by the addition of calcium ions in the form of gypsum.

**Other Phenomena Related to Zeta Potential.** Because laundering operations consist in part of suspending dirt particles in water a correlation might be expected between charge on the particles and detergency. Work and several synthetic soils led to the conclusion by Durham (27) that there was a qualitative correlation between zeta potential and redeposition of soil, but that other factors were involved. Doscher (22) attributes detergency largely to the degree of adsorption of the surface active agents. Other workers have also investigated this relation, with varying results (26, 75–77).

The microelectrophoretic method is a useful tool to workers studying bacteria (58). It has been used to identify the nature of the surface of living bacteria by comparing their migration rates under varying conditions with those of model systems under the same conditions. James (54), for instance, showed that *Aerobacter aerogenes* had a polysaccharide surface under normal conditions, but a lipid surface when grown in the presence of crystal violet. Normal and abnormal blood cells have been studied (89).

Other phenomena are no doubt associated with zeta potential, although in many cases quantitative data are lacking. Soyenkoff (92), in an early review of the behavior of fine particles in organic liquids, concluded that electrokinetic potential was not important in oil dispersions. Later work, however, indicated that this is often not true. Reising (81) studied the appearance of several paint pigments suspended in organic oils when a 450-volt potential was impressed across a 1/50-in. gap containing the suspension. Some pigments migrated to the anode, some to the cathode, and others assumed a lines-of-force arrangement. Similar behavior was found for coal particles suspended in oil (46). Winslow (110, 111) found that certain substances such as powdered silica gel suspended in oil assumed a lines-of-force arrangement in strong electric fields. He designed an electrostatic clutch making use of the increased viscosity. Gemant (39), in a study of transformer oil, used a novel radioactive tracer technique to measure magnitude of the zeta potential of magnesium oxide, graphite, and high molecular weight fatty acid salts.

### Direct Applications of Electrokinetic Phenomena

Electrokinetic phenomena have been or are being used directly to some extent. Any process that involves the separation of particles with differences in zeta potential suggests itself as a likely candidate for an electrokinetic separation technique. In the field of lyophilic colloids, for instance, the electrophoretic separation of proteins and amino acids is commonplace. Except as noted below, there does not appear to have been much application to the separation of lyophobic colloids, probably because separations are more easily accomplished by other methods. Electrophoretic deposition of colloidal particles, however, has been used in several cases. Electroosmosis has also been used for dewatering.

**Separations.** A recent study by Todd and Wild (101) describes a unique separation procedure that is related in some way to the electrical character of a solid-liquid interface. Their separation procedure was applied to 1- to 30-micron particles of mineral mixtures suspended in nonconducting organic liquids. When a d.c. potential of 1750 v. was applied to the suspension across a 0.4-cm. gap, materials of the mixture would usually plate out on the electrodes. With the proper choice of liquid and surface active agent, Todd and Wild were able to separate completely such mixtures as $\alpha SiO_2$–$MoC_2$, talc–aluminum oxide, and garnet–$FeTiO_3$. In many other cases, a considerable increase in the concentration of one of the components was obtained.

**Electrophoretic Deposition.** At one time, the electrophoretic deposition of rubber latex was a common method of forming thin rubber goods. Natural rubber latex was deposited on an anode of the desired shape. This method has largely been replaced by simpler dipping techniques.

Electrophoretic deposition of paints has aroused considerable interest in recent years and is in commercial use on a limited scale. The process, while not new (16), appears to be gaining favor in the industrial application of paint film to metal parts as large as automobile bodies. The usual commercial practice is to make the metal part the anode and electrophoretically deposit the paint materials from a water emulsion. The paint system can usually be made to behave as if it consisted of particles of only a single electrophoretic mobility. If the conductivity of the paint batch is kept low, power costs are small.

Electrophoretic deposition of paint usually gives a denser and more coherent coating than is obtainable by conventional dip or spray methods. In addition, little paint is wasted—there are no sags or runs and the coating is very uniform, even over rough spots, sharp edges, and within boxed sections. A number of recent papers show the great current interest in the subject (6–8, 33, 40). For further information, see page 60 of IND. ENG. CHEM., August 1965.

**Electrical Dewatering.** Electrophoresis and the liquid counterflow, electroosmosis, suggest themselves as a means of dewatering fine particle size suspensions that are not amenable to filtration. In fact, the capillary rise phenomenon observed in 1808 by Reuss in Moscow was essentially an electroosmotic dewatering process.

In the early part of the present century Count Schwerin made extensive studies of the electrophoretic and electroosmotic dewatering of peat and clay and obtained some 50 patents on various aspects of the process.

In a clay plant of his design, the clay was made to deposit on a partially immersed rotating drum from which it could be removed by a scraping mechanism. The process was apparently more efficient than the filtration processes of the day. A good review of electrical dewatering of clay is given by Curtis (*17*). Stanczyk (*94*) made a study of the dewatering of phosphate rock slime by electrophoresis and electroosmosis (*94*).

An interesting application of electroosmosis for the temporary stabilization of high moisture content soils prior to excavation has been described (*61, 62, 71*). The process consists of driving a solid anode and a perforated cathode into the ground several feet apart; when a voltage is applied, water collects inside the cathode and may be pumped out. Removal of a small amount of water usually markedly increases bearing strength of the soil.

An electrophoretic method known as electrodecantation (*56, 93*) can be used for the concentration of colloidal dispersions. In the electrodecantation process, two electrodes are used to impress a potential across a colloidal suspension; the electrodes are separated from the bulk of the suspension by a membrane which allows the migrating colloidal particles to build up on the membrane, rather than on the electrodes. If the concentrated colloid is more dense than the suspension, it will frequently sink to the bottom in a fairly dense layer that can be removed from the system. Should the concentrated colloidal material have a tendency to stick to the membrane, it can usually be released by a momentary reversal of the current. A multicompartment cell with several membranes may be used to increase the efficiency of the separation. The process has been used for concentrating rubber latex (*67*).

## LITERATURE CITED

(1) Abramson, H. A., Moyer, L. S., Garin, H. M., "Electrophoresis of Proteins," Reinhold, New York, 1942.
(2) Agnello, L. A., Morris, H. H., Gunn, F. A., IND. ENG. CHEM. **52**, 370 (1960).
(3) Aplan, F. F., Fuerstenau, D. W., in "Froth Flotation," D. W. Fuerstenau, Ed., p. 170, American Institute of Mining, Metallurgical and Petroleum Engineers, Inc., New York, 1962.
(4) Ballou, E. V., *J. Colloid Sci.* **10**, 450 (1955).
(5) Benton, D. P., Elton, G. A. H., "Second International Congress of Surface Activity," Vol. 3, p. 28, Academic Press, New York, 1957.
(6) Berry, J. R., *Paint Technol.* **27** (12), 13 (1963).
(7) *Ibid.*, **28** (1), 24 (1964).
(8) *Ibid.*, **28** (3), 53 (1964).
(9) Bolt, G. H., *J. Colloid Sci.* **10**, 206 (1955).
(10) Buchanan, A. S., Heymann, E., *Proc. Roy. Soc.* (*London*) **195A**, 150 (1948).
(11) Buchanan, A. S., Heymann, E., *J. Colloid Sci.* **4**, 137 (1949).
(12) *Ibid.*, p. 151.
(13) *Ibid.*, p. 157.
(14) Burton, E. F., *Phil. Mag.* **11**, 425 (1906).
(15) Chapman, D. D., *Ibid.*, **25** (6), 475 (1913).
(16) Crosse and Blackwell Ltd., Brit. Patent **455,810** (Oct. 28, 1936).
(17) Curtis, C. E., *J. Am. Ceram. Soc.* **14**, 219 (1931).
(18) DeBruyn, P. L., Agar, G. E., in "Froth Flotation," D. W. Fuerstenau, Ed., p. 91, Am. Inst. Mining, Metallurgical and Petroleum Engs., Inc., New York, 1962.
(19) Debye, P., *J. Chem. Phys.* **13**, 1 (1933).
(20) Debye, P., Huckel, E., *Physik Z.* **24**, 185 (1923).
(21) Dorn, E., *Wied. Ann.* **10**, 70 (1880).
(22) Doscher, T. M., *J. Colloid Sci.* **5**, 100 (1950).
(23) Douglas, H. W., Walter, R. A., *Trans. Faraday Soc.* **46**, 559 (1950).
(24) Dulin, C. I., Elton, G. A. H., *J. Chem. Soc.* **1952**, p. 286.
(25) *Ibid.*, **1953**, p. 1168.
(26) Durham, K., *J. Appl. Chem.* (*London*) **6**, 153 (1956).
(27) Durham, K., "Second International Congress of Surface Activity," Vol. 4, p. 60, Academic Press, New York, 1957.
(28) Einstein, A., *Ann. Physik.* **4**, 19 (1906).
(29) Elton, G. A. H., *Proc. Roy. Soc.* (*London*) **197A**, 568 (1949).
(30) Elton, G. A. H., *J. Chem. Phys.* **19**, 1317 (1951).
(31) Elton, G. A. H., Hirschler, F. G., *J. Chem. Soc.* **1952**, p. 2953.
(32) Elton, G. A. H., Mitchell, J. W., *Ibid.*, **1953**, p. 3690.
(33) Finn, S. R., Mell, C. C., *J. Oil Colour Chemists Assoc.* **47**, 219 (1964).
(34) Freundlich, H., "Kapillarchemie," 1st ed., Leipzig, 1909.
(35) Fuerstenau, D. W., *Mining Eng.* **8**, 834 (1956).
(36) *Ibid.*, **9**, 1365 (1957).
(37) Fuerstenau, D. W., Modi, H. J., *J. Electrochem. Soc.* **106**, 336 (1959).
(38) Gaudin, A. M., Fuerstenau, D. W., *Mining Eng.* **7**, 958 (1955).
(39) Gemant, A., *J. Phys. Chem.* **56**, 238 (1952).
(40) Gloyer, S. W., Hart, D. P., Cutforth, R. E., *Off. Dig., Federation Soc. Paint Technol.* **37**, 113 (1965).
(41) Gouy, G., *Ann. Phys.* **7** (9), 129 (1917).
(42) Gouy, G., *J. Phys.* **9** (4), 457 (1910).
(43) Graham, K., Madeley, J. D., *J. Appl. Chem.* (*London*) **12**, 485 (1962).
(44) Grahame, D. C., *Chem. Rev.* **41**, 441 (1947).
(45) Hardy, W. B., *Proc. Roy. Soc.* (*London*) **66**, 110 (1900).
(46) Hedrick, J. E., Andrews, A. C., Sutherland, J. B., IND. ENG. CHEM. **33**, 1055 (1941).
(47) Helmholtz, H., *Wied. Ann.* **7**, 337 (1879).
(48) Henry, D. C., *Proc. Roy. Soc.* (*London*) **133**, 106 (1931); *Trans. Faraday Soc.* **44**, 1021 (1948).
(49) Hunter, R. J., Alexander, A. E., *J. Colloid Sci.* **17**, 781 (1962).
(50) *Ibid.*, **18**, 820 (1963).
(51) Iwasaki, I., Cooke, S. R. B., Choi, H. S., *Trans. AIME* **217**, 237 (1960).
(52) Iwasaki, I., Cooke, S. R. B., Colombo, A. F., *U. S. Bur. Mines, Rept. Invest.* **5593**, 1960.
(53) Jacobs, G., *Trans. Faraday Soc.* **48**, 355 (1952).
(54) James A. M., "Second International Congress of Surface Activity," Vol. 4, p. 254, Academic Press, New York, 1957.
(55) Johansen, P. G., Buchanan, A. S., *Australian J. Chem.* **10**, 392 (1957)
(56) Kirk, R. E., Othmer, D. F., "Encyclopedia of Chemical Technology," Vol. 5, p. 549, Interscience Publishers, New York, 1950.
(57) Kruyt, H. R., "Colloid Science," Vol. I, Elsevier, New York, 1952.
(58) *Ibid.*, Vol. II, Elsevier, New York, 1949.
(59) Levy, B., Fritsch, A. R., *J. Electrochem. Soc.* **106**, 730 (1959).
(60) Linder, S. E., Picton, H., *J. Chem. Soc.* (*London*) **61**, 148 (1892).
(61) Loughney, R., *Const. Methods and Equip.* **36**, No. 8, 70, 74, 78, 82 (1954).
(62) Loughney, R., Hickey, W. E., *Eng. News Record* **162**, No. 15, 41, 45 (1959).
(63) Lyons, J. W., *J. Colloid Sci.* **19**, 339 (1964).
(64) Maron, S. H., Bowler, W. W., *J. Am. Chem. Soc.* **70**, 3893 (1948).
(65) Modi, H. J., Fuerstenau, D. W., *Ibid.*, **61**, 640 (1957).
(66) Modi, H. J., Fuerstenau, D. W., *Trans. AIME* **217**, 381 (1960).
(67) Murphey, E. J., *Trans. Inst. Rubber Ind.* **18**, 173 (1942).
(68) Neogy, R. K., *J. Indian Chem. Soc.* **31**, 291 (1954).
(69) Oakes, P. T., Burcik, E. J., *Natl. Acad. Sci.–Natl. Res. Council, Publ.*, No. 456, 225 (1956).
(70) O'Connor, D. J., "Second International Congress of Surface Activity," Vol. 3, p. 319, Academic Press, New York, 1957.
(71) Olinger, W. A., "Sixteenth Annual Minerals Symposium," Univ. Minn., p. 46, Jan. 11–12, 1955.
(72) Peace, J. B., Elton, G. A. H., *J. Chem. Soc.* **1960**, p. 2186.
(73) Perrin, J., *J. Chim. Phys.* **2**, 601 (1904).
(74) *Ibid.*, **3**, 50 (1950).
(75) Porter, A. S., "Second International Conference of Surface Activity," Vol. 3, p. 103, Academic Press, New York, 1957.
(76) Powney, J., Wood, L. J., *Trans. Faraday Soc.* **36**, 420 (1940).
(77) *Ibid.*, p. 57.
(78) Quinke, G., *Pogg. Ann.* **113**, 513 (1861).
(79) Quirk, J. P., Schofeld, R. K., *Soil. Sci.* **6**, 163 (1955).
(80) Quist, J. D., Washburn, E. R., *J. Am. Chem. Soc.* **62**, 3169 (1940).
(81) Reising, J. A., IND. ENG. CHEM. **29**, 565 (1937).
(82) Reuss, F. F., *Mem. Soc. Imperiale Natural. Moscou* **2**, 327 (1809).
(83) Riddick, T. M., *TAPPI* **47**, 171A (1964).
(84) Roy, C. B., *J. Indian Chem. Soc.* **38**, 903 (1961).
(85) Rutgers, A. J., *Nature* **157**, 74 (1946).
(86) Rutgers, A. J., de Smet, M., *Trans. Faraday Soc.* **48**, 635 (1952).
(87) Rutgers, A. J., Nagels, P., *Nature* **171**, 568 (1953).
(88) Ruyssen, R., Loos, R., *Ibid.*, **162**, 741 (1948).
(89) Schulze, H., *J. Prakt. Chem.* **25** (2), 431 (1882).
(90) *Ibid.*, **27**, 320 (1883).
(91) Seaman, G. V. F., Pethica, B. A., "Second International Conference of Surface Activity," Vol. 4, p. 277, Academic Press, New York, 1957.
(92) Soyenkoff, B., *J. Phys. Chem.* **35**, 2993 (1931).
(93) Stamberger, P., *J. Colloid Sci.* **1**, 93 (1946).
(94) Stanczyk, M. H., Feld, I. L., *U. S. Bur. Mines, Rept. Invest.* **6451**, 1964.
(95) Stern, O., *Z. Elektrochem.* **30**, 508 (1924).
(96) Street, N., *Australian J. Chem.* **9**, 467 (1956).
(97) Street, N., *J. Colloid Sci.* **12**, 1 (1957).
(98) Street, N., Buchanan, A. S., *Australian J. Chem.* **9**, 450 (1956).
(99) Thomas, Arthur H. Co., Catalogue No. 65, Philadelphia, Pa.
(100) Tiselius, A., *Trans. Faraday Soc.* **33**, 524 (1937).
(101) Todd, G., Wild, G. A., *Anal. Chem.* **36**, 1025 (1964).
(102) Ueda, S., Tsuji, F., Watanabe, A., "Second International Conference o Surface Activity," Vol. III, p. 3, Academic Press, New York, 1957.
(103) Van Olphen, H., "Clay Colloid Chemistry," Interscience, New York, 1963.
(104) Van Wazer, J. R., Besmertnuk, E., *J. Phys. and Colloid Chem.* **54**, 89 (1950).
(105) Verwey, E. J. W., Overbeek, J. T. G., "Theory of the Stability of Lyophobic Colloids," Elsevier, New York, 1948.
(106) Von Smoluchowski, M. "Graetz Handbuch Der Elektrizitat Und Des Magnetismus," II, p. 385, Leipzig, 1921.
(107) Weiser, H. B., Merrifield, P., *J. Phys. and Colloid Chem.* **54**, 990 (1950).
(108) Wiedemann, G., *Pogg. Ann.* **87**, 321 (1852).
(109) *Ibid.*, **99**, 177 (1856).
(110) Winslow, W. M., *J. Appl. Phys.* **20**, 1137 (1949).
(111) Winslow, W. M., U. S. Patent **2,417,840** (March 25, 1947).
(112) Zeta Meter, Inc., Bull. 6-61, 1720 First Ave., New York, N. Y.

# 8

# Zeta Potential Measurement Applications in the Paper Industry

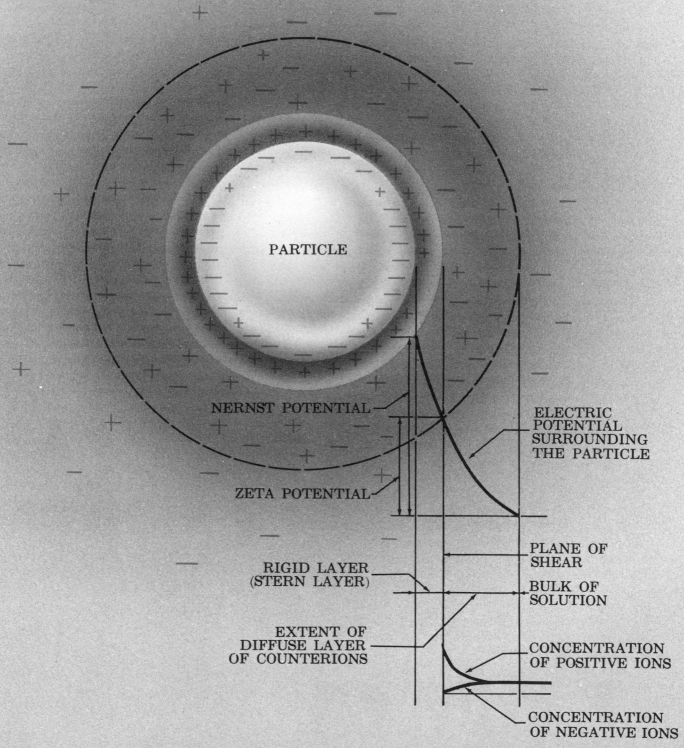

PARTICLE

NERNST POTENTIAL

ELECTRIC
POTENTIAL
SURROUNDING
THE PARTICLE

ZETA POTENTIAL

PLANE OF
SHEAR

RIGID LAYER
(STERN LAYER)

BULK OF
SOLUTION

EXTENT OF
DIFFUSE LAYER
OF COUNTERIONS

CONCENTRATION
OF POSITIVE IONS

CONCENTRATION
OF NEGATIVE IONS

FIGURE 1. The concept of the zeta potential. Most colloidal particles have a negative charge, as shown here, surrounded by stationary positive charges. These in turn are surrounded by a diffuse layer of negative charges. The zeta potential is the difference between the charge of this moveable layer and that of the bulk of the suspending liquid. For most natural substances, zeta potential is negative.

# Zeta Potential Measurement
## Applications in the Paper Industry

RUDOLF SCHMUT

> *Even in very complex systems, the properties of colloids can be assessed by simplified approaches. Electrophoretic mobilities, as measured by the Zeta-Meter, are descriptive, reproducible, and useful in control of the dispersion*

Ever since W. Ostwald's pioneering book, "Die Welt der vernachlässigten Dimensionen" in 1915, the study of colloidal phenomena has been largely an experimental science. The formulation of exact theories has been hindered by the large number of variables involved and the difficulty or complexity of accurate measurements. Theories, therefore, are largely limited to particular phenomena.

The paper industry has several problems which are based at least partially on colloidal phenomena. These include formation, flocculation, retention of fillers and fines, dispersion of additives, treatment of water and effluent and waste gases, foam, sizing, and preventing pitchy deposits. The aqueous solutions are extremely complex, and many interrelated variables affect the nature of these colloids. For technical applications, one attempts to stabilize or destabilize a dispersion by mutual repulsion or attraction of particles through adsorption of charged ions, using as guides flocculation indexes, sedimentation values, zeta potential measurements, or related descriptive test methods.

Recently developed instruments, for example, the Zeta-Meter, permit improved measurements of electrophoretic mobilities. We have found that studies of electrophoretic mobilities, with or without conversion of readings to zeta potentials, can be simplified so far as to permit rapid evaluations of additives and their effects in complex aqueous industrial systems. The results are both descriptive and quantitative depending upon the experience and judgment of the investigator. Modern instrumentation permits measurements which are reliable and reproducible in standardized systems.

Though absolute measurements may be doubtful, the relative values obtained are sufficient.

Some of the results of tests using a Zeta-Meter to control deposits in papermill systems are given in this article. The effects of variables in such systems (dilution, pH, ionic effects, additives, mixing effects, and so forth) are illustrated. Since this article is a review as well as a report of industrial experiences, some duplication of previous information is unavoidable and the industrial rather than the academic approach is used.

### Electrokinetic Colloidal Phenomena

Four groups of related electrokinetic colloidal phenomena have been reported at boundary surfaces in systems containing at least one liquid phase.

*Electrophoresis.* An externally applied potential difference causes suspended particles to migrate to the pole which carries the charge opposite to that of the particles.

*Electrosmosis.* An externally applied potential difference causes a liquid to move through a capillary tube or a membrane in a container.

*Streaming or flow potential.* An electrical potential results when a liquid is moved against another phase (e.g., liquid flowing through a tube).

*Migration potential or fall potential.* An electrical potential results when suspended particles are forced to migrate through a dispersion medium.

These four phenomena provide most of the experimental data on behavior and effects of charged small particles. Detailed exposition is given in available textbooks on colloid chemistry.

### Sols and Some of Their Properties

Sols are colloids of a solid dispersed in a liquid and are classified according to the liquid used as medium of the dispersion. The dispersed particles range usually between 1 and 500 m$\mu$ in size. If the medium of dispersion shows an attraction to the dispersed solids, the sol is named lyophilic (hydrophilic in case of water). If there is little or no attraction between the medium of dispersion and the dispersed solid the sol is named lyophobic (hydrophobic in case of water).

A beam of light passed through a sol becomes visible because of the Tyndall effect (light scattering by the dispersed solids). The Tyndall effect is the underlying principle of the ultramicroscope and the Zeta-Meter; both use beams of light focused in a sol and observations of the images obtained at angles to the direction of the beam. Particles can be observed directly, or as flashes of scattered light, or by adsorption on larger carriers if they are much below the wave length of visible light.

Particles of a hydrophobic sol are electrically charged and will migrate toward the electrode of opposite charge in an electric field. This migration is called electrophoresis. The charge on the dispersed solid is usually caused by adsorption of ions. The stability of colloidal particles in a lyophobic sol is a function of the zeta potential (mutual repulsion of particles with equal charges).

Hydrophilic sols are prepared by adding the solid to water and heating. They are reversible, that is, a solid obtained by evaporation can be made into a sol again by wetting. Hydrophilic sols may be both charged and hydrated.

### Coagulation and Precipitation

Though the charge on a dispersed solid in a lyophobic sol is usually caused by adsorption of ions, additional factors (polarity, hydration, swelling, macromolecular structure, and so forth) affect lyophilic sols and obscure the picture. The exact source of all charges on cellulose or wool, for example, has not been determined. For industrial applications, however, this is of secondary importance. As stated previously, the problem becomes that of stabilizing or destabilizing a dispersion by mutual repulsion or attraction of particles using adsorption of charged ions, measured by flocculation indices, sedimentation values, conductance, zeta potential, and related descriptive test methods.

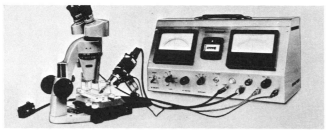

COURTESY ZETA-METER, INC., NEW YORK

*Figure 2. The Zeta-Meter, an instrument for measuring electrophoretic mobility*

Ions of opposite charge precipitate sols and the effectiveness of precipitation increases with the valence of the precipitating ions (Schulze-Hardy rule). Ions of the same valence and sign differ somewhat in their precipitation and flocculation values depending on their size, expressed as ionic radius. In extreme cases this effect can obscure the Schulze-Hardy rule (Hofmeister series). Lyophilic sols added to lyophobic sols may coat the lyophobic colloidal particles and stabilize them against precipitation by electrolytes (protective colloids).

Since hydrophilic sols may be charged and hydrated, both electrical discharge and dehydration may be required for precipitation or coagulation.

### Application of the Zeta-Meter

The Zeta-Meter measures the electrophoretic mobility (converted to zeta potential) of suspended colloids and suspensoids, by indirect determination of the ionized or electrokinetic charge surrounding the particles (Figure 1). Most colloid particles have a negative charge, which is surrounded by stationary positive charges which are in turn surrounded by a diffuse layer of negative charges. The zeta potential is the difference between the charge of such a diffuse or movable layer and the bulk of the other phase (suspending liquid). The charges involved are electrokinetic (adsorption of ions) and not electrostatic (excess or absence of electrons). Most natural substances show a negative zeta potential. These charges prevent flocculation and precipitation of colloids by electrokinetic repulsion. Polyelectrolytes will change the system and the zeta potential, permitting precipitation or further dispersion. For precipitation it is necessary to adjust the zeta potential close to zero and to assist floccing with polymers or flocculants.

The Zeta-Meter is more applicable to lyophobic than to lyophilic dispersions since their stability is controlled by the zeta potential, they respond to small amounts of electrolytes, the electrokinetic charge is stable, and they respond always to an applied potential. In technical application ranges, however, this consideration may be neglected if one controls, or at least monitors, electrolyte concentrations, ionic strengths, pH, hydration, conductance, temperature, time, etc. A standardized procedure is fairly easily established for a system.

Since water is the essential medium of dispersion in current pulping and papermaking, this paper is limited to common materials and additives in such a system.

The readings obtained from the Zeta-Meter are converted to the zeta potential by monographs based on the Helmholtz-Smoluchowski formula, assuming spherical colloidal particles. This assumption is incorrect for pulp and papermill systems because of size and shape of the majority of investigated materials; however, for the sake of simplicity and for fast comparison of various samples it is adequate. Electrophoretic mobilities reduced to standard conditions seem more appropriate.

### Description of the Zeta-Meter

The instrument has been described in connection with pitch control and water treatment (1, 2) The system consists of an illuminator, a plastic electrophoresis cell and an electrical control unit (Figure 2). It permits quick and convenient measurements of electrophoretic mobilities. Tests on pulp and paper stocks show discernible differences between various samples, as will be discussed below.

The instrument has advantages and drawbacks. The main advantages lie in its simplicity of operation and its suitability for samples of wide ranges in particle size and concentration. Its drawbacks include the use of a binocular microscope (a long focus monocular appears sufficient), the individual focusing required for each sample (a predetermined focal plane would obviate this), the size of the cell (a shorter cell with less volume would

**AUTHOR** *Rudolf Schmut is Senior Research Chemist, Covington (Va.) Research Dept. of the West Virginia Pulp & Paper Co. He wishes to acknowledge the assistance of H. B. Casey and F. B. Warlitner, Jr., during sampling and testing.*

## TABLE I. DILUTION EFFECTS

| Dilution | Sample A | | $B_2$ | | C | | $D_1$ | | $E_1$ | |
|---|---|---|---|---|---|---|---|---|---|---|
| | EM | ZP | EM | ZP | EM | ZP | EM | ZP | EM | ZP |
| as is | | | | | 27 | −35 | | | | |
| 1:1 | | | 2.5 | −32.5 | 2.3 | −29.9 | | | | |
| 1:2 | | | | | 2.5 | −32.5 | | | | |
| 1:2.5 | 2.35 | −30.5 | | | | | | | | |
| 1:5 | 2.48 | −32.0 | 2.3 | −29.9 | 2.4 | −31.1 | | | | |
| 1:7.5 | 2.48 | −32.0 | | | | | | | | |
| 1:10 | 2.45 | −31.6 | | | 2.8 | −36.3 | 0.73 | − 9.3 | 0.54 | −7.0 |
| 1:15 | 2.44 | −31.4 | 2.2 | −28.5 | 2.7 | −35.0 | 0.86 | − 8.6 | | |
| 1:20 | 2.45 | −31.5 | | | 2.5 | −32.5 | 0.89 | − 8.9 | 0.46 | −5.9 |
| 1:25 | 2.47 | −31.8 | | | | | | | | |
| 1:50 | 2.20 | −28.7 | 2.7 | −35.0 | 2.4 | −31.1 | 0.81 | −10.4 | 0.39 | −5.1 |
| 1:100 | 2.35 | −30.5 | | | | | | | | |
| pH range | 7.85 to 7.35 | | 7.7 to 7.5 | | 7.7 to 7.4 | | 4.7 to 5.4 | | 4.8 to 5.3 | |

*Samples A, $B_2$, and C are from unsized, unbleached furnishes, $D_1$ and $E_1$ from sized, bleached furnishes.*

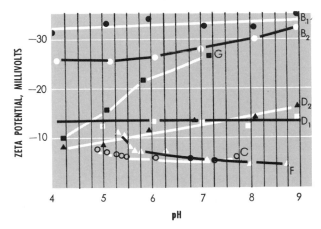

*Figure 3. Effect of pH on zeta potential of paper machine furnishes. Curves B and D, adjusted with HCl and NaOH; Curve C, sodium carbonate; Curve F, sodium aluminate; Curve G, alum*

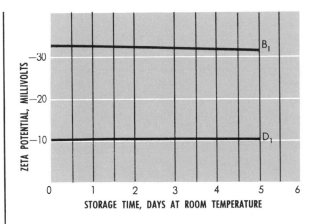

*Figure 5. Effect of storage time on zeta potential. Little change was observed*

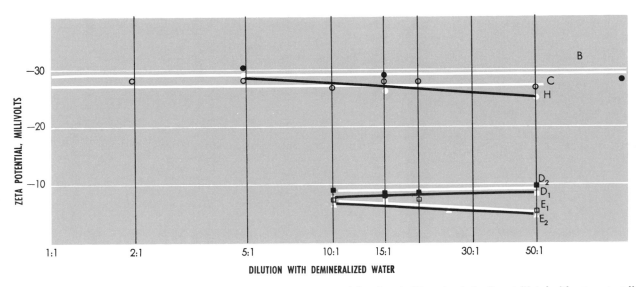

*Figure 4. Effect of dilution with demineralized water on zeta potential. Sample H consisted of sediment diluted with supernatant liquid (see Table I)*

be adequate), the electrode arrangement (permanently embedded electrodes with plugs seem preferable to the crocodile clamps), the bulk of the system, its current limitation to aqueous dispersions, and finally its sensitivity to vibrations.

Ideally, one would desire two different instruments—a small compact preset one for routine work, and a more versatile one suitable for such uses as low conductance high voltage applications in nonaqueous systems.

**Experimental Work**

Deposits in paper mill systems and additives for their control have been discussed in other papers (*1*, *3*). A list of materials commonly used for deposit control appears on page 33. The relationship between these and the application of electrophoretic mobility is self-explanatory. Electrophoretic mobilities permit one, in many cases, to distinguish between chemical and colloidal precipitates.

The tables and figures shown below give a comparison of paper machine process waters (white water) under various test conditions. The Zeta-Meter Co. has published data and bulletins stressing the necessity of careful sample preparation in dilution, proportioning, mixing, ionic strength, viscosity control, and so forth. The test results reported here indicate that sample preparation and handling are much less critical, at least in the tested system, than reported in these bulletins. Their data on paper mill systems are very limited, except for water treatment and effluent control. It was therefore decided to investigate bleached and un-

bleached papermill systems and to study various test conditions. Application data are, however, not included, and applications are only discussed in general terms.

Figure 3 shows the effect of pH variations on paper machine furnishes; the samples were diluted 10:1 with demineralized water and the pH was adjusted with HCl, NaOH, alum, soda ash, and sodium aluminate. In the absence of multivalent ions the changes in electrophoretic mobilities are slight. Electrophoretic mobilities ($EM$) are expressed in $10^{-4}$ cm.$^2$ per volt-sec. Zeta potentials ($ZP$) are expressed in millivolts. Specific conductances are not included in the graphs or tables. They follow straight lines if plotted against dilutions with demineralized water (specific conductance 1 to 3 micromho/cm.).

Figure 4 and Table I show the effect of dilution with demineralized water on the zeta potential; there are no definite trends. One sample ($H$) consisted of sediment diluted with supernatant liquid; it was not significantly different.

Figure 5 shows the effect of storage time on the zeta potential. Little change, if any, was observed during a storage period of five days at room temperature. The relationship between zeta potential of a sample and the time required for a sedimentation level of 50% in a 1000-ml. graduate was checked for several points. As expected, the closer the sample is to the isoelectric point, the shorter is the sedimentation time.

Figures 6 and 7 show comparisons of zeta potential distribution curves (as staple diagrams) of white water samples and mixtures of white water samples. Mixtures

*Figure 6. Zeta potential distribution curves before and after blending samples $B_4$ and $D_4$ (white water samples)*

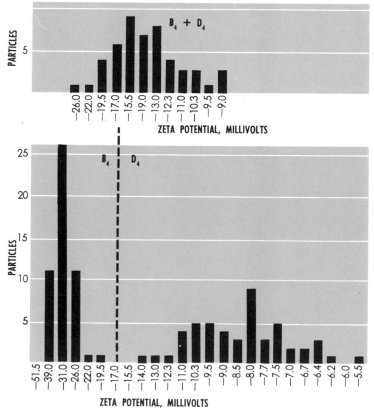

*Figure 7. Zeta potential distribution curves before and after blending samples $B_5$ and $D_5$ (white water samples)*

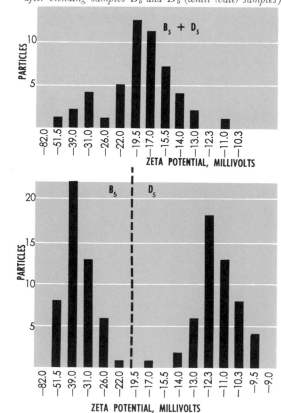

show only one peak and are flatter than the original samples because of an equilization of charges. The mixtures, due to different solid contents of the original samples, do not show a numerical average of the distributions of the components; this effect probably overshadows differences in ionic strengths.

Table II shows the effects of an anionic oil-ester base defoamer. On an unbleached unsized furnish, the change in the system points to an electrokinetic effect which may lead to precipitation with counter-ions present and may deactivate the defoamer, particularly at excessive defoamer applications. The mechanism of foaming is complicated and pulp and paper defoamers are designed in many cases for specific applications. The emulsifier may be anionic, nonionic, or cationic; the same applies to the active ingredients. Electrokinetic incomptabilities can lead to defoamer breakdown, deposits, defoamer inefficiences, interference with the resin–size–alum system, and so forth.

Table III shows a comparison of two commercial polyphosphate-chelate complexes which are used as anionic dispersants. Both behave in a similar manner—they exhibit an optimum point of addition beyond which the effect flattens out or is reversed. Various other anionics were evaluated in a similar manner, particularly naphthalene sulfonates, permitting cost-efficiency comparisons in presence of various counter-ions.

#### TABLE II. ADDITION OF DEFOAMER

| Defoamer, % of liquid | EM | ZP |
|---|---|---|
| 0 | 2.17 | −28 |
| 0.05 | 2.38 | −30.8 |
| 0.10 | 3.4 | −42.0 |
| 0.15 | 3.7 | −47.5 |
| 0.20 | 4.0 | −51.8 |
| 0.25 | 4.6 | −69.5 |

#### TABLE III. ADDITION OF DISPERSANTS

| Addition Level, P.P.M. | Compound I | | Compound II | |
|---|---|---|---|---|
| | EM | ZP | EM | ZP |
| Sample B₃—unbleached, unsized | | | | |
| 0 | 2.12 | −27.3 | 2.12 | −27.3 |
| 10 | 2.2 | −28.5 | 2.2 | −28.5 |
| 20 | 2.32 | −30.0 | 2.35 | −30.5 |
| 30 | 2.35 | −30.5 | 2.32 | −30.0 |
| 50 | 2.40 | −31.0 | 2.39 | −30.9 |
| 100 | 2.38 | −30.8 | 2.30 | −29.8 |
| 150 | 2.39 | −30.9 | 2.28 | −29.6 |
| Sample D₃—bleached, sized | | | | |
| 0 | 0.63 | −8.2 | 0.63 | −8.2 |
| 10 | 0.88 | −11.5 | 0.88 | −11.5 |
| 20 | 0.88 | −11.5 | 0.88 | −11.5 |
| 30 | 0.93 | −12.0 | 0.94 | −12.2 |
| 50 | 0.96 | −12.5 | 0.95 | −12.4 |
| 100 | 1.46 | −19.0 | 1.39 | −18.1 |
| 150 | 1.27 | −16.7 | 1.25 | −16.4 |

### Wet End Additives for Deposit Control

ADSORBENTS are characterized by fine particle size, large surface area, and acceptable papermaking qualities (brightness, capacity, low abrasiveness, low reaction rate with other furnish constituents). They have organophilic surfaces or edges, adsorb organics selectively, and keep them dispersed by their own dispersion or by coating the pitch particles. Most other deposit control agents interfere with the action of the adsorbents.

POLYPHOSPHATES are negatively charged polyelectrolytes. They complex or sequester some of the polyvalent metal ions which assist in the formation and precipitation of sticky deposits. Negative charges are imparted to particles after adsorption of the polyphosphate on polyvalent cations at their surface. The negative charge causes the particles to repel one another. The formation of surface layers on interfaces tends to inactivate them and to decrease the tendency of deposition.

SEQUESTERING AGENTS, alone or combined with polyphosphates, sequester excess alkaline earths and polyvalent metals, which augment the agglomeration and precipitation of deposits. In particular, they sequester calcium, iron, copper, and magnesium-ions.

SURFACTANTS AND POLYELECTROLYTES in general act by changing surface charges (electrokinetic charge measured as electrokinetic mobility). Anionic materials impart negative charges leading to mutual repulsion and dispersion at zeta potentials lower than −20 millivolts. Cationic materials act by increasing the zeta potential close to 0 millivolts, or to the positive side, leading to precipitation and retention of materials on the paper fibers. Cationic surfactants may require the use of nonionic hydrophilic additives or of amphoteric additives to prevent agglomeration before the particles are retained on the fibers. It is claimed that some of the cationics dissolve pitch or disperse pitch; however, it seems that a zeta potential of about +20 millivolts for cationic dispersions would be hard to reach and may interfere with the whole system.

SULFITES, SULFATES, AND ACIDS harden pitchy deposits and may fix them on the fiber surfaces.

ALKALIS assist in the dispersion of pitch, but may lead to difficulties since calcium and magnesium ions contribute to pitch precipitation at pH 6.0 and above. Alkali treatments are usually combined with a subsequent stabilizing treatment, for instance the formation of protective colloids.

PROTECTIVE COLLOIDS AND EMULSIFIERS stabilize existing dispersions and lower the surface tension. In many cases, they depend on pH for other effects (for instance, retention). The changes in surface tension can lead to foaming and from there back to deposits through the precipitating action of defoamers.

CLOSED SYSTEMS AND HARD WATER tend to increase deposit troubles as do large amounts of dissolved solids and salts; these act by salting-out and destabilizing emulsions or dispersions.

### LITERATURE CITED
(1) Jacobsen, N. Å., Schmut, R., *Tappi* 47, No. 1, 210A–213A (1964).
(2) Riddick, T. M., *Chem. Eng.* 68, No. 26, 28: 121–26, 141–46 (1961).
(3) Schmut, R., *Paper Mill News* 86, No. 12, 22–3 (1963).

# 9

# Adsorption and Condensation Processes

*Figure 1.  Circular islands of condensed phase, one monolayer thick, are seen in a sea of the uncondensed monolayer phase.  Electron micrograph of a monolayer of stearic acid at 10 dynes per cm. spread on water (9)*

A specialist in nucleation and condensation theory and a specialist in physical adsorption theory combine their separate approaches to two-dimensional film formation on the surface of an adsorbent.

# ADSORPTION AND CONDENSATION PROCESSES

JOHN B. HUDSON    SYDNEY ROSS

In the present paper, we consider the relation of processes of physical adsorption to the occurrence of first-order phase changes in systems where surface considerations play a significant role. We begin with a review of the phenomena involved, some of which have long been recognized and treated as first-order phase changes, though others have not been treated in those terms. The thermodynamic treatment of phase changes, applied to these systems, yields a generalized phase diagram that takes into account the presence of a chemically inert adsorbent surface. This phase diagram enables us to see clearly the relation between bulk and monolayer condensation, and the conditions wherein to expect one or the other. We consider next the kinetics of the phenomena and the added effects thereby introduced into our predictions. We consider finally the application of this treatment to systems of practical interest and show its relevance to processes of technological importance.

## Systems of Interest

What systems can be considered as undergoing first-order phase changes? The criterion for such a change is that material be transferred from one thermodynamically well-defined phase to another by a process involving a discontinuous change in the state functions of the material so transferred. In other words, for such a process to occur at constant $T$ and $p$, there must be a $\Delta H$ and a $\Delta S$ of transformation. This contrasts with the concept of a second-order phase change, in which occurs a discontinuous change in the partial derivatives of the state functions, but not in the state functions themselves. Obvious and well defined examples of first-order

changes are the bulk-phase transformations, such as ice $\leftrightharpoons$ water; water $\leftrightharpoons$ steam; or dry ice $\leftrightharpoons$ carbon dioxide gas, wherein one macroscopic bulk-phase is transformed to another with the attendant change in the bulk thermodynamic properties. The process of physical adsorption, involving the transfer of sorbate molecules from a bulk vapor to a two-dimensional adsorbed phase, with attendant discrete changes in the enthalpy and entropy of the sorbed material, is another and, at least in the context of this symposium, a fairly common example of the first-order phase change:

$$_{gas}M \leftrightharpoons {}_{ads}M$$

In addition to these well-known examples, we may similarly consider several other processes occurring in systems where a one-component, sorbable material is in contact with a chemically inert surface. For example, the vertical discontinuities observed in adsorption isotherms of gases on solids, and the horizontal discontinuities observed during the compression of monolayers spread on liquids, both display the thermodynamic characteristics of a first-order phase change—the change in these cases being from a two-dimensional gas to some sort of two-dimensional condensed phase. For monolayers spread on water, the correctness of this interpretation has been shown by direct observation with an electron microscope. Figure 1 (9) is an electron micrograph of a film of stearic acid spread on water, observed at a degree of compression in the middle of the two-phase region. Circular "islands" of condensed phase, one monolayer thick, are seen in a "sea" of the uncondensed monolayer phase. Similar photographs show that the islands grow reversibly from the uncondensed phase as the area of the film is decreased at constant temperature.

The same kind of analogy to bulk systems, for gases adsorbed on solid surfaces, can be shown by comparison of the $p$–$V$ behavior of examples of the bulk system and the sorption-system, which shows a two-dimensional transition of adsorbed gas to monolayer condensed-phase. This comparison is shown in Figure 2 (6, 10). The bulk-phase data are presented in terms of density rather than volume to facilitate comparison with the conventional $p$–$\theta$ curve for the adsorbed phases. Note that both isotherms contain a region of low slope at low pressure corresponding to compression of the uncondensed phase; a vertical discontinuity in density at the equilibrium pressure for formation of the condensed phase, during which the condensed phase grows at the expense of the gas; and a further slow rise following the phase change, attributable to compression of the condensed phase (plus, in the two-dimensional case, possible beginning of second-layer formation).

We may range still further from the usually recognized phase transformations to consider such processes as the spreading of a bulk liquid or solid to form a monolayer (gaseous or condensed, depending on the pressure) on a foreign surface, solid or liquid; or the reverse of these processes—the growth of bulk phases from monolayers as the pressure is increased.

In all cases involving two-dimensional phases, the surface energy of the substrate involved, and more particularly the way in which this surface energy changes as gaseous or condensed layers form upon it, is critical to the production of these phases and the transformations that may occur among them, as dealt with later.

### Thermodynamic Basis

Let us review briefly the thermodynamic basis for first-order phase changes, considering in all cases the change in Gibbs free energy, $\Delta G$, involved in transferring a given amount of material from one phase to another by an isothermal, isobaric process. This free-energy change consists of a term $\Delta H = \Delta E + \Delta(pV)$, characteristic of the difference in the enthalpy of material in the present and newly formed phases; a term $-T\Delta S$, characteristic of the difference in entropy between the two phases at the temperature of transformation; and, where a surface phase is involved, the term $\Delta(A_f)$, the change in the total surface free energy when a monolayer phase is formed on a previously clean substrate. The bulk variables, $H$ and $S$, are expressed in terms of a chemical potential, $_g\mu = (\partial G/\partial n)_{T,p,A\gamma}$, per mole thus: $_g\mu = H - TS$. This $_g\mu$ is related to the standard state of the gas phase at one atmosphere by the relation $_g\mu = _g\mu_s + RT \ln p$. The surface area is expressed in terms of adsorbate molecular density on the surface, $\Gamma$ mole/sq. cm., that is, $A = n/\Gamma$. The condition for equilibrium between any two phases is thus

$$_xG \rightleftharpoons _yG \tag{1}$$

or

$$_x\mu + \left(\frac{f}{\Gamma}\right)_x = _y\mu + \left(\frac{f}{\Gamma}\right)_y \tag{2}$$

Equilibrium relations among the phases that may be found in systems of interest to the study of surface processes can now be written. These equilibrium relations can then be used to construct phase diagrams indicating the phase equilibria involved in systems where surface phases are present.

Consider first a system of a one-component vapor phase in contact with an energetically uniform, chemically inert surface. In this system, for the transformation bulk vapor $\rightleftharpoons$ bulk crystal, we have, at equilibrium

$$\Delta G = (n_s\mu - n_g\mu) = 0 \tag{3}$$

where $n$ is the number of moles transferred, or:

$$_g\mu = _s\mu = _g\mu_s + RT \ln (_sp_0) \tag{4}$$

*Figure 2.   Typical p–V behavior for two-dimensional and three-dimensional systems.   At left, bulk condensation, water vapor $\rightleftharpoons$ liquid water at 100° C.; at right, monolayer condensation, ethane adsorbed on sodium chloride crystals at 90° K. (10)*

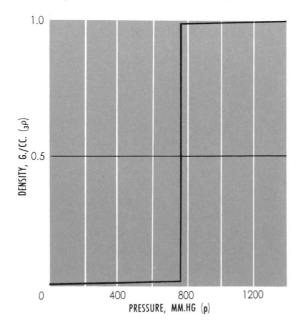

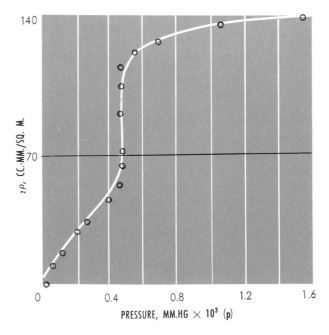

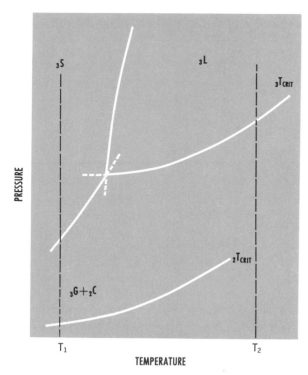

*Figure 3. Generalized phase diagram for the case $_2P_0 < {_3P_0}$*

where $_3p_0$ is the equilibrium vapor pressure of the bulk crystal phase.

Again, similarly, for the transformation

$$\text{bulk vapor} \leftrightarrows \text{adsorbed gas}$$

$$\Delta G = (n_a{}^\theta \mu + n_a{}^\theta f/\Gamma) - (n_g \mu + n_a{}^0 f/\Gamma) = 0 \quad (5)$$

or:

$$_g\mu = {_a}{}^\theta\mu + \frac{1}{\Gamma}({_a}{}^\theta f - {_a}{}^0 f) = {_g}\mu_s + RT \ln p \quad (6)$$

This may readily be rearranged to give:

$$\Gamma = -\frac{({_a}{}^\theta f - {_a}{}^0 f)}{{_a}{}^\theta\mu - {_g}\mu} \quad (7)$$

which is a statement of the Gibbs adsorption theorem.

These first two transformations were fairly obvious examples; a slightly less obvious situation is that of forming a monolayer condensed phase on the adsorbent surface—a two-dimensional liquid or crystal if you will—from the bulk vapor phase. For this case:

$$\Delta G = [n({_{ac}}{}^1\mu) + n({_{ac}}{}^1 f/{_{ac}}{}^1\Gamma)] - [n({_g}\mu) + n({_a}{}^0 f/{_{ac}}{}^1\Gamma)] = 0 \quad (8)$$

$$_g\mu = {_{ac}}{}^1\mu + \frac{1}{{_{ac}}{}^1\Gamma}({_{ac}}{}^1 f - {_a}{}^0 f) = {_g}\mu_s + RT \ln ({_2}p_0) \quad (9)$$

where $_{ac}{}^1\Gamma$ is the molecular density on the surface at saturated monolayer concentration and $_2p_0$ is the pressure of the gas in equilibrium with condensed monolayer.

We now have equilibrium relations among four phases: bulk vapor, bulk crystal, adsorbed gas, and monolayer condensate. Similar relations involving bulk liquid phases and/or phase transitions from one monolayer condensed phase to another could likewise be formulated but need not be further elaborated.

These equilibrium relations can be graphically illus-

trated by a phase diagram generalized to take account of the presence of the surface and the phases that form upon it. The phase rule, generalized to account for interfacial phases, states that (2)

$$F = C - P + 2 + i$$

where $i$ is the number of interfaces of different $_a{}^0 f$ or $df/d\mu$. For the system we have been considering, in which $C = 1$, $i = 1$, making only the one further assumption that $_2p_0$ is always less than $_3p_0$, the resulting generalized phase diagram is shown in Figure 3.

In addition to the familiar stability curves for the bulk phases we have an additional line representing the equilibrium between monolayer gaseous and condensed phases. Furthermore, the areas in which the surface is exposed to the bulk vapor phase are now two-phase regions, a condition allowed by the extra degree of freedom introduced by the term $i = 1$ in the generalized phase rule.

This phase diagram can be used to trace the course of any $p$–$T$ process in this system. For example, an adsorption isotherm at $T_1$ is represented by the vertical line so labeled. In such a process at low pressures an adsorbed gas is present, increasing in density as the pressure is increased. When the pressure exceeds the equilibrium value for the two-dimensional condensed phase, $_2p_0$, this phase will nucleate and grow until a complete condensed monolayer is formed. As the pressure is increased still further, additional adsorption takes place on this monolayer condensate. When the pressure exceeds the equilibrium value for the bulk condensed phase, $_3p_0$, the appropriate phase (bulk solid or bulk liquid, depending on the temperature) will nucleate and grow. An experimental example of such an isotherm, taken from the published literature, (1) is given in Figure 4 for krypton at 77° K. on P-33 (2700°), a graphite of high surface homogeneity.

Again, an isotherm taken at $T_2$ would show the general rise in coverage with pressure observed at lower temperatures, but no discontinuity associated with the formation of a monolayer condensate would be observed, as $T_2 > {_2}T_{crit}$, the critical temperature for the two-dimensional phase transition. It has been shown (3) that $_2T_{crit}$ is approximately half of $_3T_{crit}$. Figure 5 is an experimental isotherm corresponding to this example taken from the published literature (7) and represents nitrogen on graphite at 77° K.

The condensation of a fatty-acid monolayer spread on water, as shown in Figure 1, is an additional example of the same adsorbed gas $\rightleftarrows$ monolayer condensate transition, occurring as the film pressure, in this case the pressure against the barrier confining the film, is increased beyond $_2p_0$.

We now consider a phase diagram for a second case: that in which $_2p_0$ is greater than $_3p_0$. The diagram is shown in Figure 6. Isotherms for this case, at $T_1$ for example, would show limited adsorption up to the equilibrium pressure of the bulk condensed phase, with much less than monolayer coverage even at that point. As the equilibrium pressure is exceeded, the appropriate three-dimensional phase will nucleate and grow. The illustrative experimental isotherm for this case is shown in Figure 7 for water on graphite (*11*), which is a third example taken from the published literature.

Thus it is seen that not only is the course of well-recognized phase transformations such as melting and boiling described by a path on the generalized phase diagram; but also transitions among surface phases, such as are encountered in adsorption from the vapor or the spreading of monolayers on liquid substrates, are equally well specified. By extending the above treatment to multicomponent systems one could also cover such processes as wetting, detergency, and the stabilization of emulsions.

### Kinetic Basis

The argument to this point has been purely thermodynamic; it has developed the relations between various adsorption and condensation processes occurring at surfaces. The argument is now extended to cover the added complication of the kinetic effects during monolayer and bulk-phase changes, and how they influence the behavior in a given real system.

The equations that were written earlier for phase equilibria between various bulk and surface phases in the system chosen all relate to phases that are infinite in extent; no account was taken of the presence of phase boundaries, e.g., between adsorbed gas and monolayer-condensate in the monolayer case. Nevertheless, any new condensed phase must form by the nucleation of a minute particle of that phase and by its subsequent growth to macroscopic size. When this is taken into account our picture of the system in the vicinity of monolayer-phase or of bulk-phase transformations is quite different.

Consider the free energy change involved in forming a small particle of the bulk-solid phase at a pressure a little greater than $_3p_0$ on the isotherm previously drawn ($T_1$ on Figure 3). For simplicity we will assume the particle to be a cylinder of height $h$, and radius $r$. For this case

$$\Delta G = \pi r^2(_{x/s}f + _xf - _sf) + 2\pi rh(_xf_e) + \pi r^2 h(_x\mu - _0\mu) \quad (10)$$

In this equation the second term is inherently positive (unfavorable), the third term is inherently negative, and in most cases, the first term is also inherently positive. Note that the surface energy terms, which are always unfavorable to growth of the particle are in the second power of particle size, while the volume free energy term, which is favorable to growth when $_x\mu < _0\mu$, is in the third power of particle size. Therefore at very small particle sizes the unfavorable surface terms will predominate and the particle will be unstable relative to the vapor phase and, on the average, will break up. As we consider larger and larger particles, the volume-free-energy term eventually predominates and the particle will become stable relative to the vapor and grow. In other words, a plot of $\Delta G$ *vs.* cylinder size would show an initial rise in $\Delta G$ up to a maximum $\Delta G^*$ at $r^*$, $h^*$, the dimensions of the so-called critical nucleus, followed by a decrease in $\Delta G$ with further increase in $r$ or $h$, $\Delta G$ becoming negative with continued particle growth.

We may obtain $r^*$ and $h^*$, the dimensions of the critical nucleus, by successive differentiation of Equation 10 by these quantities, yielding

$$\frac{h^*}{r^*} = \frac{(_{x/s}f + _{x/0}f - _sf)}{_xf_c} \quad (11)$$

and from this

$$\Delta G^* = \frac{4\pi(_xf_e)^2 (_{x/s}f + _{x/0}f - _sf)}{(_x\mu - _0\mu)} \quad (12)$$

We may further relate this $\Delta G^*$ to the nucleation rate in the system through the rate equation

$$j = K\Gamma e^{-\Delta G^*/RT} \quad (13)$$

which simply states that the nucleation rate, $j$, is the product of the concentration of clusters of size $r^*$, $h^*$, which is $\Gamma e^{-\Delta G^*/RT}$, and the collision frequency of single atoms with these clusters, which is contained in $K$.

The form of Equation 13 is such that as $\Delta G^*$ is slowly reduced by increasing $(_x\mu - _0\mu)$, that is, by increasing the supersaturation in the vapor phase, $_3P/_3p_0$ the nucleation rate rises abruptly from a negligibly small value to an easily observable value over a very narrow range of supersaturation. Experimentally this is observed as a "critical" supersaturation $_3p^*/_3p_0$ below which nothing nucleates and above which the transformation is rapid.

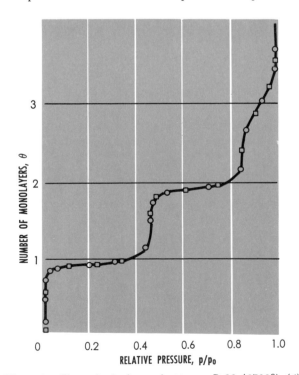

Figure 4. *Illustrative isotherm—krypton on P-33 (2700°) (1)*

**AUTHOR** *John B. Hudson is Research Associate, Department of Materials Science, Rensselaer Polytechnic Institute, Troy, N. Y. Sydney Ross is Professor of Colloid Science, Chemistry Department, Rensselaer Polytechnic Institute. Figure 1 is reproduced through the courtesy of H. E. Ries.*

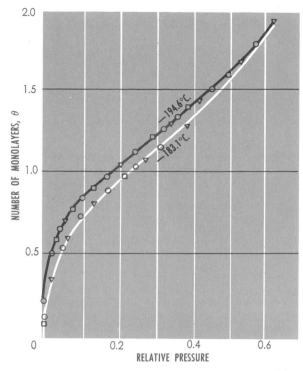

*Figure 5. Illustrative isotherm—nitrogen on graphite (7)*

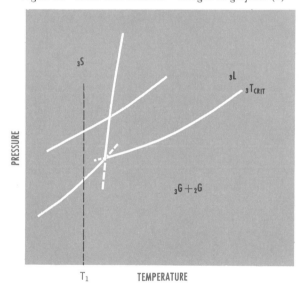

*Figure 6. Generalized phase diagram for the case $_2P_0 > _3P_0$*

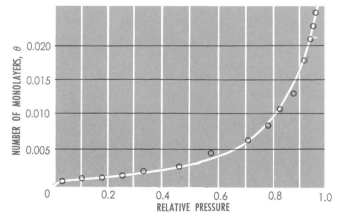

*Figure 7. Illustrative isotherm—water on graphite (11)*

These kinetic considerations introduce two complications into the isotherm picture derived from the previously calculated phase diagrams. First, in those cases where $(_{x/s}f + _{x/g}f - _sf)$ is negative, the solid phase would spontaneously spread as a monolayer on the surface. This behavior is actually observed, for example, with benzophenone crystals on a liquid-mercury surface. Second, because of the requirement of attaining a critical supersaturation $_3p^*/_3p_0$ prior to nucleation of the bulk phase, the isotherm would continue in a smooth curve beyond $_3p_0$ until $_3p^*$ was reached, then drop back discontinuously to $_3p_0$ and rise vertically from that point.

A similar argument holds for the formation of the monolayer-condensed phase in the vicinity of $_2p_0$. For this case, $h$ is constrained to be one molecular diameter, and the relation between $\Delta G$ and disk size is

$$\Delta G = N[(_{ac}{}^1\mu) - {}_g\mu] +$$
$$\frac{N}{(_{ac}{}^1\Gamma)} [(_{ac}{}^1f) - (_a{}^0f)] + 2(_{ac}f_e)\left[\pi \frac{N}{(_{ac}{}^1\Gamma)}\right]^{1/2} h \quad (14)$$

where the expression is now written in terms of the number of molecules in the disk, rather than of the radius. Once again, the first two terms are inherently negative in systems in which monolayer condensation is known to occur, and the third term is inherently positive, and again of lower order in $N$ than the first term. Thus the same sort of "critical" supersaturation behavior is to be expected in this situation, and the isotherm predicted can be further modified to indicate that the nucleation would be observed at a critical supersaturation $_2p^*$ which is greater than the equilibrium pressure $_2p_0$.

This effect is well known experimentally in the bulk case, and has been extensively studied (4). It is less common in the monolayer case but has been observed in a limited number of systems (5).

## Applications

We have developed the concept of applying the thermodynamics and, in terms of a theoretical model, the kinetics of first-order phase changes to processes occurring in systems where surface phases are involved, with a few illustrative examples from published experimental data. The results obtained are in effect predictions of the behavior of general types of systems, and they can be used to answer certain questions.

Consider first whether monolayer condensation will occur in a given system. No unequivocal criterion yet exists for this process. The scanty data that are available, notably that for chloroform vapor (8) on graphite and for water vapor on graphite (11), indicate that, should the heat of adsorption exceed the corresponding change of enthalpy for bulk condensation, monolayer condensation will occur at a pressure less than that at which bulk condensation occurs. Should the reverse relation for the heats pertain, no monolayer condensation is to be expected. That is, if the adsorbate-adsorbent interaction is *strong*, considerable adsorption and probably monolayer condensation are favored at pressures below $_3p_0$. If the interaction is *weak*, an adsorbate concentration sufficient for monolayer condensation is never reached below $_3p_0$. Considering further the question of the extent to which adsorption takes place as the pressure approaches the bulk-phase equilibrium value, $_3p_0$, here again a relation between the heats of adsorption and of bulk condensation appears to hold: a heat of adsorption greater than the heat of bulk condensation implies extensive adsorption ($\theta > 1$) at pressures below $_3p_0$. A second generalization is that if the surface energy of the bulk adsorbate phase be small compared to that of the adsorbent surface, high coverage at low pressures, and monolayer condensation at temperatures below $_2T_{\mathrm{crit}}$ are favored. The latter rule is rather more speculative than the former, as few pertinent experimental data are available at present.

Turning to predictions based on our kinetic treatment, we see that if the surface energy of the adsorbent be large compared to that of the bulk phase nucleating on it, then *rapid* nucleation at small supersaturations will be favored; and vice-versa. These two opposite situations can each be used to advantage: the first in cloud seeding, where the object is to maximize the nucleation probability; the second in the coating of windshield surfaces with a low energy film, where the object is to minimize or completely inhibit condensation, which is effected by the extremely slow rate of nucleation on the coated surface.

In addition to the general rules deduced so far, continued theoretical and experimental development of this subject will doubtless lead to other significant correlations: for example, the relation between monolayer condensation and spreading or wetting; the relative magnitudes of the supersaturation required for nucleation of bulk and of monolayers in a given system; and a theory of physical adsorption in terms of the more pertinent parameter $_2p_0$ rather than $_3p_0$, which has been used in many previous treatments. Furthermore, extension of what we have developed here to multi-component systems, such as those involving a surface-active agent at the interface between two bulk or mono-layer condensed phases, will serve to clarify the processes occurring in such phase changes as the monolayer condensed $\rightarrow$ bulk condensed phase change observed in detergency and the reverse bulk condensed phase $\rightarrow$ monolayer phase transformation involved in the spreading of a material by means of a wetting agent.

Thus it appears that results to date, while they do indicate that relations such as those we seek do indeed exist, are not adequate for complete specification of the systems involved. These results must be greatly amplified, both through additional experimental study of systems in which phase changes involving monolayer phases occur and through continued development of the theoretical treatment. Only then will more concrete generalizations regarding many systems be justified.

## NOMENCLATURE

$A$ = Area of surface in sq. cm.
$C$ = Number of components in a system
$E$ = Internal energy
$f$ = Surface free energy, ergs/sq. cm.
$_a^0f$ = Surface free energy of substrate entirely free of adsorbed phase (equivalent to $_sf$)
$_a^\theta f$ = Surface free energy of substrate covered with adsorbed monolayer at coverage $= \theta$
$_{ac}^1f$ = Surface free energy of adsorbed-condensed monolayer at coverage = unity
$_{ac}f_e$ = Surface free energy of the edge of the adsorbed-condensed monolayer
$_{x/s}f$ = Surface free energy of $x/s$ interface
$_{x/g}f$ = Surface free energy of $x/g$ interface
$_sf$ = Surface free energy of bare substrate
$_xf_e$ = Surface free energy of the edge of the $x$-phase
$F$ = Number of degrees of freedom in a system
$G$ = Gibbs free energy
$\Delta G^*$ = Free energy difference between vapor phase and nucleus of critical dimensions
$h$ = Height of nucleus of condensed phase
$h^*$ = Height of nucleus of critical dimensions
$i$ = Number of interfaces to be considered in applying phase-rule to a system
$J$ = Nucleation rate, Equation 13
$K$ = Arbitrary constant in Equation 13
$k$ = Boltzmann's constant ($= 1.38 \times 10^{-16}$ ergs/deg.)
$M$ = A generalized component: any molecular species that undergoes a phase change
$n$ = Number of moles of material transferred from one phase to another
$N$ = Number of molecules transferred from one phase to another
$P$ = Number of phases, both bulk and interfacial, in a system
$p$ = Pressure of gas
$_2p_0$ = Pressure of gas in equilibrium with two-dimensional phase
$_3p_0$ = Pressure of gas in equilibrium with three-dimensional phase
$_2p^*$ = Pressure of gas at critical supersaturation of two-dimensional condensed phase
$_3p^*$ = Pressure of gas at critical supersaturation of three-dimensional condensed phase (nucleus)
$r$ = Radius of nucleus of a condensed phase
$S$ = Entropy
$T$ = Temperature in degrees Kelvin
$_2T_{crit}$ = Critical temperature of a phase change between two-dimensional states
$_3T_{crit}$ = Critical temperature of a phase change between three-dimensional states
$x$ = Three-dimensional phase, in process of nucleating
$x/s$ = Interface between $x$ and substrate
$x/g$ = Interface between $x$ and its own vapor
$\Gamma$ = Molecular density in two-dimensional phase (moles/sq. cm.)
$_{ac}^1\Gamma$ = Molecular density in adsorbed-condensed monolayer at coverage − unity
$\theta$ = Fractional coverage in adsorbed-monolayer phase
$\mu$ = Chemical potential
$_a^0\mu$ = Chemical potential of substrate entirely free of adsorbed phase (equivalent to $_s\mu$)
$_a^\theta\mu$ = Chemical potential of substrate covered with adsorbed monolayer at coverage $= \theta$
$_s\mu$ = Chemical potential of bare solid substrate
$_{ac}^1\mu$ = Chemical potential of adsorbed-condensed monolayer at coverage = unity
$_g\mu$ = Chemical potential of gas phase
$_g\mu_s$ = Chemical potential of gas phase at standard state
$_x\mu$ = Chemical potential of $x$-phase

## LITERATURE CITED

(1) Amberg, C. H., Spencer, W. B., Beebe, R. A., *Can. J. Chem.* **33**, 305 (1955).
(2) Crisp, D. J., pp. 17–35, "Surface Chemistry," Butterworth's Scientific Publn., London, 1949.
(3) DeBoer, J. H., p. 147, "The Dynamical Character of Adsorption," Clarendon Press, Oxford, 1953.
(4) Hirth, J. P., Pound, G. M., *Progress in Materials Science* **11**, Macmillan, New York (1963).
(5) Hudson, J. B., *J. Phys. Chem.* **67**, 1884 (1963).
(6) "International Critical Tables," McGraw-Hill, New York, 1928.
(7) Joyner, L. G., Emmett, P. H., *J. Am. Chem. Soc.* **70**, 2353 (1948).
(8) Machin, W. D., Ross, S., *Proc. Roy. Soc. (London)* **265A**, 455 (1962).
(9) Ries, H. E., Jr., Kimball, W. A., *Nature* **181**, 901 (1958).
(10) Ross, S., Winkler, W., *J. Am. Chem. Soc.* **76**, 2837 (1954).
(11) Young, G. J., Chessick, J. J., Healy, F. H., Zettlemoyer, A. C., *J. Phys. Chem.* **58**, 313 (1954).

# 10

# Structure of Macromolecules at Liquid-Solid Interfaces

F. ROWLAND
R. BULAŠ
E. ROTHSTEIN
F. R. EIRICH

# Structure of Macromolecules at Liquid–Solid Interfaces

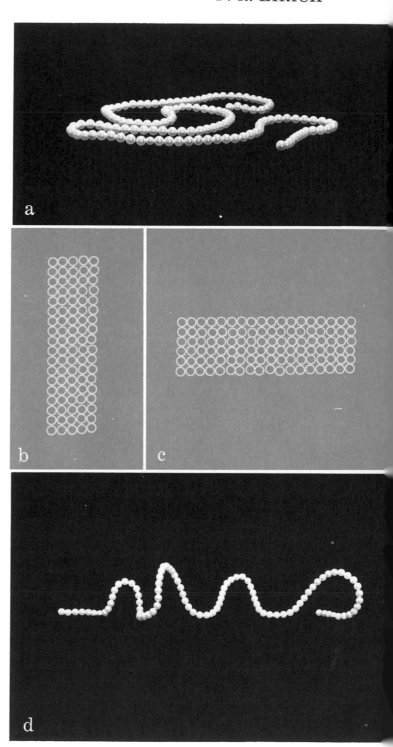

The hypothesis underlying much of the work reported below is that the adsorption of polymers is the primary step of contact-making in the formation of all polymeric interfacial bonds, such as occur in organic adhesion, in coatings, in dispersion-stabilization (affecting viscosity), and in biological membranes. It is further assumed that there is good reason for the observation that all adhesives are macromolecular in character—macromolecules can adhere to the interfaces by multiple points of physical adsorption as well as by extending into the adjacent phase. They thereby form a bridge of multiple van der Waals strength, as if they had diffused into the adjacent phases (which may or may not actually be true), and thus can accomplish a stitching action. The function of primers or the adherence of various paints or coatings can be understood on the same basis, as can the action of fillers. Stabilization of a dispersion is assumed to function via solvated protective jackets formed by adsorbed macromolecules. Finally, many biological structures are of composite nature and contain folded or helical macromolecules in contact with solid materials—e.g., inorganic constituents of bone and teeth. Thus, the study of adsorption of polymers from solution is of both academic and practical value.

In such a study, the experimental techniques should measure the amount of solute removed by the solid, and should recognize whether the adsorbate is present directly in the interface. Apart from the problem of how much is adsorbed, there is also the problem of finding out how the material is adsorbed. On an idealized plane surface with idealized spherical hard molecules as adsorbate, one can assume at first a monolayer, as described by Langmuir's theory, which can be a densely or loosely packed condensed solid or liquid layer, or a gaseous one, with changes between the types either continuous or marked by sharp phase transitions. If more material is to be adsorbed it has to be accommodated in multilayers. When the molecules have a complicated shape, are triaxial, for instance, they can be packed on the surfaces with respect to any of their three axes and thus exhibit a

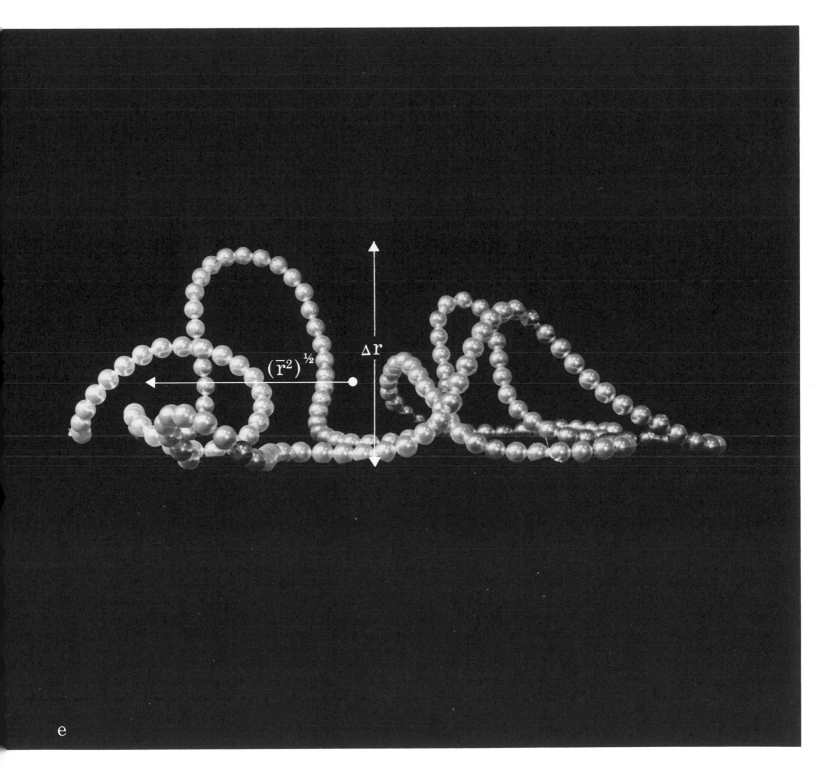

e

Figure 1. *Hypothetical conformations of adsorbed chain molecules:*
*a, lying on surface; b, condensed standing chains; c, flat multilayer;*
*d, looped chain; e, random coil, where* $[(\bar{r}^2)/6]\pi = (2nl^2/6)\pi \cong$
$nl^2$, *l = length of bead in the chain, n = number of beads*

variety of amounts adsorbed as well as a variety of structures of the monolayers.

Inasmuch as in adsorption from solution the solvent also plays an important part, the solvent will also influence the structure of the adsorbed layer. Solvent has to be desorbed from the solid surface before any solute adsorption can take place and keeps on interacting with the adsorbate. For a full understanding of the total system, therefore, it would be necessary to know either the complete thermodynamic functions of all components before and after adsorption, as well as the relations of these functions to the molecular states encountered; or it would be necessary, in addition to a measure of the polymer removed from the supernatant, to know also the fraction lying directly in the interface and, if the fraction is much less than 1, either the density or the thickness of the interfacial boundary zone. This situation will be greatly accentuated in the case of linear macromolecules which may be assumed to pack poorly under many adsorptive conditions and to lie rather incompletely on an interface (Figure 1).

We have conducted studies to develop information of this kind. Our main concern was to determine the thicknesses of adsorbed layers, in addition to measuring amounts of polymer removed from the supernatant liquid. Because we were interested in the consequences of adsorption for transport processes, for the packing of particles, and in interactions between adsorption-coated solid surfaces, it was natural to look for methods which would measure adsorbed thicknesses by mechanical means. In particular, we were applying methods which measure the so-called hydrodynamically effective thicknesses or dimensions of dispersed particles or of capillaries as such and in solid filter beds (Figure 2).

Our results leave, in our opinion, no doubt that under many conditions polymers adsorb from dilute solution on solid-liquid interfaces in the form of monolayers of molecular coils whose dimensions are proportional to those of the free coils in that particular solution. Thus, the thickness of the adsorbed layer, its density, and the nature of the macromolecular conformations can be derived from intrinsic viscosity measurements. The adsorbed molecular coils seem to retain also the tendency of the free coils to be mutually repelling within the monolayer, as well as between monolayers on different particles. This repulsion leads, among other things, to an increased stability of dispersed particles thus coated; the more complete the monolayer is, the better the stability. Given a certain degree of coating, the dispersive power then depends further on the degree of wetting of the uncoated particles by the solvent; on the state of solution of the macromolecules; and on the molecular weight, which must not be too low. If the polymer coils are well extended in a good solvent, the adsorbed layer is of low density and yet protects well against inelastic collisions. Conversely, dense adsorbed layers in nearly precipitating solvents are poorly protective. However, a polymer may extend far into the solvent because it has a low affinity for (few segments in) the surface. In that case, because it is more readily

desorbed, it will not stabilize dispersions well. Consequently, an adsorption isotherm on the particles to be dispersed and in the solvent to be used, which exhibits a high affinity but only moderate capacity, combined with an intrinsic viscosity of the polymer in the same solvent about twice that in a theta solvent, should provide the best conditions for a stable nonionic dispersion.

**Experimental Methods**

Adsorption from solution of low and high molecular weight materials alike is, as a rule, measured by difference. The adsorbent is finely divided and shaken with a solution of the adsorbate. The system is centrifuged and it is assumed that the state of adsorption is not altered thereby. The amount taken down with the adsorbent is calculated from the change of concentration in the

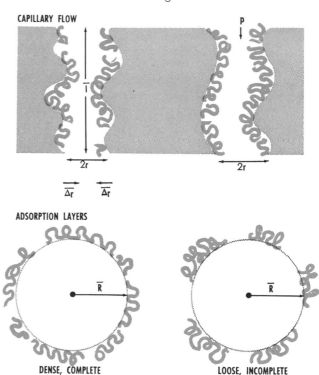

*Figure 2. Changes in hydrodynamic dimensions due to adsorption. For capillary flow, Poiseuille's law applies—i.e., $Q = \pi p (r - \Delta r)^4 / 8\eta \bar{l}$. For the coated particles, Einstein's law holds—i.e., $\eta = \eta_0 (1 + 2.5\phi + 14\phi^2 + \ldots)$ and $\phi = n/V \times 4\pi/3 \, (d/2 + \overline{\Delta r})^3$. $Q = $ flow rate; $p = $ pressure; $\eta = $ coefficient of viscosity; $\phi = $ dispersed volume; $n = $ number of particles per unit volume of dispersion; $d = $ particle diameter*

supernatant liquid, and the further assumption is made that the adsorbent is not bridged by the adsorbate.

The amount of solute removed, when calculated on the basis of the two above assumptions, is not tantamount to adsorption, except in the specific case in which all removed material lies in the interface. However, to elucidate the state of dispersion created by a protective colloid, this method does show how much of the latter moves with the dispersed particles and how much is independently contained in the intermicellar serum.

Data are usually presented in the form of adsorption isotherms (Figure 3) and may have to be qualified with respect to the quantity removed from the supernatant but held by bridging or entanglement.

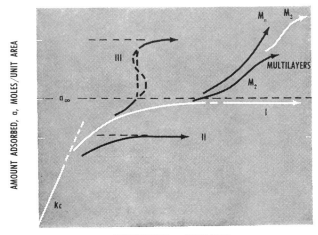

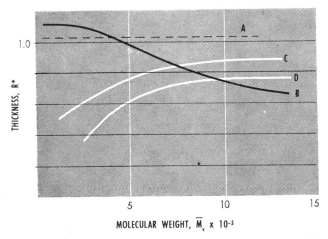

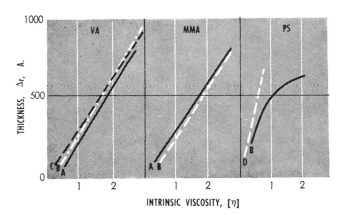

*Figure 3. Various kinds of adsorption isotherms. Monolayers exhibit an initial straight line with slope equal to the affinity constant, k, and a saturation capacity (complete monolayer) of $a_\infty$. Multilayers are indicated by a subscript; concentration, c, represents equilibrium concentration of supernatant*

I—Langmuir type, where $a = (a_\infty kc)/(1 + kc)$
II—Intralayer repulsion
III—Intralayer condensation
*Polymers follow a Type II isotherm*

*Figure 4. Relative adsorbed film thickness vs. molecular weight. Curve A, PS in cyclohexane; curve B, PS in benzene; curve C, VA in benzene; curve D, MMA in benzene*

*Figure 5. Change in adsorbed film thickness with intrinsic viscosity. A, benzene at 50° C.; B, benzene at 30° C.; C, methylethyl ketone at 30° C.; D, cyclohexane at 34.2° C.*

In principle, one could think of methods which recognize whether the adsorbate is present directly in the interface, provided the latter can be molecularly defined, as is usually true for the interfaces between liquids, when surface tension and optical reflection methods have been applied. If the adsorbent is particulate, the latter methods cannot be used. In the case of smooth metallic plates, ellipsometry has given good results (25, 26), as has infrared spectroscopy (9, 27); the latter also can be applied to dispersions. However, as can be readily understood, these methods count the material within 3 to 30 A. from the surface, in addition to that within the van der Waals bonding distances.

### TABLE I. METHODS OF AVERAGING

*Particle Mean Diameters*

| | | |
|---|---|---|
| $d_1$ | Arithmetic mean | $\dfrac{\Sigma n_i d_i}{\Sigma n_i}$ |
| $d_2$ | Surface mean | $\dfrac{\Sigma n_i d_i^2}{\Sigma n_i d_i}$ |
| $d_3$ | Volume-surface mean | $\dfrac{\Sigma n_i d_i^3}{\Sigma n_i d_i^2}$ or $\dfrac{6}{\rho A_{sp}}$ |

*Pore Size Averages*

| | | |
|---|---|---|
| $d_v$ | Volume mean | $\left(\dfrac{\Sigma n_i d_i^3}{\Sigma n_i}\right)^{1/3}$ or $(d_1 \cdot d_2 \cdot d_3)^{1/3}$ |
| $\lvert r \rvert$ | $\dfrac{2V_{pore}}{S}$ | $\dfrac{\Sigma n_i r_i^2}{\Sigma n_i r_i}$ |
| $\lvert r^2 \rvert$ | $\dfrac{\vartheta C}{\pi N}$ | $\dfrac{\Sigma n_i r_i^2}{\Sigma n_i}$ |
| $\lvert r^4 \rvert \equiv \lvert\lvert r \rvert\rvert$ | $\left(\dfrac{1}{N}\Sigma r_i^4\right)^{1/4}$ | $\dfrac{\Sigma n_i r_i^4}{\Sigma n_i}$ |

$V_{pore}$ = pore volume; $S$ = pore surface; $\Sigma n_i = N$; $\vartheta = V_{pore}/V_{total}$; $C = R^2\pi$; $R$ = disk radius; $A_{sp}$ = specific surface area.

To provide the more specific information needed in this study, the experimental methods consisted of two kinds of measurements. In the first series, the flow rate of polymer solutions and of the corresponding pure solvents through capillaries (17) or sintered glass disks (21) was measured. In the second series, Bulas and Rothstein measured viscosities of coated and uncoated dispersions (3, 20). The average pore size of the Corning disks was obtained by a gas flow technique (22), and the pore size distribution by the mercury intrusion method (28). The amounts adsorbed per unit area were determined by independent adsorption studies on the same glass powder that was sintered into the disks. The isotherms were determined by the methods of Koral et al. (7, 14, 16) and of Ellerstein and Ullman (8, 18) and were in good agreement with those reported. The isotherms of polystyrene showed a markedly lower affinity and rapid partial reversibility. The amounts adsorbed at the surface at saturation were equivalent to approxi-

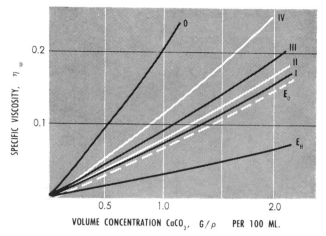

Figure 6. Variation in specific viscosity with concentration of calcium carbonate dispersions in tetrachloroethylene. $E_H$, Einstein curve for hard spheres; $E_O$, "Einstein" curve for fully dispersed $CaCO_3$ (irregular particles plus surfactant); O, curve for unstabilized $CaCO_3$ dispersion; I, II, III, IV, curves of $CaCO_3$ dispersion with 0.2% MMA of increasing molecular weight added

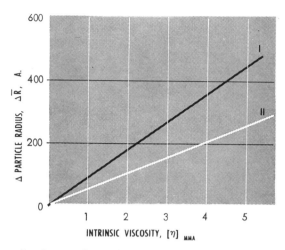

Figure 7. Increase in particle radius by adsorption of MMA of increasing intrinsic viscosity. I, calculated as $\Delta\phi/A$; II, calculated as $\Delta d_r/2$

mately 2 to 8 dense segmental (monomeric) monolayers for all polymers.

Great care was taken to ensure reproducibility and internal consistency of the porous disk method. A fourth power averaging calculation (Table I) was worked out (21), blanks and standards were run concurrently, the applicability of Poiseuille's law was verified, and additional adsorption isotherms were run with stearic acid to determine the effective surface area for nonpolymeric solutes. As a final check, the adsorption of stearic acid in the filter disk showed, in fact, an average narrowing of the capillary radius by approximately 30 A.

For an independent method, study of changes of hydrodynamic particle radii in dispersion, based on Einstein's equation, was designed along the lines described by Amborski and Goldfinger (2), in collaboration with Bulas (3). Calcium carbonate was suspended in organic solvents, and the average particle size and surface area were determined by adsorption of stearic acid tagged with carbon-14, by sedimentation analysis, and by microscopic particle counting. An average cube root diameter (Table I) was determined and the hydrodynamically effective volume measured from a viscosity-concentration series of suspensions which were made to be fully dispersed (no particle aggregation) by surface active agents. These agents could be replaced by polymers, in this case by fractions of polymethylmethacrylate, of which the lowest fraction (mol. wt. ≈ 75,000) produced a dispersion of a viscosity almost identical with that obtained using the surface active agents; the higher fractions exhibited increasingly larger suspensoid viscosities. From these data the increase of the dispersed volume due to adsorption could be calculated according to Einstein's equation and, by dividing it through the surface area, an effective thickness of the adsorbed layer could be calculated (Figure 2).

Whereas the efficiency of the adsorbed MMA layer at full coverage as a dispersant for calcium carbonate in organic solvents under conditions of equilibrium adsorp-

tion was thus demonstrated as an incidental but important result, it became also of interest to find at which density of surface coverage—i.e., at which fraction of the surface coated, or at which coating thickness—full particle dispersion could be achieved. This study was undertaken by Rothstein (20). With the investigation slanted toward the problem of pigment dispersion in alkyd paints, a silica, an anatase, and a phthalocyanine powder were chosen as adsorbents; three molecular weights of three fatty acid–extended glycerophthalic polyesters were chosen as polymers; and xylol, n-butyl acetate, and methylethylketone were chosen as solvents. All adsorption isotherms were determined and the viscosities of a given concentration of the dispersions measured as a function of relative surface coverage as derived from the adsorption isotherm in a given system of pigment, polymer, and solvent. The details of the results have been discussed and published (19). Some facts particularly relevant to our present discussion shall be discussed later in conjunction with the other results.

The materials used, apart from the already mentioned Corning glass, were six fractions of bulk polymerized polyvinyl acetate, $M_W$ 75,000 to 1,200,000; six fractions of a commercial polystyrene, $M_W$ 60,000 to 1,400,-000; and a Sartomer polymethylmethacrylate freed from gel and fractionated into five fractions from $M_W$ 75,000 to 1,400,000. The latter material and some

**AUTHORS** *F. R. Eirich is Professor of Chemistry at Polytechnic Institute of Brooklyn. Material in this article is taken from dissertations submitted by the other authors in partial fulfillment of requirements for the degrees of M.Sc. and Ph.D. at that college. R. Bulas is now Senior Chemist, International Corp., Clifton, N. J.; E. Rothstein is Research Engineer, Keuffel and Esser Co., Hoboken, N. J.; and F. Rowland is Research Chemist, Carothers Research Laboratory, E. I. Du Pont de Nemours and Co. F. Rowland wishes to acknowledge financial support from the AFOSR.*

slightly different fractions of it were also used by Bulas, who employed a suspension in benzene or tetrachloroethane of a calcium carbonate No. 2924 supplied by Whittaker, Clark, & Daniels of a volume average particle diameter $d_v = 4.4 \times 10^{-5}$ cm. The alkyds and pigments used by Rothstein are described in detail (*19, 20*). The $M_W$ varied from 4 to 12,000, the oil length from 30 to 60%. Well defined fractions were used. The silica was Berkshire ground quartz, the anatase was Titanox ANO, and the phthalocyanine was GAF heliogen. All polymers were characterized by their intrinsic viscosity and all pigments by particle size.

**Results and Discussion**

The adsorption of polymers from solution on liquid-solid interfaces exhibits isotherms which closely resemble Langmuir's. The explanation for this curious finding is probably that if adsorbed particles have a tendency to repel one another within the surface layer, this produces an isotherm similar to Langmuir's but with lower capacity. Adamson (*1*) and De Boer (*5*) have shown that this can be quantitatively explained by a repulsion term in the equation of state for the surface layer. This is briefly explained by Figure 3.

Generally, any adsorption process which yields a monolayer will have an initial linear slope proportional to affinity times concentration and show saturation or a plateau, so that at least the low and high concentration sectors of any isotherm can be characterized by two constants as if it were a Langmuir isotherm. In addition, one is interested in the fraction of the adsorbing surface which is covered in a particular case, and in the thickness and structure of the adsorbed layer.

Previous work elsewhere (*4, 11–13*) and at the Polytechnic Institute of Brooklyn (*7, 14, 16*) has established a number of important basic facts. First, there is the preponderance of isotherms whose shapes indicate the presence of monolayers of some kind. Second, the amounts held at the interface at or near equilibrium saturation are, in most cases, appreciably larger than can be accounted for by a monolayer of monomer units, with the exception of the adsorption of polyelectrolytes on surfaces of opposite charge when capacities of mono-

mer monolayers are often approached. Third, the saturation values depend weakly on molecular weight. Fourth, there is a weak dependence on temperature which can be positive or negative. Compensations of the accompanying enthalpy and entropy changes probably account for this small temperature dependence. Finally, there is a strong dependence on the solvent.

A number of theories have been developed to explain these observations—notably those by Frisch, Simha, and Eirich (*10, 24*), by Silberberg (*23*), and, more recently, by DiMarzio and coworkers (*6*). These theories differ primarily in the way the polymer is pictured at the interface. The first theory considers that the polymer will, in most cases, be only partially adsorbed, with short sequences of segments held on the surface and random loops extending into the solvent. Should the forces of surface-polymer attraction become strong, or the solvent be poor, then the polymer will lie more and more in the interface. Silberberg's theory assumes, on the contrary, a preponderance of positions in or near the surface with looping into the solvent only in the case of weak interactions. There are other physical and mathematical differences which, however, need not be considered here. More recent theories concern themselves largely with the choice of the right statistics of conformation counting.

All findings to date say little with respect to the structure of the polymeric layer. Certain of the possible structures can be excluded—for instance, a dense packing of the polymer molecules, standing on end like soap molecules in a condensed water-air interface, would lead to a capacity dependence on molecular weight much higher than is observed. On the other hand, the low molecular weight dependence of the capacity found is ambiguous because the flat model as well as the random coil or looped model give a dependence of $M^0$. The thickness of adsorbed polymer layers would be independent of molecular weight in the case of Silberberg's model; nearly proportional to it for stiff, end-on packed rods; and to $M^{1/2}$ for random coils. The models are therefore better distinguished by thickness than by capacity or affinity measurements (Figure 1).

Our results show now that the thicknesses in a wide variety of physical adsorptions are generally of the order

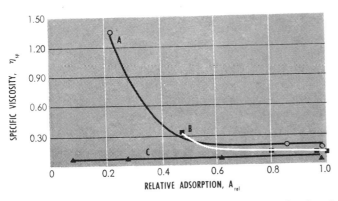

*Figure 8. Specific viscosity of silica-alkyd suspensions as a function of solvent and surface coverage. A, from xylol; B, from n-butyl acetate; C, from methylethyl ketone*

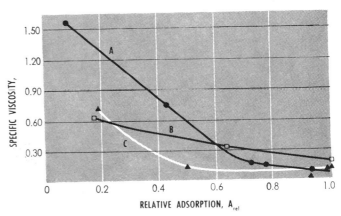

*Figure 9. Specific viscosity of alkyd-anatase suspensions as a function of solvent and surface coverage. A, from xylol; B, from n-butyl acetate; C, from methylethyl ketone*

of the diameter of the free coils in solution—that is, approximately proportional to $M^{1/2}$. A convincing way to express this is to plot a relative thickness, such as the ratio $R^*$ of the thickness adsorbed, $\Delta r$, to the mean square diameter of the free molecule in solution $2\overline{r^2}$—i.e., $R^* = \Delta r/2\overline{r^2}$. If this is done, an interesting difference can be observed between polystyrene (PS) on the one hand, and methylmethacrylate (MMA) and vinyl acetate (VA) on the other. As shown in Figure 4, the ratio falls off with molecular weight for PS, but rises for MMA and VA. Another interesting fact is that the values of $\Delta r$ always rise faster than the adsorption isotherms, so that the final thicknesses reach their limiting value prior to the saturation of the surface. When the solvent power changes, the thicknesses reflect this in a sensitive manner—that is, the coils reach further into the solvent the better it is, and contract toward the surface with a poorer solvent. Interestingly enough, in theta solvents the relative thickness $R^*$ no longer varies with molecular weight. Changes of the temperature change $R^*$ relatively little. Altogether, the changes for $\Delta r$ and $R^*$ closely follow those which the free molecules would undergo in solution (as measured by intrinsic viscosity)—so much so, in fact, that a plot of $\Delta r$ vs. intrinsic viscosity, whether affected by solvent, temperature, or molecular weight, is linear over a wide range for the ester polymers and for polystyrene in the theta solvent (Figure 5).

When adsorbed thicknesses at constant molecular weight are plotted against amounts adsorbed, an almost constant value of $\Delta r$ was found even though the amounts adsorbed almost triple from the best to the poorest solvent. This means that adsorbed layers become much more compact as the solvent power decreases. Because this is about the same factor of densification which the free polymer coil experiences when the solvent changes in the above manner, the increase of compactness found on the surface does not necessarily indicate coil interpenetration. On the other hand, depending on the validity of the surface area determinations, the coils are about two to six times denser at the surface than in free solution, a state which is compatible with the view of coils adsorbed on multiple sites, but still reaching extensively into the solution.

If thicknesses and amounts adsorbed are compared in the same solvent at rising molecular weight, fairly straight lines are obtained which do not point to the origin of the diagram. Because adsorption measurements at low molecular weight are difficult, an extrapolation may be permissible, the interpretation of which indicates that low molecular weights of all polymers form relatively short loops and lie more directly on the surface, but that longer loops occur above a critical molecular weight. In the case of PS on a polar surface, $\Delta r$ rises rapidly at first to almost the free coil value at a molecular weight of 50,000–100,000 and then it declines; in the case of the ester polymers, $\Delta r$ rises eventually to approximately one half of the free coil diameter. All of these data are compatible with the view that these polymers are adsorbed in the form of monolayers of coils which are somewhat, but not much, denser than in solution and which

have dimensions perpendicular to the surface which are substantial fractions of the free coil diameters.

In view of the many assumptions on which these conclusions had to be based, the results obtained by Bulas (3) may be considered as independent confirmation. He found that the increase in radius of dispersed particles caused by adsorption, calculated according to Einstein's equation, agreed extremely well with the $\Delta r$ values established by Rowland, and, moreover, the same linear dependence was found between adsorbed thicknesses and intrinsic viscosities (Figures 6 and 7).

Rothstein (19, 20) slanted his investigation toward the problem of pigment dispersion in alkyd paints and compared states of dispersion, as disclosed by reduced viscosities, with degree of surface coverage by adsorbed alkyd molecules, as established by adsorption isotherms. The adsorbed thicknesses were again a linear function of intrinsic viscosity, even though in this case the molecular weights were low. The adsorption could be shown to be a sensitive function of details of polymer structure and of solvent—again, the amounts adsorbed decreased with solubility. The thicknesses increased with the fatty acid content (oil length) of the esters, which may be explained by decreasing affinity toward polar surfaces of increasingly hydrocarbon-rich polyesters. There is, again, a uniform and rapid increase in the density of the adsorbed layer as the film thickness drops with decreasing solvent power. Most interestingly, there is a striking decrease in viscosity—that is, increase in dispersing power—with relative surface coverage. The critical percentage of coverage which is required to produce complete dispersion (minimum viscosity of the dispersed system) varies greatly, as shown in Figures 8 and 9. When the wetting power of the solvent for the pigment is smaller, or when the alkyd solubility in a given solvent is poorer, the surface coverage must be more complete if good dispersion is to be achieved. Similar findings have been discussed recently by LaMer and Healy (15).

## LITERATURE CITED

(1) Adamson, A., "Physical Chemistry of Surfaces," Interscience, New York, 1960.
(2) Amborski, L. E., Goldfinger, G., *Proc. Int. Coll. Macromolecules*, Amsterdam, 1949.
(3) Bulas, R., thesis, Polytechnic Institute, Brooklyn, N. Y., 1963.
(4) Claesson, I., Claesson, S., *Phys. Review* **73**, 1221 (1948).
(5) De Boer H., "Dynamic Character of Adsorption," Clarendon Press, Oxford, 1953.
(6) DiMarzio, E. A., Peyser, P., Hoeve, C. A. J., *J. Chem. Phys.* **42**, 2558 (1965).
(7) Eirich, F. R., Consiglio Naz. Ricerce, Roma (1963).
(8) Ellerstein, S., Ullman, R., *J. Polymer Sci.* **55**, 123 (1961).
(9) Fontana, B. J., Thomas, J. R., *J. Phys. Chem.* **65**, 480 (1961).
(10) Frisch, H., Simha, R., *J. Chem. Phys.* **27**, 702 (1957).
(11) Gottlieb, M., *J. Phys. Chem.* **64**, 427 (1960).
(12) Hobden, J., Jellinek, H., *J. Polymer Sci.* **11**, 365 (1953).
(13) Jenkel, E., Rumbach, B., *Z. Elektrochemie* **55**, 612 (1951).
(14) Koral, J., Ullman, R., Eirich, F. R., *J. Phys. Chem.* **62**, 541 (1958).
(15) LaMer, V. K., Healy, T. W., *Rev. Pure Appl. Chem. (Australia)* **13**, 112 (1963).
(16) Lauria, R., thesis, Polytechnic Institute, Brooklyn, N. Y., 1962.
(17) Ohrn, O., *Arkiv Kemi* **12**, 397 (1958).
(18) Perkel, R., Ullman, R., *J. Polymer Sci.* **54**, 127 (1961).
(19) Rothstein, E., *Off. Digest Paint Manuf.* **36**, 479 (1964).
(20) Rothstein, E., thesis, Polytechnic Institute, Brooklyn, N. Y., 1964.
(21) Rowland, F., *Ibid.*, 1963.
(22) Schwartz, F. A., *J. Appl. Phys.* **20**, 1070 (1949).
(23) Silberberg, A., *J. Phys. Chem.* **66**, 1872, 1884 (1962).
(24) Simha, R., Frisch, H., Eirich, F. R., *Ibid.*, **57**, 584 (1953).
(25) Stromberg, R. R., Passaglia, E., *J. Res. Natl. Bur. Stand.* (1964).
(26) Stromberg, R. R., Passaglia, E., Tutes, D. J., *Ibid.*, **67A**, 431 (1963).
(27) Thies, C., Peyser, P., Ullman, R., Proceedings, 4th International Congress on Surface Activity, 1964.
(28) Winslow, N., Shapiro, J., *ASTM Bull.* **236**, Philadelphia, Pa., 1959.

# 11

# Gas Adsorption

# Extreme Limits of Surface Coverage

# GAS ADSORPTION

## The Extreme Limits of Surface Coverage

VICTOR R. DEITZ

*Adsorption is divided into fairly distinct categories by the use of surface coverage*

The experimental effort in adsorption at the gas/solid interface is very extensive. In this review it is proposed only to survey some recent researches of interest to surface chemistry, to mention some of the important current trends in their broader aspects, and to present the material from the point of view of surface coverage.

Grouping of adsorption phenomena by coverage (denoted by $\theta$) has practical value. A realistic view of the boundary of a solid is never the mathematical plane that must be assumed in theoretical models. On an atomic scale the boundary includes crystal faces having composition, extent, and orientation that are fixed during the formation and pretreatment of the solid. The residual reactants and products of side reactions may accumulate in the boundary in trace and larger quantities. These and other imperfections of the boundary become more significant with decreasing coverage at the gas/solid interface and as experimental techniques attain greater sensitivity to cope with properties of low coverage. Four classifications of coverage are:

—multilayer formation
—completion of the monolayer
—fractional monolayer
—sparsely covered surfaces

The BET model (*19*) has furnished the required estimate of monolayer coverage (usually designated by $V_m$, the volume adsorbed at STP) and the coverage is then given by $\theta = V/V_m$. Fractional coverage is, of course, a calculated quantity since molecular clusters having possibly both variable width and depth may exist at isolated sites. The sparsely covered surface has attained considerable importance as a result of its accessibility via the new ultrahigh vacuum techniques.

The many applications of adsorption in research and technology involve approximately a range of $10^6$ in surface coverage corresponding to a range of $10^{12}$ in pressure, although this may not have been observed for any one gas/solid system. Some examples are given in Table I for a number of physical adsorption and chemisorption operations. It is quite an accomplishment to reach a level where the absolute total surface coverage is about $10^{-5}$. In order to gain a feeling for this magnitude, consider the area of clean surface ascribed to the tungsten tip of the field emission microscope; this has been given as approximately $10^{-10}$ cm.$^2$ or $10^6$ A.$^2$ When only three molecules, each about 10 A.$^2$ in cross section, are on this surface, $\theta$ is about $10^{-5}$. A surface of 100 A. $\times$ 100 A. having one percent of a monolayer (either adsorbed or as replaced surface atoms) would contain 10 such molecules. Solid state investigators have used this practical level as a definition of "an atomically clean surface" (*1*). It is readily attained in ultrahigh vacuum systems.

The over-all reaction at a gas/solid interface is:

$$X_{\text{solid}} + A_{\text{gas}} \rightleftharpoons X \ldots A_{\text{complex}} \qquad (1)$$

This formulation emphasizes the need to characterize both the starting material and the adsorption complex.

## TABLE I. ADSORPTION PHENOMENA

| Coverage | Application |
|---|---|
| **PHYSICAL ADSORPTION** | |
| 0.9 to 1.1 | Surface area estimates |
| 0.1 to condensation | Industrial separations |
| | Solvent recovery |
| | Water vapor removal |
| 0.001 to 0.1 | Gas phase chromatography |
| 0.0001 to 0.01 | Retention of toxic gases |
| 0.0001 | Inert gas adsorbed at $10^{-10}$ torr |
| 0.01 to 0.00001 | After outgassing to $10^{-6}$ torr |
| **CHEMISORPTION (BEHAVIOR VERY SPECIFIC)** | |
| 1.0 | Completion of monolayer |
| 0.01 to 0.10 | Commercial catalytic processes |
| 0.001 to 0.0001 | Coverage with oxidation gases on hot carbon |
| <0.00001 | After gettering action and high temperature treatment in ultrahigh vacuum (<$10^{-7}$) torr |

It also provides a division of researches into those concerned with the adsorption complex and those attempting to give to a large degree, the properties of the initial adsorbing surface. The thermodynamic activity of both complex and solid in Equation 1 cannot be taken as unity and it is usually the solid in its standard state that is considered as having unit activity. The experimenter must, of course, be alert to the possibility that the formation of the adsorption complex may modify or deform on an atomic scale the original surface of the solid. Hence, the experimentalist must characterize the initial and the final states of a gas/solid interaction to a degree that is consistent with his objective.

Information concerning the adsorbent itself has been obtained by a variety of techniques. The boundary surface can be modified by a variety of pretreatments, intentional or otherwise. Knowing how sharply intermolecular forces decrease with increase in separation, it is not surprising that a knowledge of the chemical composition in the gas/solid interface—i.e., the impurity defects—is of prime importance. Many researches have sought to define the surface in terms of the known underlying crystal structure. Geometric or steric factors are then evoked to bring out the close fit or misfit between atomic separations of the adsorbate and surface.

Finally, the chemical reactivity of groups in the gas/solid interface has for a long time occupied the attention of scientists and technologists, encompassing as it does the field of heterogeneous catalysis. The complexity of surface structure of a catalyst and the amazing range of properties will require decades of research to unravel. Studies in the semiconductor field have introduced new experimental techniques, but these have added another magnitude of new problems to the surface chemistry and physics of solids. The task of the experimental investigator today is to make the pertinent observations needed to define the initial and final states of the gas/solid process in terms of atomic structure and energy levels, in addition to mass balance which has dominated research studies hitherto.

## THE ADSORBATE COMPLEX

### Completion of the Monolayer

Measurements of nitrogen physically adsorbed on the sample in the relative pressure range of 0.05 to 0.25 are used to determine the monolayer capacity. The available methods have been reviewed recently (123).

A general procedure for determining the area of a solid is the "point B" method. Figure 1, used by Brunauer and Emmett (18) in their pioneering studies of iron catalysts, summarizes the typical behavior of nitrogen adsorption isotherms at −195° C. The point B is associated with that adsorption where the first layer of nitrogen is completed. This "knee" in the isotherms is frequently followed by an almost linear portion BD. The position where the linear portion breaks away from the observed isotherm is used to determine the point B. The surface area is calculated from the number of molecules in one layer of adsorbed gas. The number of

moles adsorbed at point B is multiplied by Avogadro's number and by the area per nitrogen molecule (16.2 A.²). The other positions noted on the curve have not correlated with actual surface area as well nor have they proved to be of theoretical interest.

The point B is now identified with $V_m$ of the BET (Brunauer-Emmett-Teller) theory (19) and the equations of this theory may be viewed as analytical methods of locating point B. The usual relationship for $V_m$ is:

$$\frac{P}{V(P_o - P)} = \frac{1}{V_m c} + \frac{c - 1}{V_m c} \frac{P}{P_o} \qquad (2)$$

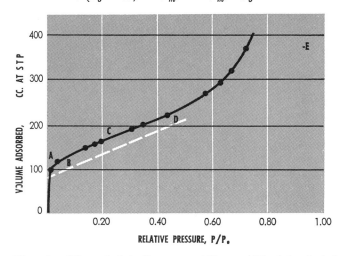

Figure 1. The analysis by Brunauer and Emmett (18) of the physical adsorption isotherm of nitrogen on an iron catalyst. Point B is the beginning of the linear portion of the isotherm. (Adsorption of $N_2$ on Fe–Al₂O₃ catalyst at −195.8° C.)

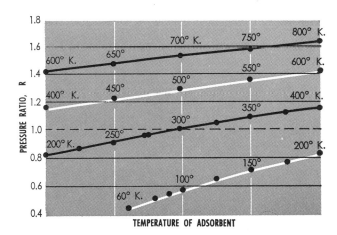

Figure 2. The ratio of pressure in an adsorbent vessel at various temperatures to pressure measured at 25° C. All pressures are in the Knudsen region

## TABLE II. EXPERIMENTAL ERROR IN NITROGEN ADSORPTION

| | Weight, G. | BET Area, M.²/G. | Dead Space, Ml. | Error, δn/n, % |
|---|---|---|---|---|
| Titanium oxide | 1.08 | 9.9 | 4.1 | 2.1 |
| Coconut charcoal | 0.71 | 1700 | 5.7 | 0.1 |
| Glass spheres | 12.29 | 0.93 | 16.3 | 1.9 |
| Bone char | 1.92 | 120 | 7.0 | 0.3 |
| Cotton | 31.1 | 0.7 | 121 | 10.4 |

All values at 78° K. (81).

where $P$ = pressure, $V$ = volume adsorbed, $P_o$ = saturation pressure, $V_m$ = monolayer coverage, and $c$ is a constant characteristic of the particular interaction at the gas/solid interface. The slope $(m)$ and intercept $(i)$ of the linear plot of $P/V(P_o - P)$ against $P/P_o$ are used to determine the value of $V_m$ where $V_m = 1/(m + i)$. The $c$ value may then be obtained $[c = 1 + (m/i)]$.

The practical advantage of the BET procedure over the point B method is that fewer experimental points are required, and thus the economics of laboratory operations favor the BET procedure. However, with commercial instruments now available to record automatically the complete adsorption isotherm, the point B method may be a practical procedure.

Usually a volumetric method is used, with nitrogen gas as the adsorbate and liquid nitrogen at atmospheric pressure as the refrigerant. For materials of small surface area, it is necessary to use large samples, and hence to employ sample containers with comparatively large dead space. It is important to have an estimate of the experimental error inherent in the conventional volumetric apparatus. If ideal gas laws are assumed, the number of moles, $n$, of gas adsorbed at constant temperature for the initial adsorption measurement is

$$n = \frac{P_i V_b}{300 \, R} - \frac{P_e V_b}{300 \, R} - \frac{P_e V_d}{78 \, R} \qquad (3)$$

where $P_i$ = initial pressure of nitrogen introduced into the buret system (300° K.)

$P_e$ = equilibrium pressure after contact with the sample at 78° K.

$V_b$ = volume of $N_2$ (STP) in buret space

$V_d$ = dead space

$R$ = gas constant

The variation in the number of moles adsorbed, $\delta n$, can be used to express the percentage error [81]. The

values of $\delta P_i$ and $\delta P_e$ are no greater than 0.1 since an accuracy in pressure of $\pm 0.1$ torr may be readily attained. Also, a value of $\delta V_b = 0.1$ is possible, since the calibration of the buret space with mercury is conveniently made before the apparatus is assembled. A reasonable value for the accuracy of the dead space volume (calibration with helium) is one percent; hence, $\delta V_d$ is 0.01 $V_d$. This analysis has been applied to the first points for a number of measurements, and the results are given in Table II. The error in obtaining subsequent adsorption points is cumulative; nevertheless, the treatment given indicates the dependence of accuracy on the magnitude of adsorption.

When the amount adsorbed is small, the determination depends on a small difference between the relatively large amounts introduced and those left in the gas phase. This experimental difficulty has been partly overcome by reducing the temperature and hence $P_o$ so that the same relative pressures can be realized at smaller absolute pressures. As a result, the residual gas not adsorbed at equilibrium is smaller. In addition, the dead space need not be reduced to a minimum to achieve the desired precision, nor does the volume of the pressure gage. Table III lists a few gas/solid systems which have been used in such a procedure.

It is not known how far the strategy of decreasing $P_o$ can be pushed in order to measure yet smaller surface coverages. Clarke [24] has determined adsorbed krypton (Kr-85) directly by counting the $\gamma$-emission of the sample in liquid nitrogen. A thermistor pressure gage was used to determine the pressure of the equilibrating gas. This method is applicable over a wide range of surface areas (10 cm.$^2$ to 10 m.$^2$/g.) and to sample sizes of 0.5 g. or less. The precision is given as two percent for $8 \times 10^3$ counts in 5 minutes when the background count is less than $10^3$/minute. The above procedure, however, is not without some complications.

### TABLE III. ADSORBATES USED IN DETERMINATION OF BET MONOLAYER COVERAGE

| Adsorbate | Temp. | $P_o$, Torr | Solid | Pressure Gage | Ref. |
|---|---|---|---|---|---|
| Nitrogen | −195° C. | 760 | Fe catalyst | Hg manometer | (19) |
|  | −183.1° C. | 2700 |  |  |  |
| n-Butane | −116° C. | 0.17 | Coated cathode | McLeod | (121) |
| Ethylene | −183° C. | 0.0305 |  |  |  |
| Ethylene | −183° C. |  |  |  | (38) |
| Ethylene | −183° C. | 0.033 | Al foil | McLeod | (20) |
|  |  | 0.021 |  |  |  |
|  | 90° K. | 0.010 | NaCl | McLeod |  |
| Ethane | 122.9° K. | 3.92 |  |  |  |
|  | 136.0° K. | 19.00 | KCl | Manometer | (102) |
| Ethane | −183° C. | $10^{-2}$ | Cu films | Pirani | (2) |
| Krypton | −195° C. | 2.63 to 3.72 | Anatase, porous glass, etc. | McLeod | (13) |
| Krypton | 77.8° K. | Super-cooled liquid | Ge powder | Thermistor | (101) |
| Krypton-85 | −195° C. | Super-cooled liquid | Graphite | Thermistor | (24) |

It is necessary to correct observations at low pressures for the change in pressure due to thermal transpiration. In the Knudsen range (mean free path several times the tube diameter), the ratio of pressures in the reaction vessel at two temperatures is $P_2/P_1 = \sqrt{T_2/T_1}$. Figure 2 illustrates the pressure ratio for the Knudsen effect above and below 25° C., the temperature assumed for the pressure measurement. In the intermediate pressure range where $P_2/P_1$ is between these values and unity, a correction must be made. A number of procedures

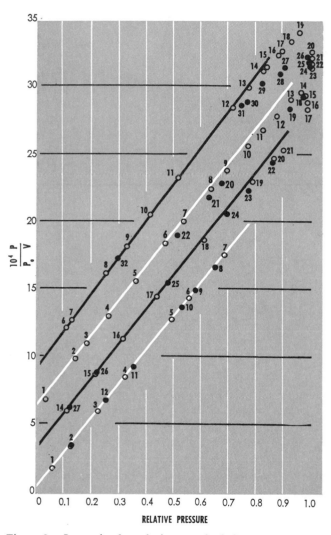

Figure 3. Langmuir plots of nitrogen adsorbed on a coconut shell charcoal at 78° K. Open circles show adsorption; closed circles show desorption. Note onset of hysteresis at high relative pressures

is available, that of Takaishi and Sensui (111) being the most recent. There is some uncertainty as to the exact lower limit for the thermal transpiration ratio of hydrogen and neon (93a) and of helium (67a).

There are solids for which the BET plots are not sufficiently linear to give an acceptable value for $V_m$. These are characterized by small values of the constant c. In some of these cases the original point B method may be used, and then more experimental points are needed. An interesting exception is the Type III iso-

therm of the Brunauer classification (17), where nothing in the observed isotherm indicates the completion of a monolayer. In such cases the BET theory with the parameter $c = 1$ furnishes a reasonable value of $V_m$. The completion of the first layer before appreciable formation of the second layer is valid only for large values of c. Hill (62) has shown that for small values of c the adsorption takes place at $V = V_m$ by the gas molecules interacting with adsorbate molecules rather than with the bare surface. Examples of such low-energy surfaces will be given in a later paragraph.

The adsorption of nitrogen on coconut shell charcoal has been represented by the Langmuir equation, and the calculated $V_m$ then corresponds to adsorption near saturation pressure. However, in this case it is necessary to discount the Langmuir behavior and use a value based on point B. Ross and Olivier (104) have demonstrated that an apparent Langmuir behavior can occur by a special distribution of energy sites for mobile physical adsorption. A careful experimental study of the nitrogen isotherm on coconut shell charcoal (51) has shown that the Langmuir equation actually does not hold at relative pressures above 0.7. Figure 3 gives the plots of $P/P_oV$ vs. $P/P_o$ and demonstrates, in fact, that a small hysteresis may take place. Nitrogen adsorption on other gas adsorbent charcoals obeys the

**TABLE IV. BOUNDARY AREA AND PARTICLE SIZE**

(Cubic particle of density 2 g./cm.³)

| Size | Particles/G. | Area, Sq. Cm./G. |
|---|---|---|
| 1 mm. | 500 | 30 |
| 149 μ | 150,000 | 200 |
| 44 μ | 6 × 10⁶ | 700 |
| 10 μ | 500 × 10⁶ | 3,000 |
| 1 μ | 500 × 10⁹ | 30,000 |
| 100 mμ | 500 × 10¹² | 300,000 |

three-constant BET equation in which the parameter $n$ is a measure of the restricted number of adsorbed layers at saturation. In these cases, $V_m$ is close to point B.

The BET surface area measurement may be used for a variety of purposes; one is to estimate the entrapped surfaces in the closed voids within a solid. Particle size diminution increases the surface area per unit weight to a greater extent than can be attributed to the decrease in particle size alone. The boundary area of 1 g. of cubes (density 2 g./cm.³) varies with size of the cubes as shown in Table IV. The opening of the internal voids in several basic calcium phosphates was reported by Hendricks and Hill (58); the BET area in Figure 4 varied linearly with boundary area. The total surface area increases 20 times faster than the boundary area. Recently, Clarke (24) has demonstrated the presence of closed voids in nuclear graphites and Figure 4 also shows these results. In the case of graphite the total area increased 200 times faster than the boundary area. The linear dependence indicates a uniform distribution of very small closed voids within

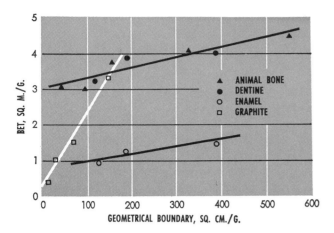

*Figure 4. Evidence of the entrapped surface associated with closed voids within a solid when exposed by particle diminution*

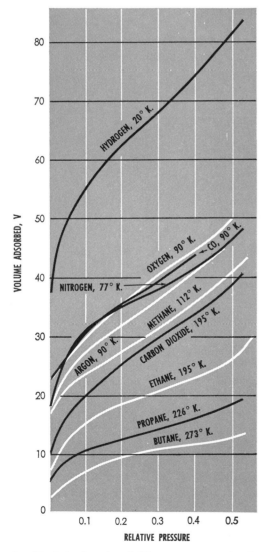

*Figure 5. Physical adsorption of 10 gases on a sample of new bone char (34)*

these solids.    The technique may be applied to a number of solids as a test for homogeneity, but as Savage (*106, 107*) has shown, it is necessary to be alert to chemisorption effects with the environment during the grinding.

It is preferred, when possible, to define the monolayer in terms of changes in several adsorption characteristics rather than to base it on some one particular system. The physical adsorption of nitrogen at liquid nitrogen temperatures, however, appears to have unique correlation with other adsorption phenomena associated with monolayer coverage and comes close to being a universal technique.    Heat of adsorption is usually high enough to give a $c$ that furnishes a well defined point B.

### Multilayer Region

The study of multilayer adsorption has developed along several directions since Brunauer's classic volume (*17*).    Up to that time the main objective had been to predict the shapes of adsorption isotherms which was accomplished by the BET theory with good success. Later developments included calculation of the thermodynamic properties of carefully selected systems, extension to a variety of adsorbates and solids, and influence of molecular structure on the properties of the adsorption complex.    Other than to demonstrate the great complexity of the problem, there has been no real breakthrough since the BET theory was formulated.

In the period after World War II, careful measurements of reversible adsorption isotherms enabled the thermodynamic properties of the adsorbed phase to be determined.    The desired precision of volumetric gas analysis and the determination of the amount adsorbed gravimetrically made special demands on manometers and microbalances.    It may be noted that many of the necessary components are now available on a commercial basis.    For example, the entire adsorption and desorption isotherms may be determined volumetrically in completely automated apparatus (*5*).

Early investigators in multimolecular adsorption were still concerned with monolayer coverage and studied the availability of a surface to molecules of increasing size and complexity.    An example for a porous adsorbent (bone char) is shown in Figure 5 (*34*).    The adsorption of hydrogen and that of *n*-butane differ by a factor of almost eight at the same relative pressure.    The homologous series $CH_4$, $C_2H_6$, $C_3H_8$, and $C_4H_{10}$ indicated a progressive decrease in BET area of 115, 90, 76, and 66 m.²/g., respectively.    The sequence was not proportional with $V^{2/3}$ ($V$ = molar volume of adsorbate species as a liquid), nor could it be correlated with any obvious packing arrangement on the surface.    The situation was similar for nine other carbon adsorbents.    Recently, Kini (*73*), using two carbon adsorbents with Ar, $CO_2$, Kr, Xe, or $CH_3OH$, has shown that the BET theory in its original form gave good agreement for surface area.    The area problem is also treated by a technique known as "high temperature" physical adsorption which will be discussed below.

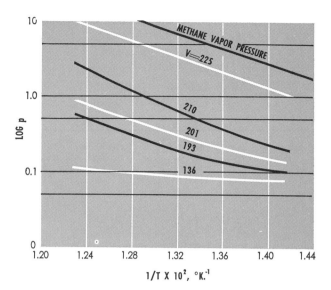

*Figure 6.   Adsorption isosteres of methane on a charcoal (72)*

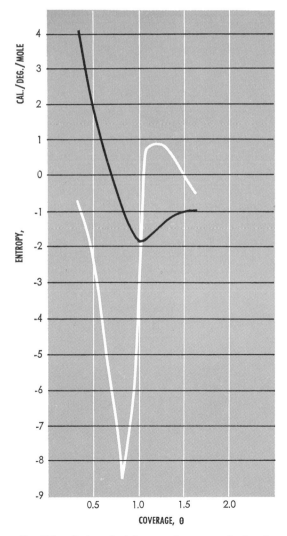

*Figure 7.   The criterion of minimum molar entropy for locating mono-layer coverage in the physical adsorption of nitrogen on graphitized carbon black (65). The upper curve is the integral entropy cal-culated from spreading pressures; the lower curve is the differential (isosteric) entropy*

The packing of adsorbate molecules in multilayers and the corresponding entropy changes present problems of great complexity.

The theoretical treatments of multilayer formation, recently reviewed by Young and Crowell (*123*), indicate that the difficulties are similar to those encountered with problems of the liquid state.   Multilayer adsorption has been considered as the precursor to the condensed phase.

The packing of adsorbate molecules at different coverages should influence the density of the adsorbed phase relative to that of the condensed phase.   Several careful measurements using helium as the displaced fluid have been reported (*30, 87, 114*) and, while no absolute values for density are given, the results have a definite trend.   At surface coverages up to a monolayer, the density is close to the normal value of the liquid. In the multilayer region a more dilute type of coverage forms which then increases gradually until the normal density is reached at saturation.   More work is required to establish the concept of "holes" in the multilayer structure.   This concept of the multilayer appears compatible with the original BET model of a random vertical stacking of adsorbed molecules, although an alternative cluster model would behave similarly.

The adsorption isostere is particularly useful for expressing experimental results.   An example is the system methane/charcoal taken from the work of Kidnay and Hiza (*72*) and shown in Figure 6.   It is important, of course, that the data be reversible in order to calculate the heats of adsorption.   Figure 6 brings out a marked curvature (slope increases with temperature) and, more-over, shows that the heats of adsorption for this system may be less than the heat of condensation.   Other systems have shown a similar behavior: argon with graphitized carbon black (*94*), nitrogen or argon with diamond or mineralogical graphite (*82*), and nitrogen or argon with polypropylene and polytetrafluoro-ethylene (*52*).   Calorimetric measurements to verify these findings would be interesting.   It is important to obtain data at close temperature intervals in order to bring out fine-structure behavior.   There is need for a simple cryostat not tied too strongly to normal boiling and melting points of available refrigerants.

Hill, in a series of theoretical papers (*63*), developed a thermodynamic model in which the adsorbent is assumed inert and the presence of the surface provides an attractive force field for the adsorbate molecules. This one-component model presents all the measured heat and entropy changes as taking place in the ad-sorbate.   In addition to affording a simplicity in theory, the model did provide new information.   For example, Hill, Emmett, and Joyner (*65*), independent of the BET theory, were able to locate the point of monolayer coverage by the position of minimum entropy for the system nitrogen/graphitized carbon black (Figure 7).

One aspect of physical adsorption that delineates it from chemisorption is the absence of strong specificity between the interacting gas and solid.   This, however, is only true to a moderate degree.   Actually, multilayer formation does sense the structure of the bare solid.

Singleton and Halsey (*109*), using argon isotherms on graphitized carbon black, showed progressive change in the shape of the isotherms as the thickness of preadsorbed xenon layers increased (up to six layers). Heats of adsorption from isotherms of hydrogen, deuterium, and helium on Graphon agree with calorimetry (*93*).

The calorimetric studies of Morrison *et al.* (*37, 88, 89*) on the systems argon, oxygen, and nitrogen/titanium dioxide (rutile) were invaluable in showing the difficulties inherent in fundamental interpretation of the measurements. The data were evaluated in terms of statistical models that placed restrictions on rotational, transitional, and vibrational degrees of freedom ascribed to the free molecule. The extremes of gas/solid interaction are those of a strictly localized bond to the surface site and a completely mobile adsorbate which permits two-dimensional gas behavior. The careful studies of Morrison *et al.* showed that argon adsorbed on rutile at 14–25° K. was localized, but at the higher temperatures the results could not be accounted for on the basis of any simple model; they did suggest a limited mobility of the adsorbed argon. The melting process in multilayer adsorption of nitrogen on rutile is completely reversible and takes place at temperatures well below the normal melting point of nitrogen.

Current researches in multilayers attempt to express the surface nonuniformity in terms of energy distribution as a function of surface coverage. On an atomic scale there may be a distribution of crystal faces, each having different atomic spacings. In many cases a distribution of defects (impurities, etc.) exists over the boundary surface which varies with the techniques employed to pretreat the surface. Finally, the properties of the surface may change with time (*27*) as the strain-stress relationships set up in pretreatment of the solid adjust slowly toward a minimum surface free energy.

The dimensional changes that take place in physical adsorption in many gas/solid systems demonstrate that the adsorbent is definitely not inert geometrically or energetically. Yates (*122*) developed a vacuum interferometer and measured the length changes upon

adsorption of several gases on porous glass. Some of these results are shown in Figures 8*a* and 8*b*. The general phenomena are very complex with interesting temperature effects and fair reproducibility; these take place in systems free of chemisorption possibilities.

Many current researches are concerned with the interaction among the molecular groups located in the multilayer system. The infrared adsorption technique has been applied rapidly, but progress is handicapped by the breakdown of the selection rules for the optically active modes of vibration. In chemisorption systems, new molecular species are formed; in physical adsorption, there are significant changes in the normal vibrational modes of the free molecule and forbidden frequencies appear in the perturbation field of the surface groups. Galkin, Kiselev, and Lygin (*50*) have shown that aromatic molecules and silica have an interesting dependence of the adsorption on both molecular structure and surface coverage. Specifically, the interaction is between the $\pi$-electron system of the aromatic molecule and the surface OH group.

The electrical properties of gas/solid systems have been studied widely with relatively little success. In the multilayer region there are sufficient numbers of surface groups to affect the nuclear magnetic resonance spectra of certain nuclei, which fortunately include hydrogen. Recently, nuclear magnetic resonance relaxation times (*98*) were observed for water adsorbed on a hardwood gas charcoal. The observations were compatible with a model of supercooled water in the capillaries of the charcoal. The dielectric properties (*92, 125*) of surface hydrates and other polar adsorbates have been recorded, but there is considerable difficulty in factoring out the particular electrical properties of the adsorbate.

The phenomenon of hysteresis remains an intriguing and largely unexplained behavior in the region of multilayer coverage. When an adsorbent contains microscopic open voids, the process of "capillary condensation" occurs (*17*). This structural model has been the basis of attempts to understand hysteresis and many

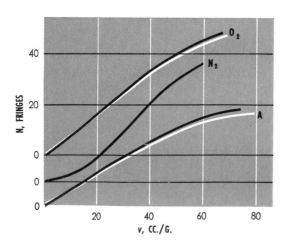

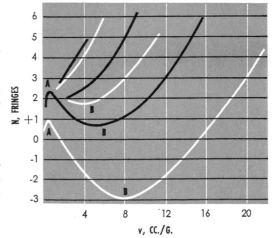

*Figure 8a (left). Expansion of porous glass (interference fringes) after adsorption of argon, oxygen, and nitrogen (122). Black lines at 90° K., white lines at 79° K.*

*Figure 8b (right). Length change of porous glass upon the adsorption of sulfur dioxide. From the top, curves at −78°, 0°, 24°, 50°, 75°, and 100° C. (122)*

publications have been based on it. The hypothetical cylindrical capillary and the realistic texture based on crystal structures constitute an anomaly that has yet to be resolved. An alternate explanation of hysteresis may be found in some low-energy modification on the adsorbent surface during the adsorption process [see the domain concept of D. H. Everett (*43*) and J. A. Enderby (*42*)]. There may be steric factors that influence the orientation of surface groups in which the weaker bending forces of the surface bonds are involved. A cooperative orientation effect may be a function of the amount adsorbed in a manner similar to adsorbed films on liquids. It is interesting that hysteresis of a surface film of ovalbumin on several buffer solutions has recently been reported (*68*). Thus, for each orientation of the bonds in the surface, there is a different gas/solid system to study; it would be interesting if means were found to freeze each for individual study.

### Fractional Surface Coverage

Only a fraction of the total gas/solid interface is covered by physical adsorption at temperatures above the critical temperature of the gas and at relative pressures below 0.05 to 0.10. Chemisorption processes usually involve only a fractional part of the BET surface. The importance of the BET theory, and also the constructive criticism that has followed, should again be appreciated. Only after this development was a general means available to determine fractional coverage.

**Analyses of the Gas Phase.** The experimenter today has a tremendous advantage over his colleagues of only five to ten years ago. With the development of modern gas chromatography and mass spectrometry procedures, the means are available to follow the partial pressures of all reactants and products. In fact, facility of data collection makes possible quite elaborate experimental designs so as to include binary, ternary, and multiple gas mixtures. Adsorption studies with multiple gas component systems were first reported with commercial adsorbents (*79*) and, with the introduction of gas phase chromatography, many studies have followed (*8, 9*).

Reliability of gas/solid studies in the past has sometimes been questioned because of possible competitive gaseous impurities. Although a start could be made with high-purity gases, it was not known to what degree solid and stopcock manipulations might introduce gaseous contaminations. Now, a continuous monitoring of the gas phase with built-in components permits greater attention to be given to this factor. Systems involving fractional surface coverages, in general, deal with more demanding experimental procedures.

**Pretreatment of the Solid.** The pretreatment of the solid is probably the most important experimental parameter in current researches. The usual degassing in vacuum at some specified temperature has generally been selected for convenience and expediency. For many commercial adsorbents this may contribute effectively to the subsequent adsorption and in some cases the treatment may generate an adsorption site on the solid. The

recipes for the manufacture of some solid state devices have depended upon the generation of special sites at the surface and junction of the crystallites. Only recently has some rationality replaced uncertainty.

The outgassing of solids may be monitored by measuring the rate of gas formation at an elevated temperature. Deitz and Carpenter (*32*) recorded pressure-time curves after the heated sample was isolated, and a typical record is shown in Figure 9. A memory effect is indicated in the time and temperature of the evacuation. Points A, B and E, F are typical of successful operation. Point C resulted when an accidental back-diffusion of oxygen to the heated sample took place, but subsequent degassing gradually progressed to the initial rate of decay. This study raises questions as to the advantages and disadvantages to be gained by some high-temperature pretreatments. The impurities removed from the surface may be renewed by the volatile products of decomposition originating in the bulk of the solid. A poorly defined substrate such as glass spheres can hardly be expected to give a better defined surface by thermal pretreatment alone. Liang (*80*) showed that such glass surfaces are quite heterogeneous and that the gas/glass interface is non-reproducible (90 hours at 300° C.) in the adsorption of krypton at 77.6° K. at low coverage (<0.05). The cleaning of a solid surface is really a three-dimensional problem. The two-dimensional concentration of impurities has been recognized, but the concentration may change on moving inward from the surface. For the present, however, much interesting work can be done with surface impurities depleted to a level knowingly set by the design of the experiment.

The thermal treatment in vacuum may be supplemented by chemical treatments. Examples are the reaction of HCl or $Cl_2$ with NaCl crystals to restore the anion vacancy (*7*); of $O_2$ with oxides to restore the stoichiometric balance desired (*120*); and of hydrogen with some metals to eliminate trace oxygen and nitrogen (*74*). Adequate pumping must always be available to

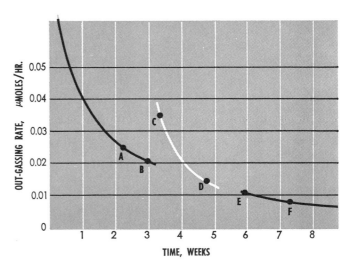

*Figure 9. The outgassing behavior of a diamond powder at 600° C. in terms of the rate of gas formation*

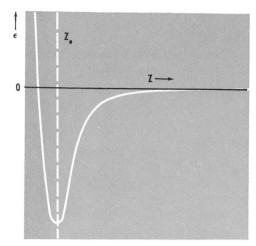

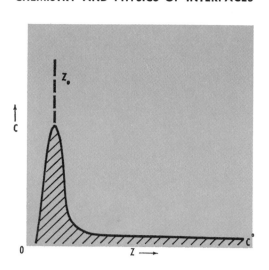

*Figure 10. Left, dependence of the potential energy of the molecule on the normal distance to the plane of the surface. Right, dependence of the coverage concentration in the potential field on the normal distance to the plane of the surface*

assure that the desorption dominates over the simultaneous adsorption process.

The flushing of a solid by repeated adsorption and desorption with the gas of interest has long been advocated (85, 86). High purity gases are obviously required for such a procedure. Special techniques are available to pretreat metals: atomic hydrogen treatment, rare gas ion bombardment, filament flashing, and others. Organic solids require very special care so as not to introduce decomposition impurities.

The objectives sought in a pretreatment process are reproducibility, known chemical composition and known structure of the boundary planes at an atomic level. Not all of these objectives are achieved, although good progress has been made toward reproducibility in a number of cases.

**"High-Temperature" Adsorption.** Considerable interest is now being expressed in the field of "high-temperature" physical adsorption. The significant factor is the low fractional surface coverage with minimum adsorbate–adsorbate interaction.

The Steele-Halsey (S-H) model (26, 47, 110) is concerned with an integration of the gas/solid interaction given by an interatomic energy potential over a structureless semi-infinite solid. The Ross-Olivier (R-O) model (103, 104) applies the de Boer-Hill isotherm (16) for a two dimensional mobile film interacting with a surface having a Gaussian distribution of adsorption energies. The experimental data used in applications of the S-H model have been obtained at 0 to 50° C. and correspond to fractional coverages of 0.01 to 0.02. The applications of the R-O model have been to coverages between 0.1 and 0.6. The objectives of this work are an independent method of determining surface area, a technique for dealing with heterogeneous surfaces, and a physical adsorption process independent of adsorbate and temperature. The definition of physical adsorption involved here has been discussed (64).

Baker and Everett (6) have expressed the Steele-Halsey model in terms of conventional adsorption theory, and their simplified presentation will now be given.

Potential energy of the molecule varies with the normal distance $z$ to the plane in the usual way and the average concentration $c$ in the potential field $\epsilon$ varies according to a Boltzman distribution (Figure 10)

$$c = c_o e^{-\epsilon/kT} \tag{4}$$

where $c_o$ is the bulk phase concentration at $\epsilon = 0$. By using the Gibbs definition of adsorption and placing the dividing line where $\epsilon = 0$

$$dn_a = dx \, dy \int_{z_o}^{\infty} (c - c_o) dz \tag{5}$$

and substituting Equation 4 in Equation 5

$$dn_a = c_o \int_x \int_y \int_{z_o}^{\infty} (e^{-\epsilon/kT} - 1) \, dz \, dy \, dx \tag{6}$$

For a uniform surface and an ideal gas ($c_o = P/RT$)

$$n_a = AP/RT \int [\exp(-\epsilon/kT) - 1] \, dz$$
$$n_a = AP(k_h) \tag{7}$$

if $\epsilon$ is a known function of $z$, then $k_h$ can be calculated. If $n_a/P$ is found experimentally, area $A$ can be found.

The small adsorption may be readily measured by gas chromatography procedures. Hanlan and Freeman (56) have shown that the gas/solid interaction coefficient can be obtained from the retention volumes calculated under the given set of experimental conditions. The potential energy of the interaction can then be found from the temperature dependence of the retention volumes. The necessary experimental results are readily obtained on a routine basis and the calculations, although involved, may be handled by computers with dispatch. The method may, therefore, prove to be a research tool of considerable value.

Ross and Olivier (103, 104) deal with adsorbed mobile films with an interaction given by the two-dimensional van der Waals gas constants. The de Boer-Hill isotherm (16) is used

$$P = K_t \frac{\theta_t}{1 - \theta_t} \exp\left[\frac{\theta_t}{1 - \theta_t} - \frac{2\alpha\theta_t}{\beta \, kT}\right]$$

where $K_i$ = a term giving the adsorbate-adsorbent interaction

$\theta_i$ = coverage of a given patch of energy $U_{oi}$ at pressure $P$

$\alpha, \beta$ = two-dimensional van der Waals constants (assumed independent of surface heterogeneity)

A Gaussian distribution of adsorption energies is assumed and a series of model isotherms computed for particular adsorbates and temperature expressing the total coverage by

$$\theta = \int \Phi(U_o) \, \Psi \, (P, U_o) \, d \, U_o$$

Actually, a machine summation is made over 50 patches instead of an integration. The experimental isotherm is compared with the model isotherms and four results are immediately obtained:

—the monolayer capacity is determined

—quantitative measure of heterogeneity is given by the constants of a particular Gaussian curve

—a value of the mean energy of adsorption is given which can be related to the isosteric heat of adsorption

—the theory predicts a temperature-coefficient of adsorption.

There is a need to provide the experimental isotherms for a large variety of solids and adsorbates to test these two aspects of gas/solid interaction. The means are available to record the isotherms in the pressure regions desired, namely $10^{-4}$ to $10^3$ torr, and the temperatures selected to cover a wide range in close intervals.

**Materials.** Powders, films, and filaments have been studied in a variety of fundamental investigations, each requiring a different experimental technique. Only a few solids have been studied in all three forms; one example is tungsten. To these forms must be added the tungsten point used in the field emission microscope.

Table V presents some of the relative advantages and disadvantages in pursuing investigations at the gas/solid interface by the three techniques. Such an analysis may have value when viewing the gas/solid interface in its broadest aspects. Actually, each system has its own share of individual idiosyncrasies. All solids can be studied as powders or crystals, and a relatively few (metals) can be studied as filaments. Films can be formed of any substance that has a finite vapor pressure or that can be formed from volatile reactants. De Boer (31) obtained films of calcium, strontium, and barium fluorides by sublimation and studied their interesting surface chemistry. Continuation of such studies would be extremely valuable.

The study of films has the major advantage of large surface-to-volume ratio. Consequently, the amount adsorbed per unit weight of material is greatest for films, next for powders, and least for filaments. Moreover, films share with filaments the capability of being studied in ultrahigh vacuum. Since the sublimation process in itself may be used as a purification step, the films may be of good chemical purity.

**Rate of Adsorption.** The rates of adsorption vary in magnitude from the rapid values for physical adsorption to much slower values for diffusion-controlled adsorption. Various solid state sensors have been devised for very fast reactions at solid surfaces (116).

Modern methods of investigation began with the studies on clean filaments (99) and with evaporated metal films (15). Trapnell (113) has reviewed the status of the field in his volumes published in 1955 and 1964; Ehrlich (39) has recently given an account of current work on clean surfaces. In the last decade the emphasis has been on the rates of mass transfer at solid/solid and gas/solid interfaces using isotope tracers. Films evaporated under ultrahigh vacuum conditions are finding preference because the surface boundary can be defined with more confidence and the transfer of the heat of adsorption is more effective.

The factors that influence rates of adsorption are given by functions in which the variables are assumed

**TABLE V. ADVANTAGES OF SURFACES IN DIFFERENT SOLID FORMS**

| | Powders or Crystals | Metal Filaments | Films |
|---|---|---|---|
| General applicability | 1 | 3 | 2 |
| Cleanness | 3 | 1 | 2 |
| Surface/volume | 2 | 3 | 1 |
| Amount adsorbed | 2 | 3 | 1 |
| Thermal stability | 2 | 1 | 3 |
| Ultrahigh vacuum | 3 | 1 | 2 |
| Chemical purity | 3 | 1, 2 | 2, 1 |
| Structure determination | 1 | 2, 3 | 3, 2 |
| Calorimetric measurements | 1 | 3 | 2 |
| Electrical measurements | 3 | 1 | 2 |
| Heat transfer | 3 | 2 | 1 |

*Rating is indicated in the order of desirability, 1, 2, or 3.*

separable. The following expressions for the rates of adsorption $\mu_a$ and desorption $\mu_d$ are typical.

$$\mu_a = \frac{P}{\sqrt{2\pi \, mkT}} \sum n_i \, \sigma_i \, f(\theta_i) e^{-E_i/RT}$$

and

$$\mu_d = \sum n_i K_i f'(\theta_i) e^{-E_i/RT}$$

where $n_i$ sites of type $i$ each of an energy $E_i$ and coverage $\theta_i$. The four factors are:

—the number of collisions with a surface ($\sim P/\sqrt{2\pi mkT}$)

—the condensation probability ($\sigma$)

—the activation energy ($E$)

—the fraction of the surface covered ($\theta$)

When surfaces are heterogeneous, these four factors are applied to each type of site available. Experimental procedures are selected in an attempt to simplify interpretation of the data; the selection of constant pressure and constant temperature permits an analysis in terms of distribution of surface sites.

Gas phase chromatography lends itself readily to many studies in physical adsorption in which the adsorbates on various column materials are maintained at fractional surface coverage. Molecular exchange on carefully conditioned surfaces is the basis of the gas chromatographic process. The delicate interaction at the many gas/solid interfaces in the column presents a very difficult system to analyze on a fundamental basis.

**Surface Migration.** The extremes of surface migration are readily apparent experimentally. The early observations of Volmer on the migration of benzophenone on glass and mercury surfaces proved that adsorbed molecules move many thousands of atomic distances. There are today scores of examples of crystal growth from the gas phase that involve adsorption and surface diffusion (66).

The complete absence of surface migration has been shown for strongly chemisorbed species. The classical example is oxygen on tungsten which was demonstrated by Langmuir (78) to have a heat desorption of atomic oxygen of 160 kcal. per gram atom. It is now known that, at elevated temperatures, surface migration in this system can also be detected. Becker (12) has observed in the field emission microscope the mobility of oxygen on tungsten at temperatures lower than those required for evaporation. The mobility was observed to vary with the different planes of the tungsten crystal and with the fields applied. Between 650° and 800° K. some oxygen is desorbed, and the first layer is stable between 800° and 1400° K. Above 1400° K. some planes desorb; at about 2200° desorption is complete.

This direct observation of surface migration by field emission contrasts strongly with the many indirect means that have been used in the past. However, indirect means are still required in order to work with a greater variety of surfaces. Migration on boundary surfaces is an essential step in crystal growth, as already mentioned. It has been necessary to assume diffusion along a surface in order to account for the migration of gas molecules through porous packings (11). The intriguing mechanism of the "hopping molecules" has been proposed by de Boer (16), but has not as yet been demonstrated experimentally. Dacey (29) has shown that surface diffusion through systems in which the dimensions of the internal voids are smaller than the mean free path at subatmospheric pressures can be by both Knudsen and surface flow.

The mobility of hydrogen atoms on nickel films has been used by Deitz and McFarlane (35) to account for the low-temperature formation of methane when hydrogen was contacted with stacked films of carbon and nickel. All of the carbon in methane had to come from the carbon film. In their proposed model

$$Ni + H_2 \rightarrow Ni\text{—}H \text{ (mobile)}$$

$$C + H_2 \rightarrow C\text{—}H \text{ (localized)}$$

$$Ni\text{—}H + C\text{—}H \rightarrow Ni + CH_4$$

The multiple hydrogenation of carbon to form methane is favored by the ready transport of H atoms to a site located at the Ni/C interface.

**Heat of Adsorption.** The simplest indirect measure of gas adsorption is the temperature change of the solid. Adsorption takes place with a decrease in both free energy ($\Delta F$) and entropy ($\Delta S$). For reversible adsorption

$$\Delta F = \Delta H - T\Delta S$$

It follows that $\Delta H$ must decrease; in other words, adsorption is always exothermic.

The heats of physical adsorption have been measured with good precision and, in general, good reproducibility is found when the surface is well defined. An outstanding case for the adsorption of argon on titanium dioxide is the work of Morrison, Los, and Drain (89). Approximate heat values may be estimated from the parameter $c$ of the BET equation, the values of which range from 1 to 250 $\delta$. The heats are obtained as follows

$$c = e^{q_1 - E_l/RT}$$

where $q_1$ is the heat of adsorption in the first layer and $E_l$ is the heat of liquefaction.

In recent developments the technique of gas chromatography has been applied to the determination of heats of adsorption [Habgood and Hanlan (55); Hanlan and Freeman (56); Beebe and Emmett (14); Ross, Saelens, and Olivier (105)]. Gale and Beebe (49) have made a number of comparisons with heats of adsorption determined by calorimetric measurements at low coverage and report good agreement with their chromatographic results. The accuracy, simplicity, and speed of chromatography may be expected to expedite the accumulation of heat of adsorption data for a variety of gas/solid systems at very low surface coverage. The application of these techniques to surface area determinations has been pursued recently by Hansen, Murphy, and McGee (57) and by Freeman and Kolb (48), as mentioned earlier.

The heats of chemisorption have a considerably greater range because of specific interaction to form chemical bonds in the gas/solid interface. Reproducibility is difficult to attain in many such systems, as adequately documented by Trapnell (113).

**Multiple Gas Phase/Single Solid.** The experimental procedures now receiving attention in current studies are the simultaneous adsorption of two or more gases at one solid boundary and the replacement of one adsorbed gas by the introduction of another. The latter is always observed with a bulk sample because it is extremely difficult to evacuate powder and attain an ultrahigh vacuum. Raising the temperature of outgassing almost always increases the adsorptive capacity when the sample is cooled.

Observations with binary gaseous reactants on a given solid frequently show a dependence of rate on the order of admission of gases. In the ethylene hydrogenation on evaporated nickel and iron films it has been shown (76) that the relative rates were in the following descending order: (a) $H_2$ first, $C_2H_4$ second; (b) simultaneous addition; (c) $C_2H_4$ first, $H_2$ second. There is obviously an urgent need to observe a property of the surface that demonstrates the surface interaction along with measurements of gas phase composition.

One such study is the adsorption of ethylene at −195° and at 25° C. by evaporated nickel films (28) which was followed by determinations of BET area (Kr at −195° C.). The results in Table VI show a reduction in area as a result of the ethylene adsorption; no reduction in area was reported for hydrogen adsorption at either $-195°$ or $25°$ C.

### Sparsely Covered Surfaces

Ultrahigh vacuum techniques are required to prepare and maintain a surface at very low coverage ($\theta < 0.1$). Commercial equipment to do this has reached a satisfactory working level, and experimentation in this field often has the choice of alternative procedures (3, 22, 97, 100). The pumping facilities have reached a high level of performance which appears to be limited only by the means of observing residual pressures. The principles of the various pumping techniques are:

| | |
|---|---|
| Diffusion pumps | Kinetic theory |
| Cold traps | Condensation to low vapor pressure |
| Cryogenic techniques | Physical adsorption |
| Getter action | Chemisorption and chemical reactivity |
| Sputter ion pumps | Gas ion impact |

The pressure measurement depends on the region of experimentation, and a resume is given in Table VII. The outstanding device below 1-$\mu$ pressure is the mass spectrometer. Not only can it span a tremendous pressure range, but it also has the selectivity required to determine the partial pressures of a gas mixture.

Adsorption isotherms in ultrahigh vacuum are obtained essentially from pressure measurements and the accuracy realized depends on several factors: calibration procedure, background gas, container wall, and interaction with the pressure gage. The calibration is usually based on the McLeod gage in the range $10^{-3}$ to $10^{-5}$ torr. Linearity of a Bayer-Alpert ionization gage between ion current and pressure is then checked by the calculated pressure drop across apertures of known conductance. Because of the background gas and the degassing of the sample and container wall, the partial pressure of the gas of interest may be uncertain. The mass spectrometer is, therefore, a necessity in such cases.

Experimentation in ultrahigh vacuum has several unique advantages to the surface chemist. The interface maintained at $10^{-9}$ torr may be held for several

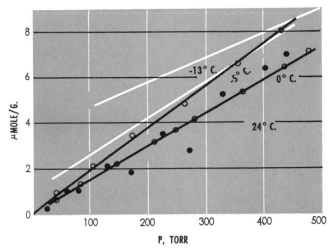

*Figure 11. Linear adsorption isotherms of carbon dioxide on a graphitized carbon black, FT (33)*

hours under a given set of conditions without fear of contamination by adsorbed gases. In building up to higher pressure, the impurities in the gas phase are critical since clean surfaces exhibit a high affinity for chemically reactive gases such as oxygen and water if present. The stability of surfaces in ultrahigh vacuum offers an opportunity to define the structure of the solid/vacuum interface unperturbed by an adsorbed phase. Significant advances in this regard have been made with W, Si, Ni, Pt, $Cu_2O$, and a few other solids. A reaction at the gas/solid interface can be studied with no lateral interaction of adsorbate molecules. Ultrahigh vacuums permit work in pressure regions where the thermal diffusion is independent of pressure ($<10^{-6}$ torr). Correction factors for observations at $25°$ C. are shown in Figure 2.

The early adsorption data in high vacuum were concerned with pressure-time experimentation. The observed reversible adsorption phenomena were superimposed with phenomena resulting from the pumping action of ionization gages. The latter can be minimized, but not avoided, by intermittent operation for short intervals and by reduction of the electronic current so as to reduce the pumping action. Many specific factors influence the results such as the kind of gas, the

### TABLE VI.   MULTIPLE GAS ADSORPTION

Kr, $-195°$ C., FOLLOWING $C_2H_4$ AT $-80°$ C. ON Ni FILMS

| Temp., °C. | BET Area, M.²/G. (Kr) | | $C_2H_4$ Adsorbed, $\mu l$. at STP |
|---|---|---|---|
| | Initial | After adsorption | |
| 0 | 0.232 | 0.128 | 20 |
| 25 | 0.196 | 0.110 | 12 |
| 100 | 0.134 | 0.078 | 8 |

*Data from (28).*

**AUTHOR** *Victor R. Deitz is Research Chemist at the U. S. Naval Research Laboratory, Washington, D. C.*

### TABLE VII.   GAGES FOR LOW PRESSURE MEASUREMENT

| Range | Absolute Pressure, Torr | Instrument |
|---|---|---|
| Subatmospheric | 1–760 | Manometers |
| Conventional vacuum | $10^{-4}$–1 | Bourdon gage Membrane gage McLeod gage Thermocouple Thermistor Pirani Thermal conductivity |
| High vacuum | $10^{-7}$–$10^{-4}$ | McLeod gage Ionization |
| Ultrahigh | $10^{-7}$–$10^{-11}$ $10^{-16}$–$10^{-5}$ $10^{-13}$–$10^{-5}$ | Ionization Mass spectrometers Cold cathode ionization |

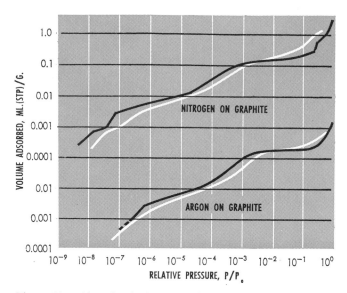

*Figure 12. Adsorption isotherms of nitrogen and argon on graphite at low relative pressures (82). Black curve of each pair at 77° K.; white curve at 90.0° K.*

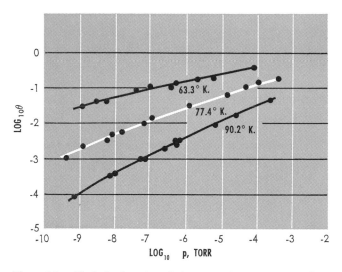

*Figure 13. Physical adsorption of nitrogen on Pyrex glass at 78° K. (67)*

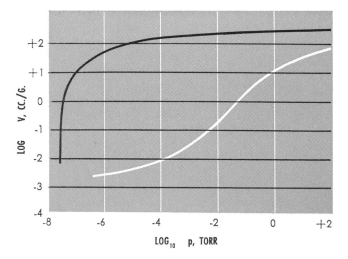

*Figure 14. Adsorption of hydrogen on a charcoal at 20.4° K. (top curve) and 80° K. (bottom curve) (45)*

nature and temperature of the adsorbing surface, and gas leakage and gas emission by impurities, etc. The surface chemist, aware of the complexity of these systems, is in a position to make a significant contribution.

**Henry's Law.** One important requirement for all models of adsorption is that the isotherm simplify to Henry's law at low coverage.

$$V = \frac{baP}{1 + aP} = baP$$

In this respect, experimentation in ultrahigh vacuum is very pertinent. Linear adsorption isotherms have been observed for many systems and good examples are the rare gases on graphitized carbon black (P-33) (25) and the system shown in Figure 11 at coverages of 0.01 to 0.05. However, linear isotherms at 273° K. have also been reported for nonuniform energy surfaces such as porous glass, some nongraphitized carbon blacks, and an alumina-silica cracking catalyst (10).

Henry's law behavior is a necessary but not sufficient condition of surface uniformity. Lopez-Gonzalez, Carpenter, and Deitz (82) showed that adsorption isotherms of nitrogen and argon at 78° and 90° K. on mineralogical graphite obeyed Henry's law between $10^{-3}$ and $10^{-4}$ relative pressure but were definitely nonlinear at lower pressures. These results are shown in Figure 12. Hobson and Armstrong (67) observed nonlinear isotherms of nitrogen at 78° K. on Pyrex glass to absolute pressures of $10^{-9}$ torr and to coverages of $10^{-4}$; some of their results are shown in Figure 13. Fedorova (45) has reported nonlinear adsorption isotherms of $H_2$ and $D_2$ on several adsorbent charcoals over a pressure range of $10^{-3}$ to $10^{-8}$ at 4, 20.4, and 80° K. It is estimated that $\theta = 0.10$ at $10^{-6}$ torr for this material. Two isotherms for hydrogen are given in Figure 14.

The failure to obtain Henry's law at low pressures may be due to the fact that a sufficiently low coverage has not been attained to realize a residual uniform surface. However, a Henry's law behavior for known heterogeneous surfaces at low coverage appears to be another matter. Barrer and Rees (10) concluded that this is due to an approximate linear relationship that exists between $T\Delta S_o$ and $\Delta E$ (where $\Delta S_o$ is the thermal entropy of adsorption and $\Delta E$ the energy of adsorption) which may occur only at some dilute coverage. A similar conclusion was reached by Everett (43) and Baker and Everett (6), who related the linear behavior to a constant value of $\Delta S_o/(T\Delta C_p + RT)$, where $\Delta C_p$ is the differential heat capacity of adsorption. Thus, $\Delta E$ at low surface coverage may depend on temperature and not on coverage, but at the lower temperatures, where the adsorption may cease to follow Henry's law, $\Delta E$ becomes dependent on coverage.

At very low fractional coverage the isosteric heats of adsorption may be quite large. A well known example is the oxygen/charcoal system for which values of 70 to 80 kcal./mole have been reported for the first increment of gas introduced (71, 83). Recently, the differential heats of adsorption of oxygen on a purified mineralogical graphite ("evacuated for a long time and degassed at $10^{-5}$ mm. Hg") (44) were determined calorimetrically. Very large heats of adsorption ($\cong$ 100 kcal./mole) were observed up to 0.3 $\mu$mole per square meter; thereafter, the heat decreased steadily with oxygen adsorption ($\cong$ 50 kcal./mole at 1.4 $\mu$mole oxygen per square meter). Such high magnitudes are probably associated with chemisorption processes. Cook, Pack, and Oblad (27) raised the question of whether physical adsorption typified by the Type II isotherm can exist in the low pressure region. These authors suggested that a mechanical strain exists at the surface of the solid and the first amounts adsorbed are associated with the relief of this strain. To this may be added a chemical aspect. When the first aliquot of gas is added to an intensively outgassed solid, the rate of adsorption is definitely slower than for succeeding doses. This behavior may be associated with chemical changes that are apparent in the composition of the gas phase as revealed by mass spectrometry techniques. Bursts of gas have been observed when a crystal is cleaved under ultravacuum conditions (117). From the surface chemist's point of view, part of the "strain" located at the surface may be associated with surface impurities that are known to concentrate at the interface. These may be released by desorption or by molecular exchange following the introduction of the gas under study.

The interaction of surface atoms and the adsorbate atoms or molecules to minimize the surface energy leads in general to ordered arrangements. This is readily accomplished given a sufficient degree of surface mobility. In the preparation of commercial solid adsorbents and catalysts, however, much effort is made to avoid minimization of surface energy. Here, disordered structures and high surface energies are sought. Fundamental knowledge of the sparsely covered surface can, therefore, indicate the direction to go to attain either goal.

The thermal desorption of gases in ultrahigh vacuum has been widely studied by the "flash-filament" technique to determine the reaction order and the dependence of activation energy on surface coverage (95). When applied to gases chemisorbed on the refractory metals, the results indicate that there are several adsorbed states on the same surface. Nitrogen has three states on tungsten (91) and two on molybdenum (91). Oxygen adsorbed at 300° K. on polycrystalline molybdenum in two states has been shown by Redhead (96) to desorb by electron bombardment (0–300 e.v.) into neutral atoms and $O^+$ ions in the ratio of 50 to 1. The surface chemistry and physics of even these well defined surfaces entails, therefore, fundamental atomic processes that require the application of several techniques simultaneously for further elucidation.

## THE ADSORBENT SURFACE

### Chemical Composition of the Boundary

The useful properties of commercial solid adsorbents and catalysts normally depend on the presence of chemical groups possibly extraneous to the bulk composition. These serve to prevent an otherwise self-minimization of the surface energy of the solid. One requirement essential to fundamental investigations is the ability to approach an ideal surface as closely as possible and then study the effect of an applied change. The impurities in the reactants forming the solid may be adsorbed or desorbed at the interface, and although they may constitute a relatively small fraction of the total solid, this segregation of impurities can involve a significant fraction of the boundary. In addition, the environment may contribute adsorbed species or decomposition products, unless very special precautions are taken.

In general, the "active centers" originally conceived by the surface chemist are now interpreted as vacancies, interstitial atoms, dislocations, and occluded impurities by the solid state physicist. The influence of surface composition was recently demonstrated in a study of sodium chloride crystals containing 2.2% calcium chloride (75) prepared from fused mixtures. The higher catalytic activity of the mixture toward ethyl chloride dehydrohalogenation than that of sodium chloride alone was accounted for by the preferential adsorption of calcium ions at the interface. Repeated extracts with acetone in which both salts are only slightly soluble showed a large difference between bulk and surface concentration of calcium and reflected the greater ease of making a cation vacancy in the surface of the sodium chloride than doing so in the interior. The nonstoichiometric behavior of some materials is based on the composition of the total sample; the well known laws of combining proportions for macrostructures need revision where applied to surface structures (77).

Adsorbed impurities have long been known to influence the growth, topography, and evaporation of crystals. The complexity of the problem is paced by the great variations possible in the chemical environment. For example, sodium chloride crystals react readily with water vapor and oxygen (7). The reaction with water vapor displaces chlorine by hydrolysis and this can be reversed by a treatment with hydrogen chloride. The oxygen ($O_2$ or $O_3$) reaction with sodium chloride forms an anion species, probably $O_2^-$ and an appreciable amount can be introduced by normal handling and annealing in laboratory atmosphere. A value for $OH^-$ concentration in NaCl of $10^{-4}$ to $10^{-5}$ mole fraction was found at 1% relative humidity (7).

The importance of adsorption impurities in a study of the gas/solid interface cannot be overemphasized (21). Figure 15 shows schematically some of the simple defects that are possible in a surface. As early as 1927 Kossel postulated that a growth process involved surface adsorption, diffusion to a step, diffusion along a step to a point defect (active site), and incorporation into the crystal. Much later, Frank (46) proposed that crystal dislocations provide a source of molecular steps required for the growth step. Very small amounts of impurities change the surface diffusion and the time of residence on a surface. Obviously, there is need to collect systematic information on individual systems prepared under highly controlled conditions.

There appear to be two limiting cases that the surface chemist might consider: immobile adsorbed impurities, and those completely mobile. In the first case, the adsorbed layer must squeeze around the impurity and thus incorporate the impurity into the adsorption complex. The degree to which this takes place depends on the concentration of impurity; it may build to an extent that stops all growth.

In the second case, the mobile-impurity concentration along the step is in equilibrium with its gaseous concentration, and the principal effect is then to maintain the impurity concentration at the active site. This lowers the rate of adsorption by direct poisoning or by an exchange process. Mobile adsorbed impurities lower the edge energy and this raises the chemical activity of the adsorption site. One current view of whisker growth

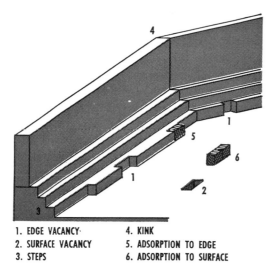

1. EDGE VACANCY       4. KINK
2. SURFACE VACANCY    5. ADSORPTION TO EDGE
3. STEPS              6. ADSORPTION TO SURFACE

*Figure 15. Simple defects ascribed to the boundary surfaces of crystals*

from the vapor is, through adsorption of atoms on perfect sidewalls of the whisker, surface diffusion to the tip, and incorporation at a step in the tip. The whisker growth of silicon crystals, however, has been ascribed to the essential presence of an impurity (*54*). This has led to a vapor-liquid-solid mechanism of single crystal growth (*118*) in which the impurity forms a droplet having a relatively low freezing temperature. This is a preferred site of vapor deposition and causes the liquid to become supersaturated. The whisker grows by precipitation of the solid from the droplet. The proposed mechanism has many applications in which controlled growth can be obtained by appropriate use of impurities.

Semiconductors are examples in which "impurities" may actually be termed the essential ingredient. Oxygen adsorption on atomically clean surfaces has shown the importance of specifying the surface condition of each crystal face (*36*), since differences in behavior were in some cases due to contamination alone and in other cases to crystal face orientation produced in a degassing followed by subsequent annealing. Some surface properties of the gas/germanium system have been reported by Zettlemoyer *et al.* (*124*). The adsorption isotherms

of argon and propanol were determined after treating the germanium 15 hours at $10^{-5}$ torr and temperatures ranging from 25 to 500° C. The interaction (chemisorption) of propanol with oxide- and/or hydroxide-covered germanium single crystals could be correlated with the electrical conductivity. This is an example of the simultaneous measurements of adsorption and some independent property, in this case, an electronic behavior of the germanium single crystal (*69*).

It is well appreciated that chemical groups in the gas/solid interface can be modified and thus bring about pronounced changes. In recent years a start has been made in relating the observed adsorption to changes in the molecular spectra. One example is the infrared absorption spectra in the OH region observed for various silicates before and after the adsorption of various organic compounds (*112*). A narrow band at 3750 cm.$^{-1}$ (the position for the free stretching frequency) is unchanged in position, but the adjacent wide absorption band (hydrogen-bonded surface OH groups) is sensitive to the thermal treatment of the silicate and to the adsorbate employed. Galkin, Kiselev, and Lygin (*50*) examined the changes in spectra of a silicate surface with adsorbed aromatic hydrocarbons. The shift in the OH adsorption band was related to the heat adsorption of the hydrocarbon. Removing the OH from the surface (dehydration and methylation) lowers the adsorption and the heat of adsorption for polar, quadrupolar, and $\pi$-electron bond molecules; the intensity of the adsorption bands for CH out-of-plane modes of vibration is also lowered. A complete understanding of the spectra of the adsorption complex will require experimental data of high resolution, and a satisfactory theoretical treatment is yet to come.

### The Geometric Factor in Gas/Solid Interaction

The terminal planes of a solid are generally considered different from the substrate planes where the forces between constituents have the symmetry of the crystal. Actually, the boundary planes may be bonded to the substrate quite differently. Either there may be strong interactions in the *z*-direction or the interaction may be strong in the *xy* plane (assumed to be in the surface). Ionic crystals and graphite are examples of these types. In all likelihood, there are intermediate degrees of interaction in surface structures where, in addition to symmetry considerations, the steric factors of fit and misfit contribute to the distance of closest approach.

Regions of low and high surface activity are accompanied by corresponding differences in atomic structure of the surface. Correlations of surface geometry and catalytic activity have been sought by many investigators [Balandin (*4*), Beeck (*15*), Rideal (*61*, *115*), Maxted (*84*)]. Definite evidence has been obtained with the field-emission microscope by Müller and Drechsler (*90*) and others. The activity of individual crystal faces in catalysis has been discussed by Gwathmey and Cunningham (*53*) and although the activity does depend on the particular lattice spacing exposed, there are regions within any one face which differ in activity. These differences are now related to defect structures.

As discussed in a previous section, the simplest method of varying the geometry of a crystal surface is by evaporation onto a suitable substrate. The evaporated film may range from a random array of small crystallites to one with a well organized structure. Changes in the surface area of a fresh deposit demonstrate that evaporated films are particularly sensitive to thermal treatment, the reduction in area depending on time, temperature, and the weight of the film. This appears to be particularly true for films that are free of serious chemical contamination. Sintering has been ascribed to the mobility of metal atoms on their own surface. According to Tammann's rule (119) atomic mobilities in a solid attain an observable rate in temperature range one-half below the normal melting point expressed in °K. This approximate rule would limit the sintering of nickel to temperatures above 600° C.; actually, it takes place at a considerably lower temperature as shown in Table VIII. With more sensitive methods based on radioactive tracers, the mobility of constituent atoms has been detected far below the melting point in numerous self-diffusion measurements for many metals and alloys.

### TABLE VIII. SINTERING OF EVAPORATED FILMS

| Copper (2) (10 Mg. Weight) | | Nickel (28) (10 Mg. Weight) | | Carbon (35) (3.23 Mg. Weight) | |
|---|---|---|---|---|---|
| Temp., °C. | A, m.²/g. | Temp., °C. | A, m.²/g. | Temp., °C. | A, m.²/g. |
| −183 | 39 | | | | |
| −183 to 18 | 12 | 25 | 0.19 | 24 | 730 |
| 18 | 6 | 100 | 0.12 | 400 | 730 |
| 100 | 4 | 200 | 0.084 | | |
| | | 300 | 0.064 | | |
| | | 400 | 0.050 | | |

Films of copper show a similar sintering behavior. The BET areas (ethane at −183° C.) of thin films of evaporated copper were determined by Allen, Evans, and Mitchell (2), and oxygen adsorption was also observed. Typical isotherms are shown in Figure 16. For films deposited at −183° C., the surface areas (39 m.²/g.) were linearly proportional to the mass of copper in the films. These facts were interpreted in terms of a uniformly porous structure. The decrease in area on annealing and the accompanying decrease in the resistance (prevented by the admission of oxygen) suggest a structure change by a surface migration of copper atoms. As in the case of nickel, the temperatures were considerably below the melting point of copper.

In contrast to the behavior of metal films, carbon films deposited at 78° K. show no sintering effect up to 400° C. In view of the very high melting point of carbon ($\cong 4000°$ K.) this may be expected. Working with stacked films of carbon and nickel, Deitz and McFarlane (35) showed that the sintering may be attributed solely to the nickel content (Figure 17).

The sintering behavior of some metal films may

depend on factors other than mobility of the constituent atoms. Caswell and Budo (23) observed that tin films deposited at 78° K. were continuous (electron micrograph), but agglomerated into separate islands in vacuum of $\cong 10^{-8}$ torr when warmed to room temperature. However, any stage in the agglomeration process could be stabilized by admitting oxygen ($10^{-4}$ torr) and warming to room temperature. A surface oxide monolayer was formed with no appreciable diffusion of oxygen into the bulk of the film. It has been proposed that oxygen be used to freeze a low temperature kinetic process (70) so that it may be examined at room temperature. This technique could be useful in certain problems and the value of ultrahigh vacuum procedures is self evident for proper control of a desired impurity.

Using a "decoration" technique with gold evaporated on graphite surfaces (in quantities only sufficient to form less than a monolayer) Hennig (59, 60) showed that the gold aggregated preferentially at surface irregularities which were thus rendered visible under electron microscopy. Adsorbed impurities caused a considerable increase in the background number of gold aggregates either uniformly or in patches—atomic hydrogen produced patches within seconds at room temperature and molecular hydrogen only above 850° C. Hennig's results, given in Table IX, show that surface compounds were surprisingly stable after heat treatment. Water could be removed below 300° C., but acetone appeared only partly removed in vacuum at 500° C., leaving residues that became "decorated" by gold.

### Chemical Reactivity

An enhanced chemical reactivity is generally found when the reactants are located on a particular gas/solid interface. As a consequence, the temperature range in which a reaction rate becomes appreciable is significantly lowered relative to the reaction between the condensed phases. The enhancement is not due only to the increase in surface area but takes place under conditions thought to be preliminary to actual catalytic activity. One or more chemisorption processes involving adsorption complexes are generally acknowledged to be involved as intermediate steps.

Many techniques are being used to study the intermediate complexes. These include infrared spectroscopy, high vacuum techniques, field emission microscopy, nuclear magnetic and electron spin resonance, contact potential measurements, and measurements of the geometric structure of the surface and substrate (41). The evidence for the existence of "hot spot" adsorption, or the adsorption bond, has been reviewed by Schuit and Reijen (108) for metal-on-silica catalyst. The bonds are covalent although slightly polarized.

In addition to forming chemical bonds with constituents in the surface, a more subtle interaction involves the bending of chemical bonds and the formation of oriented adsorbates. In regard to the adsorbate, the gas/solid interaction results in a decrease in entropy of the system. The cooperative orientation of surface-adsorbate bonds furnishes a further entropy decrease

**TABLE IX.   GOLD ON CLEAVED GRAPHITE CRYSTALS**

|  | Aggregates/$10^{-10}$ Cm.$^2$ |
|---|---|
| Freshly cleaved | 0.1 |
| Cleaved, heated to 900° C. | 0.02 |
| Adsorbed $Cl_2$ | 1 |
| Adsorbed $I_2$ | 20 |
| Adsorbed acetone | 190 |
| Reacted with ozone | 60 |

*From observations by Hennig (59).*

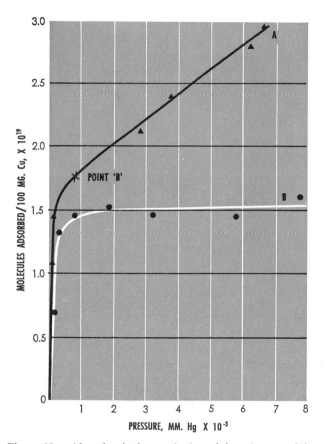

*Figure 16.   Adsorption isotherms of ethane (A) and oxygen (B) on copper films at −183° C. (2)*

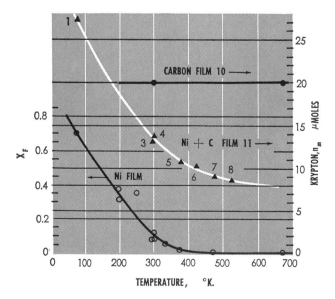

*Figure 17.   Area changes of nickel and of nickel-carbon films produced by heating to progressively higher temperatures (35)*

that can be quite significant.   In fact, this mechanism would be a plausible one to explain relocation of the atoms and groups in a surface and the relief of strain over the surface without transmitting it through the solid.   The experimental approach to this aspect of adsorption is through measurements of optical and magnetic anisotropy.

## CONCLUSIONS

This survey presents several interesting trends in current researches at the gas/solid interface.   Adsorption and desorption studies in the past have been concerned mainly with considerations of mass balance. A strong effort is now being made to define the initial state of the adsorbing surface in terms of solid state structure and surface composition and to identify the adsorbent-adsorbate complex.   The most important experimental parameter is probably the influence of the pretreatment of the solid before measurements.   The properties of some surfaces may change subsequently with time as the strain-stress relationships set up in treating the solid adjust slowly toward minimum surface free energy.   The pretreatment may include some combination of thermal, electrical, and chemical methods.

The above trend has led to an increasingly closer tie between the surface chemist and the solid state physicist. It would be very helpful to resolve some aspects of the apparently different vocabularies used by these two disciplines.

It is increasingly relevant to report a surface property in terms of unit surface.   The physical adsorption of nitrogen and krypton at low temperatures may be used to obtain the necessary data for a surface area evaluation. The determination of $V_m$ (the volume of nitrogen at standard temperature and pressure required to form a monolayer of adsorbed gas) can be accomplished by the point B method or by the BET procedure, the latter requiring fewer data.   In special cases, other adsorbates such as ethane and carbon dioxide have proved useful.

Multilayer adsorption presents many unsolved problems;   the theoretical difficulties are similar to those encountered in studies of the liquid state.   Current researches at fractional surface coverage attempt to express the surface nonuniformity in terms of an energy distribution as a function of surface coverage.   Considerable interest is now current in the field of "high-temperature" physical adsorption.   At the corresponding low surface coverage, there is minimum interaction between adsorbate molecules.

Development of modern gas chromatography and mass spectrometry makes it possible to follow the partial pressures of all gaseous reactants and products of a gas/solid system.   Facility of data collection makes possible more elaborate experimental designs.   The ability to analyze complicated gas mixtures enables new studies to be made of selective adsorption in multiple-component systems.

High vacuum technology is rapidly being applied to researches at low surface coverage.   Surface properties are very sensitive to adsorbed impurities (mobile and immobile) that originate either in the environment or as decomposition products from sample preparation. Only in ultrahigh vacuum systems can one minimize the impurity and study its influence systematically. There is an increasing use of evaporated films or otherwise vacuum-formed deposits in order to study fundamental surface properties. A greater insight into the nature of the gas/solid interaction is thus possible, thus holding great promise for the growth and development of this phase of surface chemistry.

## LITERATURE CITED

(1) Allen, F. G., Eisinger, J., Hagstrum, H. D., Law, J. T., *J. Appl. Phys.* **30**, 1563–71 (1959).
(2) Allen, J. A., Evans, C. C., Mitchell, J. W., "Structure and Properties of Thin Films," pp. 46–52, Wiley, New York, 1959.
(3) Alpert, D., *J. Appl. Phys.* **24**, 860–76 (1953).
(4) Balandin, A. A., *Z. Physik. Chem.* **B2**, 289–316 (1929).
(5) Ballou, E. V., Doolen, O. K., *Anal. Chem.* **32**, 532–6 (1960).
(6) Baker, J. A., Everett, D. H., *Trans. Faraday Soc.* **58**, 1608–23 (1962).
(7) Barr, L. W., Hoflyberg, F. P., Morrison, J. A., *J. Appl. Phys.* **33**, 225–6 (1962).
(8) Barrer, R. M., Hampton, M. G., *Trans. Faraday Soc.* **53**, 1462–75 (1957).
(9) Barrer, R. M., MacLeod, D. M., *Ibid.*, **51**, 1290–1300 (1955).
(10) Barrer, R. M., Rees, L. V. C., *Ibid.*, **57**, 999–1007 (1961).
(11) Barrer, R. M., Strachan, E., *Proc. Roy. Soc. (London)* **A231**, 52–74 (1955).
(12) Becker, J. A., *Advan. Catalysis* **7**, 135–211 (1955).
(13) Beebe, R. A., Beckwith, J. B., Honig, J. M., *J. Am. Chem. Soc.* **67**, 1554–8 (1945).
(14) Beebe, R. A., Emmett, P. H., *J. Phys. Chem.* **65**, 184–5 (1961).
(15) Beeck, O., *Advan. Catalysis* **2**, 151–95 (1950).
(16) Boer, J. H. de, "The Dynamical Character of Adsorption," Oxford Press, Oxford, England, 1953.
(17) Brunauer, S., "Physical Adsorption of Gases and Vapors," Princeton Univ. Press, 1943.
(18) Brunauer, S., Emmett, P. H., *J. Am. Chem. Soc.* **57**, 1754–5 (1935).
(19) Brunauer, S., Emmett, P. H., Teller, E. T., *J. Am. Chem. Soc.* **60**, 309–19 (1938).
(20) Burwell, R. L., Smudski, P. A., May, T. P., *J. Am. Chem. Soc.* **69**, 1525–9 (1947).
(21) Cabrea, N., Coleman, R. V., Chap. 1 in "Theory of Crystal Growth from the Vapor," Wiley, New York, 1963.
(22) Caswell, H. L., *Phys. Thin Films* **1**, 1–67 (1963).
(23) Caswell, H. L., Budo, Y., *J. Appl. Phys.* **35**, 644–7 (1964).
(24) Clarke, J. T., *J. Phys. Chem.* **68**, 884–8 (1964).
(25) Constabaris, G., Sams, J. R., Jr., Halsey, G. D., Jr., *Phys. Chem.* **64**, 1689–96 (1960); **65**, 367–9 (1961).
(26) Constabaris, G., Halsey, G. D., Jr., *J. Chem. Phys.* **27**, 1433–4 (1957).
(27) Cook, M. A., Pack, D. H., Oblad, A. G., *J. Chem. Phys.* **19**, 367–76 (1951).
(28) Crawford, E., Roberts, M. W., Kemball, C. K., *Trans. Faraday Soc.* **58**, 1761–7 (1962).
(29) Dacey, J. R., *Advan. Chem.* **33**, 172–81 (1961).
(30) Danforth, J. D., DeVries, T., *J. Am. Chem. Soc.* **61**, 873–6 (1939).
(31) Deitz, V. R., Bibliography of Solid Adsorbents, Vol. 1 (1900–1942); Vol. 2 (1943–52) National Bureau of Standards, Washington, D. C.
(32) Deitz, V. R., Carpenter, F. G., *Advan. Chem.* **33**, 146–59 (1961).
(33) Deitz, V. R., Carpenter, F. G., Arnold, R. G., *Carbon* **1**, 245–54 (1964).
(34) Deitz, V. R., Gleysteen, L. F., Unpublished results of the Bone Char Research Project, Inc., National Bureau of Standards, Washington, D. C.
(35) Deitz, V. R., McFarlane, E. F., *Carbon* **1**, 117–25 (1964).
(36) Dillon, J. A., Jr., Oman, R. M., 1962 Natl. Symposium on Vacuum Technology, 479–83, Am. Vacuum Soc., Pergamon Press, New York.
(37) Drain, L. E., Morrison, J. A., *Trans. Faraday Soc.* **48**, 316–26, 840–7 (1952); **49**, 654–73 (1953).
(38) Duncan, J. F., *Ibid.*, **45**, 879–91 (1949).
(39) Ehrlich, G., *Ann. N. Y. Acad. Sci.* **101**, 722–55 (1963).
(40) Eischen, R. P., Pliskin, W. A., *Advan. Catalysis* **10**, 1–56 (1958).
(41) Emmett, P. H., 36th Annual Priestley Lectures, "New Approaches to the Study of Catalysis" (April 1962).
(42) Enderby, J. A., *Trans. Faraday Soc.* **51**, 57–70 (1955); **52**, 139–53 (1956).
(43) Everett, D. H., *Ibid.*, **46**, 453–9, 942–57, 957–69 (1950).
(44) Fedorov, G. G., Zarif'yants, Yu. A., Kiselev, V. F., *Russian J. Phys. Chem.* **37**, 871–4 (1963).
(45) Fedorova, M. F., *Soviet Phys.-Tech. Phys.* **8**, 434–8 (1963).
(46) Frank, F. C., *Disc. Faraday Soc.* **5**, 48–54 (1949).
(47) Freeman, M. P., Halsey, G. D., Jr., *J. Phys. Chem.* **59**, 181–4 (1955).
(48) Freeman, M. P., Kolb, K., *Ibid.*, **67**, 217–21 (1963).
(49) Gale, R. L., Beebe, R. A., *Ibid.*, **68**, 555–67 (1964).
(50) Galkin, G. A., Kiselev, A. V., Lygin, V. I., *Trans. Faraday Soc.* **60**, 431–9 (1964).
(51) Gleysteen, L. F., Deitz, V. R., *J. Res. Natl. Bur. Std.* **35**, 285–307 (1945).
(52) Graham, D., *J. Phys. Chem.* **66**, 1815–18 (1962); **68**, 2788–92 (1964).
(53) Gwathmey, A. T., Cunningham, R. E., *Advan. Catalysis* **10**, 57–95 (1958).
(54) Greiner, E. S., Gutowski, J. A., Ellis, W. C., Jr., *J. Appl. Phys.* **32**, 2489–90 (1961).
(55) Habgood, H. W., Hanlan, J. F., *Can. J. Chem.* **37**, 843–55 (1959).
(56) Hanlan, J. F., Freeman, M. P., *Ibid.*, pp. 1575–88.
(57) Hansen, R. S., Murphy, J. A., McGee, T. C., *Trans. Faraday Soc.* **60**, 597–603 (1964).
(58) Hendricks, S. B., Hill, W. L., *Proc. Natl. Acad. Sci.* **36**, 731–7 (1950).
(59) Hennig, G. R., *Appl. Phys. Letters* **4**, 52–5 (1964).
(60) Hennig, G. R., *J. Chem. Phys.* **40**, 2877–82 (1964).
(61) Herington, E. F. G., Rideal, E. K., *Proc. Roy. Soc. (London)* **A184**, 434–46, 447–63 (1947).
(62) Hill, T. L., *J. Chem. Phys.* **14**, 268–75 (1946).
(63) *Ibid.*, pp. 263–7, 441–53; **15**, 767–77 (1947); **16**, 181–9 (1948); **17**, 520–35, 762–71, 772–4, 775–81 (1949); **18**, 246–56, 791–6 (1950).
(64) Hill, T. L., *J. Chem. Phys.* **63**, 456–60 (1959).
(65) Hill, T. L., Emmett, P. H., and Joyner, L. D., *J. Am. Chem. Soc.* **73**, 5102–7 (1951).
(66) Hirth, J. P., Pound, G. M., "Condensation and Evaporation, Nucleation and Growth Kinetics," Macmillan, New York, 1963.
(67) Hobson, J. P., Armstrong, R. A., *J. Phys. Chem.* **67**, 2000–8 (1963).
(67a) Hobson, J. P., Edmonds, T., Verreault, R. *Can. J. Phys.* **41**, 903–5 (1963).
(68) James, L. K., Jr., Labows, J. H., Jr., *J. Phys. Chem.* **68**, 1122–8 (1964).
(69) Katz, M. J., *Advan. Chem.* **33**, 237–8 (1961).
(70) Keith, H. D., *Proc. Phys. Soc. (London)* **69B**, 180–92 (1956).
(71) Keys, F. G., Marshall, M. J., *J. Am. Chem. Soc.* **49**, 156–73 (1927).
(72) Kidnay, A. J., Hiza, M. J., *J. Phys. Chem.* **67**, 1725–7 (1963).
(73) Kini, K. A., *J. Phys. Chem.* **68**, 217–18 (1964).
(74) Kummer, J. T., Emmett, P. H., *J. Phys. Chem.* **55**, 337–46 (1951).
(75) Kummer, J. T., Youngs, J. D., *Ibid.*, **67**, 107–9 (1963).
(76) Laidler, K. J., Townshend, R. E., *Trans. Faraday Soc.* **57**, 1590–1602 (1961).
(77) Lander, J. J., *Surface Science* **1**, 125–64 (1964).
(78) Langmuir, I., Villars, D. S., *J. Am. Chem. Soc.* **53**, 486–97 (1931).
(79) Lewis, W. K., Gilliland, E. R., Chertow, B., Cadogan, W. P., IND. ENG. CHEM. **42**, 1314–32 (1950).
(80) Liang, S. Chu, *J. Phys. Chem.* **57**, 84–7 (1953).
(81) Loebenstein, W. V., Deitz, V. R., *J. Chem. Phys.* **15**, 687–8 (1947).
(82) Lopez-Gonzalez, Juan de D., Carpenter, F. G., Deitz, V. R., *J. Phys. Chem.* **65**, 1112–9 (1961).
(83) Marshall, M. J., Bramston-Cook, H. E., *J. Am. Chem. Soc.* **51**, 2019–29 (1929).
(84) Maxted, E. B., *Advan. Catalysis* **3**, 129–77 (1951).
(85) McBain, J. W., Jackman, D. N., Bakr, A. M., Smith, H. G., *J. Phys. Chem.* **34**, 1439–53 (1930).
(86) McBain, J. W., Lucas, H. P., Chapman, P. F., *J. Am. Chem. Soc.* **52**, 2668–81 (1930).
(87) McIntosh, R. L., Rideal, E. K., Snelgrove, J. A., *Proc. Roy. Soc. (London)* **A208**, 292–301 (1951).
(88) Morrison, J. A., Drain, L. E., Dugdale, J. S., *Can. J. Chem.* **30**, 890–903 (1952).
(89) Morrison, J. A., Los, J. M., Drain, L. E., *Trans. Faraday Soc.* **47**, 1023–30 (1951).
(90) Müller, E. W., Drechsler, M., *Ergeb. Exakt. Naturw.* **27**, 290 (1953); *Z. Physik* **134**, 208–21 (1953).
(91) Oguri, T., *J. Phys. Soc. Japan* **18**, 1280–94 (1963); **19**, 77–83 (1964).
(92) O'Reilly, D. E., Leftin, H. P., Hall, W. K., *J. Chem. Phys.* **29**, 970–1 (1958).
(93) Pace, E. L., Siebert, A. R., *J. Phys. Chem.* **63**, 1398–1400 (1959); **64**, 961–3 (1960).
(93a) Podgurski, H. H., Davis, F. N. *J. Phys. Chem.* **65**, 1343 (1961).
(94) Prenzlow, C. F., Halsey, G. D., Jr., *J. Phys. Chem.* **61**, 1158–65 (1957).
(95) Redhead, P. A., *Vacuum* **12**, 203–11 (1962).
(96) Redhead, P. A., *Can. J. Phys.* **42**, 886–905 (1964).
(97) Redhead, P. A., Hobson, J. P., Kornelsen, E. V., *Advan. Electron Phys.* **17**, 323–431 (1962).
(98) Resing, H. A., Thompson, J. K., Krebs, J. J., *J. Phys. Chem.* **68**, 1621–7 (1964).
(99) Roberts, J. K., *Proc. Roy. Soc. (London)* **A152**, 445–63 (1935).
(100) Roberts, R. W., Vanderslice, T. A., "Ultrahigh Vacuum and Its Applications," Prentice-Hall, 1963.
(101) Rosenberg, A. J., *J. Am. Chem. Soc.* **78**, 2929–34 (1956).
102) Ross, S., *J. Am. Chem. Soc.* **70**, 3830–7 (1948); **76**, 2637–40 (1954).
(103) Ross, S., Olivier, J. P., "On Physical Adsorption," Interscience, New York, 1964.
(104) Ross, S., Olivier, J. P., *J. Phys. Chem.* **65**, 608–15 (1961).
(105) Ross, S., Saelens, J. K., Olivier, J. P., *J. Phys. Chem.* **66**, 696–700 (1962).
(106) Savage, R. H., *J. Appl. Phys.* **19**, 1–10 (1948).
(107) Savage, R. H., Brown, C., *J. Am. Chem. Soc.* **70**, 2362–6 (1948).
(108) Schuit, G. C. A., Reijen, L. L. van, *Advan. Catalysis* **10**, 242–317 (1958).
(109) Singleton, J. H., Halsey, G. D., Jr., *J. Phys. Chem.* **58**, 330–5, 1011–17 (1954).
(110) Steele, W. A., Halsey, G. D., Jr., *J. Chem. Phys.* **22**, 979–84 (1954); *J. Phys. Chem.* **59**, 57–65 (1955).
(111) Takaishi, T., Sensui, Y., *Trans. Faraday Soc.* **59**, 2503–14 (1963).
(112) Terenin, A. N., "Conference Surface Chemical Compounds," Edited by A. V. Kiselev, Moscow, Moscow Univ. Press, 1957 (AEC-tr-3750, pp. 227–45).
(113) Trapnell, B. M. W., "Chemisorption," Butterworth, Washington, D. C., 1955; Hayward, D. O., Trapnell, B. M. W., 2nd Edition, 1964.
(114) Tuck, N. G. M., McIntosh, R. L., Maass, O., *Can. J. Res.* **26B**, 20 37 (1948).
(115) Twigg, G. H., Rideal, E. K., *Trans. Faraday Soc.* **36**, 533–7 (1940).
(116) Ubbelohde, A. R., Chap. 11, "Chemistry of the Solid State," Butterworth, Washington, D. C., 1955.
(117) Vanderslice, T. A., Whetten, N. R., *J. Phys. Chem. Solids* **25**, 513–15 (1964).
(118) Wagner, R. S., Ellis, W. C., *Appl. Phys. Letters* **4**, 89–90 (1964).
(119) Welch, A. J. E., Chap. 12, pp. 297–310 in "Chemistry of the Solid State," Edited by W. E. Garner, Butterworth, Washington, D. C., 1955.
(120) Winter, E. R. S., *Advan. Catalysis* **10**, 196–241 (1958).
(121) Wooten, L. A., Brown, C., *J. Am. Chem. Soc.* **65**, 113–8 (1943).
(122) Yates, D. J. C., *Proc. Roy. Soc. (London)* **A224**, 526–44 (1954).
(123) Young, D. M., Crowell, A. D., "Physical Adsorption of Gases," Butterworth, Washington, D. C., 1st Edition, 1962.
(124) Zettlemoyer, A. C., Hassis, C. H., Chessick, J. J., Srinivasan, G., *Advan. Chem.* **33**, 229–37 (1961).
(125) Zimmerman, J. R., Holmes, B. G., Lasater, J. A., *J. Phys. Chem.* **60**, 1157–61 (1956); **61**, 1328–33 (1957); **62**, 1157–63 (1958).

# 12

# Immersional Wetting of Solid Surfaces

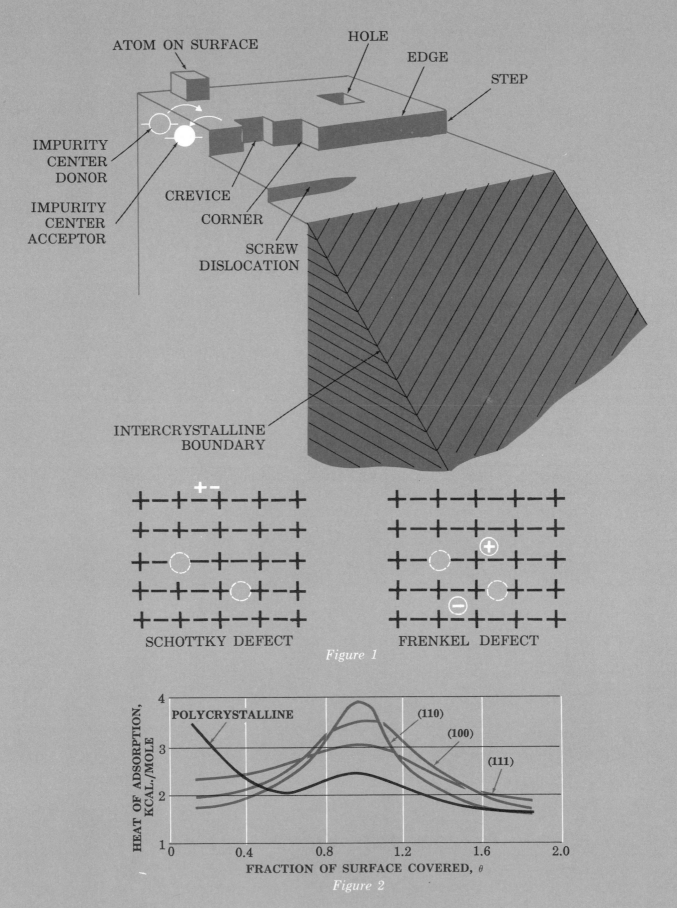

ATOM ON SURFACE

HOLE

EDGE

STEP

IMPURITY
CENTER
DONOR

IMPURITY
CENTER
ACCEPTOR

CREVICE

CORNER

SCREW
DISLOCATION

INTERCRYSTALLINE
BOUNDARY

SCHOTTKY DEFECT

FRENKEL DEFECT

*Figure 1*

POLYCRYSTALLINE

(110)

(100)

(111)

HEAT OF ADSORPTION, KCAL./MOLE

FRACTION OF SURFACE COVERED, $\theta$

*Figure 2*

EFFECT OF HETEROGENEITIES IN A SOLID SURFACE

*The heat that is evolved on wetting a solid yields a picture of the surface, with all its heterogeneities. In this article, a man who has been involved with practical problems in surface chemistry shows how to interpret this measurement*

# IMMERSIONAL WETTING OF SOLID SURFACES

## A. C. ZETTLEMOYER

FOR many systems, the crucial properties are those developed at the solid/liquid interface. The specific interactions which occur there are important to such seemingly diverse technologies as adhesives, corrosion, lubrication, detergency, heterogeneous catalysis, paints and printing inks. In some cases, such as in adhesion or in the dispersion of pigments, complete wetting or zero contact angle is desired. On the other hand, in corrosion, in catalysis, and in the attack of water on organic coatings, isolated sites provide the points of interest. In many problems, the heat of immersion technique provides one of the most fruitful methods for investigation.

Problems in these fields do not succumb to contact angle measurements or, in the case of non-volatile liquids, to vapor adsorption isotherm measurements.

◀

*Figure 1. An idealized representation of heterogeneities in a solid and of point defects in a lattice. If a lattice atom is displaced to a surface position, a Schottky defect is introduced. If the missing atom is found in an interstitial position, two point defects are introduced and these are called a Frenkel defect. In addition to these, imperfections are caused by stacking faults, nonstoichiometry and loss of order.*

*Figure 2. The graph below shows differential heats of adsorption for nitrogen on three single crystal faces of copper, and on polycrystalline copper. The large heat values at low coverages in the case of polycrystalline copper is indicative of surface heterogeneities. The low heat of adsorption on single crystal faces implies the absence of active heterogeneous sites. The heat values on single crystal faces go through a distinct maximum which corresponds, for all the three orientations, to about one monolayer. Lateral interactions between adsorbed molecules are responsible for the maxima. The combined effect of surface heterogeneities and lateral interactions lead to a monotonic decrease in heat of adsorption with coverage. The differences in the heats of adsorption in the case of single crystal faces is due to a difference in the packing of the adsorbed molecules.*

Contact angle measurements, of course, cannot be applied when the systems give zero values, nor when isolated sites provide the critical factors. Vapor adsorption measurements may also be difficult to interpret if strong chemisorption occurs as gas is admitted to the sample, the first exposed portions of the surface preferentially taking up all the adsorbate admitted.

The use of heats of immersion to attack problems in these various fields will be described. Here the solid, usually a powder, is immersed into the liquid by breaking a thin-walled sample bulb in a suitable calorimeter so that the heat liberated due to the interaction can be assayed. Included will be determinations of the average polarity of solid surfaces, site energy distribution or heterogeneity of solid surfaces, solution adsorption, interaction of surfactants with graphitic surfaces, and heat of formation of double layers. Reviews have been given elsewhere (8, 37).

The phenomenon of the evolution of heat of wetting has been known since the report by Pouillet (the "Pouillet effect") in 1822 (an even earlier observation was recorded by Leslie in 1802), and 27 more references on the subject are to be found in the literature up to 1926. By the 1930's, rather good calorimeters were developed and attention was being given to outgassing techniques prior to immersion. Yet, until the advent of the BET method (1936 to 1940) for estimating specific surface areas, the heat effects could not be put on a sound basis. The first paper which did so was that by Boyd and Harkins (5). Thereafter, the Harkins, Bartell, and Il'in groups made significant contributions. Nevertheless, the influence of immersional calorimetry in surface chemistry waned. A major reason was the difficulty

## One of the central problems in studies of solid

**TABLE I.  HEATS OF IMMERSION OF SOLIDS IN LIQUIDS**

| Solid | Surface Area, Sq. M./G. | Activation Temp., °C. | $h_{I(SL)}$, Ergs/Sq. Cm. | | | Reference |
|---|---|---|---|---|---|---|
| | | | Water | Benzene | Aliphatic hydrocarbon | |
| GeO₂ | 0.8 | 25 | 1400 | | | (4) |
| GeO₂ | 56.9 | 25 | 196 | | | (4) |
| ZrO₂ | 5.3 | 400–600 | 600 | 190 | | (5) |
| TiO₂ (anatase) | 10.5 | 100 | 504 | | 137 (hexane) | (28) |
| TiO₂ (rutile) | 5.8 | 50 | 409 | | | (40) |
| TiO₂ (rutile) | 5.8 | 100 | 498 | | | (40) |
| SiO₂ (β-quartz) | 0.07 | 160 | 847 | | | (26) |
| SiO₂ (amorphous) | 353 | 100 | 210 | 218 | | (30) |
| SiO₂ (Aerosil) | 120 | | 165 | | 118 (n-heptane) | (39) |
| α-Al₂O₃ | 2.72 | 160 | 693 | | 151 (n-hexane) | (26) |
| Al₂O₃ (amorphous) | 104 | 160 | 454 | | 85 (n-hexane) | (26) |
| BaSO₄ | 4.4 | 400–600 | 490 | 140 | | (5) |
| Graphite | 28.4 | 400–600 | 48 | 225 (5) | 122.5 (n-heptane) | (2) |
| Graphon | 97 | 25 | 32 | | 106 (n-heptane) | (35) |
| Teflon | 9.0 | 25 | 6 | | 58 (n-heptane) | (7) |

of manipulating the ever more complex calorimeters.

In the 1950's, the confluence of two factors gave new impetus to the field.  One was the appearance of simple calorimeters based on thermistors as the temperature sensing elements, and the other was the impact of various other surface chemistry developments which pointed the way toward what could be achieved through heat of immersion measurements.

Heats of immersion are usually given in ergs per square centimeter because of the convenience of these units. They appear to be small values, yet they are highly revealing.  Typical values ranging from polar solids interacting with water, to non-polar solids with non-polar liquids are listed in Table I.

### Solid Surfaces

When one passes from liquid surfaces or carefully deposited films on solid surfaces, the situation becomes vastly more complicated.  Only in the simplest cases will the crystal surface be isotropic.  Often the surface will be strained or it will contain debris, both depending on past history.  Moreover, most solids with which we may have to deal are polycrystalline and present for interaction with adsorbates different crystal faces along with intercrystalline sites.  Even a polished surface of metal or glass is likely to have an area available to adsorbed molecules which is two or three times its apparent geometric area.  This roughness is one of the central problems of solid surfaces, that of physical heterogeneities.  Some of these are idealized in Figure 1.

Screw dislocations, Schottky and Frenkel defects, and steps occur even on carefully prepared single crystal surfaces.  Powdered solids are likely to possess cracks and crevices as well, and certainly the relative abundance of edges and corners to plane surface sites is increased over that for large crystals.  Physically bound molecules are more energetically held in crevices than in declivities,

than in step positions, than on plane surfaces, than on edges or corners.  The reverse order is likely to apply in chemisorption—corners or exposed atoms more readily participate in charge sharing or transfer.

Induced heterogeneity is often prevalent—that is, the first molecules adsorbed can have a decided effect on the energy with which succeeding molecules are adsorbed. In physical adsorption, particularly on a rather homogeneous surface, lateral attraction between adsorbed molecules may lead to increased energy of interaction as indicated in Rhodin's work (18).  See Figure 2. In chemical interactions, the interaction energy usually decreases as coverage increases.  Thus, heat of adsorption curves fall (as in the physical adsorption of nitrogen for the polycrystalline copper in Figure 2).  For instance, molybdenum chemisorbs only one tenth of a monolayer of oxygen at liquid nitrogen temperature. To put it simply, the transfer of a few electrons from the metal to the oxygen makes it increasingly difficult for additional electrons to leave the metal at this low temperature.

Impurities tend to congregate in surfaces as chemical heterogeneities.  Even when present in parts per million, this effect on surface states may be noticeable or even vital to the surface properties.  Activity in heterogeneous catalysis, in corrosion, and in the interaction of semiconductors with ambients can often be ascribed to this effect.  Also, such defects can move into and out of the surface, particularly at elevated temperatures.

Quite often it is difficult to decide as to whether the interaction of a solid surface with an adsorbate is physical or chemical.  Often the amount of strong interaction varies with the water content of the surface.  For instance, a metal oxide interacts with alcohol or amine

**AUTHOR** *A. C. Zettlemoyer is Professor of Chemistry at Lehigh University, Bethlehem, Pa.  He has recently been appointed Editor-in-Chief of the Journal of Colloid Science.*

# surfaces is that of physical heterogeneities

molecules, for the most part, only weakly if outgassed at room temperature.  On the other hand, if adsorbed after high temperature outgassing, much of it can be pumped off only at elevated temperatures.

The point is raised that much surface chemistry work with metals as the substrates employs misleading nomenclature.  The interaction of a liquid with a metal (or elemental semiconductor) rarely is studied with bare surfaces.  Only under ultrahigh vacuum conditions can studies be made with such "clean" substrates.  What is really meant is "oxide-coated metal surfaces."  It seems apparent from current work in several fields that the thickness of the oxide film is important.  The thicker the film, the less is the contribution of the underlying metal to the surface properties of the oxide.  It should be recognized, however, that the surface states critical to the behavior of a given system sometimes depend on the donation or acceptance of electrons by the oxide-coating from the underlying substrate.

These current concepts of the behavior of solid surfaces are briefly summarized so that a better appreciation can be gained of the contributions the heats of immersion technique can make to the study of solid/liquid and solid/vapor interactions.

### Thermodynamics of Immersional Wetting and Relation to Vapor Adsorption

The heat of immersion of a clean solid into a pure liquid is the most straightforward quantity to consider.  Heat is almost invariably evolved so the enthalpy change is negative.  The surface area available to the wetting molecules is presumed known (as from the BET measurement) so the heat effect can be put on a more interesting and valuable basis of heat evolved per unit area:

$$\frac{\Delta H_I}{\Sigma} = h_{I(SL)} \cong e_{I(SL)} = e_{SL} - e_S \qquad (1)$$

The $\Delta$'s are often not expressed for simplicity in indicating the heat effect per unit area.  Since there is usually little $P\Delta V$ effect in the wetting process, the enthalpy change is essentially the change in the internal energy.  The last expression in Equation 1 expresses the change from the bare surface to the immersed solid.  Part of the diagram in Figure 3 (after Harkins) depicts this process.

A valuable aspect of the heat of immersion process is that it can be related to the adsorption of the same molecular species from the vapor state.  The combination of the two processes provides a valuable approach for a detailed assessment of the interactions involved.  The second path in Figure 3 is for the process of obtaining the immersed state through an intervening step in which some molecules of the liquid are first adsorbed from the vapor state.  Then, with more or less pre-coverage, the immersional step is carried out.  To make the second path equivalent to the first, the molecules for adsorption must be evaporated from the liquid.  Then the enthalpy changes for the two paths can be equated:

$$- h_{I(SL)} = - h_{A(SV)} - \Gamma h_L - h_{I(SfL)} \qquad (2a)$$

All these heat effects are considered for one square centimeter of surface and negative signs are included to make the terms positive since heat is emitted in each case as the terms are written.  When $\Gamma$ is the number of molecules/sq. cm. adsorbed during the pre-coverage, the $h_L$ is the heat of liquefaction per molecule of the vapor of the wetting liquid.  The final term represents the heat liberated when the pre-covered solid is immersed, where $SfL$ represents film-covered solid into the liquid.  When the solid is pre-covered to the extent that the film is liquid-like (at least with respect to enthalpy), then $h_{I(SfL)}$ becomes $h_{LV^\circ}$.  Sometimes this situation develops when only one monolayer has been pre-adsorbed as, for example, for the case of water on titania.  In

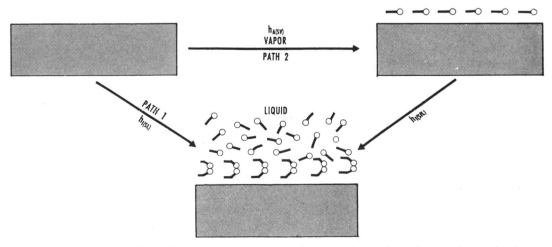

*Figure 3.  Diagrammatic representation of the relation between adsorption and immersional processes.  In Path 1, the clean surface is immersed in the liquid.  In Path 2, the surface is first covered by n adsorbate molecules from the gas phase and subsequently immersed in the liquid.  The integral and differential heats of adsorption can be calculated by following this method as indicated in the text.*

other cases, a deeper layer is needed. Then, the net heat of adsorption ($h_{I(SL)} - h_{LV°}$) is, from Equation 2:

$$h_{I(SL)} - h_{LV°} = h_{A(SV)} + \Gamma h_L \cong (e_a - e_L) \qquad (2b)$$

The last relation simply states that if the heat of immersion per unit area is reduced by the enthalpy of unit liquid surface, then, per molecule, this difference is the energy change in bringing the molecule from the liquid state into the adsorbed film. That is, the net integral heat of adsorption is obtained. Likewise, the $h_{A(SV)}$ in these equations is the integral heat of absorption per unit area up to the coverage obtained at the vapor pressure represented by $V$ in the subscript.

It is pertinent to consider further the enthalpy of liquid surfaces. If one sq. cm. of water is destroyed, 118.5 ergs are liberated. For organic liquids, surface enthalpies are considerably smaller, often 30–50 ergs/sq. cm. It is interesting to note that if the net energy required to remove a layer of liquid from a solid is 100 ergs/sq. cm., then the force required if it operates over the thickness of a molecule, say 2 A., is:

$$f = 100/2 \times 10^{-8} \text{ dynes/sq. cm.} =$$

$$5000 \text{ atm. or } 75,000 \text{ p.s.i.}$$

The surface free energy is not the same as the heat of wetting or immersion, but it is of similar magnitude and they fall in the same order from system to system (4).

Through Figure 3 and Equation 2a by rearrangement, it can also be seen that the integral heat of adsorption $h_{A(SV)}$ is:

$$h_{A(SV)} = [h_{I(SL)} - h_{I(SfL)}] - \Gamma h_L \qquad (2c)$$

Direct vapor or gas adsorption measurements produce differential heats. Immersional heats would be expected to be integral since all the interaction up to the pre-coverage or up to complete coverage is included. It becomes apparent, then, that adsorption and immersion processes are related.

In direct adsorption measurements from the vapor or gas state, differential quantities are usually determined no matter whether the heat effects are measured calorimetrically by dosing small quantities or whether they are calculated from multi-temperature isotherms. When the latter are obtained from the Clapeyron-Clausius type equation comparing isotherms at constant amount adsorbed, a so-called isosteric heat, $q_{st}$, is obtained. The relation is simply:

$$h_{I(SL)} - h_{I(SfL)} = \int_0^\Gamma q_{st}\, d\Gamma + \Gamma h_L = \Gamma(e_A' - e_L) \qquad (3)$$

The last expression relates the measured heat effects to the molar energies of the adsorbate-solid system and that for the liquid. If perturbations of the solid surface may be neglected, $e_A'$ may be regarded as the molar energy of the adsorbate itself. Adsorption indeed implies that the solid surface becomes perturbed, but the energy involved in this process is likely to be small in physical adsorptions.

Incidentally, the isosteric heat is related to the direct calorimetric heat upon adsorption of a differential amount (practically, a small increment) of vapor, $q_d$, by a work term involved in emitting the vapor. Ideally, the relation is:

$$q_{st} = q_d + RT \qquad (4)$$

The difference is often within experimental error.

Chemisorption, on the other hand, implies severe surface perturbations. Such heat effects can be readily determined by the heat of immersion technique even when vapor pressures are low or times of adsorption long. The heat effects can be followed as a function of pre-coverage, waiting as long as necessary for a given amount to be adsorbed from the vapor state. Of course, the heats of adsorption cannot be calculated from isotherms if they are not reversible.

The various heats of adsorption are therefore interrelated. Several experimental tests have been made (11, 33). Isosteric heats of adsorption generally decrease with coverage, particularly at low $\theta$'s, reflecting surface heterogeneities. We will see how heats of immersion can be used to assay the activity of sites on catalyst surfaces.

The state of the adsorbed molecules on solids can be elucidated from entropy calculations. If the entire entropy change can be attributed to the adsorbate, when perturbation of the solid is unimportant, Jura and Hill (14, 15) showed that the difference in entropy of the adsorbed film $s_A$ per molecule and the entropy of the bulk liquid $s_L$ per molecule is given by the expression

$$T(s_A - s_L) = [h_{I(SL)} - h_{I(SfL)}]/\Gamma + (\phi/\Gamma) - kT \ln p/p_o \qquad (5)$$

where $\phi = \gamma_{S°} - \gamma_{SV°}$ is the film pressure at saturation.

The entropy values thus obtained by the combination of the heats of immersion with $\phi$ values obtained from a single adsorption isotherm offer a more accurate means of evaluating the entropy data than the application of the Clapeyron-Clausius equation to multi-temperature isotherms. When this analysis was applied to the asbestos-water system (10), the uncertainty in the entropy values decreased, over the multi-temperature isotherm approach, from over 100% to 35% at low coverages and 20% to 8% at monolayer coverages.

### Work of Adhesion and the Heat of Immersion

The term adhesion has generally been used to describe the attraction at the solid/liquid interface. The work of adhesion, $W_A$, is defined as the work done in breaking one square centimeter of the solid/liquid interface in vacuum, producing solid/vacuum and liquid/saturated vapor interfaces. Thus:

$$W_A = \gamma_{S°} + \gamma_{LV°} - \gamma_{SL} \qquad (6)$$

or

$$W_A = \phi + \gamma_{LV°} (1 + \cos \theta) \qquad (7)$$

where $\phi = \gamma_{S°} - \gamma_{SV°}$ is the film pressure at saturation and $\theta$ is the contact angle of the liquid with the solid.

The value of $\phi$ is insignificant when the solid is poorly wetted. It becomes important at low contact angles or when spreading wetting occurs as desired, for instance, in adhesion. Similarly, the enthalpy of adhesion, $h_{A(SL)}$, can be expressed as:

$$h_{A(SL)} = h_{S^\circ} + h_{LV^\circ} - h_{SL} \qquad (8)$$

or:

$$h_{A(SL)} = h_{LV^\circ} - h_{I(SL)}$$

Therefore, the enthalpy of adhesion can be calculated by determining the heat of immersion and a knowledge of the enthalpy of the liquid surface $h_{LV^\circ}$. The $h_{LV^\circ}$ can be obtained by the application of the Gibbs-Helmholtz equation to the temperature variation of the surface tension of the liquid.

The entropy of adhesion is given by:

$$S_{A(SL)} = \frac{h_{A(SL)} - W_{A(SL)}}{T} \qquad (9)$$

It is thus seen that from a knowledge of $h_{I(SL)}$, $\phi$, and $\theta$ (all of these can be determined experimentally), it is possible to establish the enthalpy, free energy, and entropy of adhesion.

### Experimental Techniques

A description of the various types of calorimeters and some of the difficulties in the measurement and interpretation of heats of immersion have been discussed by Zettlemoyer et al. in earlier reviews (8, 37). Details of the construction and manipulation of the calorimeters are given in basic references by Boyd and Harkins (5), Zettlemoyer et al. (44), Berghausen (3) and Hackerman (12). There are in general two main types of calorimeters. The macrocalorimeter is constructed out of a glass Dewar flask and usually has a capacity of 250 to 1000 ml. The other type consists of metal calorimeters, usually with 5 to 10 ml. capacity, which have been generally used for microcalorimetry. The smaller heat capacity of the metal calorimeters gives a higher temperature rise and hence enhances the accuracy of the measurement. Both single and twin calorimeters of both design have been employed. Zettlemoyer and Skewis (22) have used a calorimeter constructed entirely of polyethylene and nylon to avoid the presence of trace ions which markedly influence the adsorption of surfactants.

Certain important factors that have to be taken into account in the design and construction of a calorimeter are:

— A steady and sufficient stirring rate to ensure good mixing with the minimum of heat generation.
— Accurate measurement of temperature changes.
— Accurate measurement of electrical energy when calibrating the heat capacity of the calorimeter.
— Attainment and maintenance of a steady rating period.
— A reproducible method of breaking the sample bulb.

In an experiment, in addition to the heat contribution due to the wetting process, another important source of heat is from the bulb breaking plus accessory events. Contributions could arise from the mechanical energy introduced during the fracturing of the bulb, residual strain in the glass, the $p\Delta V$ work as the residual volume from the bulb is filled with the immersional liquid, and the vaporization of liquid to fill the additional space. Usually an average correction factor is estimated by separate experiments. There have been several suggestions to minimize the errors arising out of irreproducible breaking. Young and Bursh (34) used a spring-loaded, solenoid-operated breaker to obtain a reproducible breaking of the sample bulb. They determined the heat of immersion using different sample weights. An extrapolation of the linear plot of heat of immersion versus sample weight to zero weight gives the heat of bulb breaking plus accessory events. If the bulb is filled with an inert gas (like helium) after sample activation, $p\Delta V$ work is eliminated and the correction may be much reduced (1). During the immersion of a solid into a solution there will be heat contributions due to the dilution of the solution during adsorption and due to demicellization in the case of surfactant solutions at concentrations above the cmc. These additional heat contributions can be determined and corrected for.

Special precautions have to be taken to ensure the cleanliness of the solid surfaces and immersional liquids. The need for solvent purity has been stressed for a long time (5) especially when dealing with polar surfaces and relatively non-polar wetting liquids. There are many instances where the presence of trace quantities of water are sufficient to raise the heat of immersion nearly to that due to water itself. Whalen (31) has suggested breaking several buckets of Linde sieves in the immersional liquid until the heat evolved upon the introduction of successive buckets reaches a constant level. The use of the adsorbent itself as a "getter" for last traces of water has also been successful (2, 23), here one breaks two or more bulbs in successive experiments as a check.

Considerable care has to be taken in cleaning the solid surfaces. The introduction of a liquid nitrogen trap between the sample and the final stop-cock ensures the efficient removal of organic contaminants. Often high temperature outgassing of oxides such as $TiO_2$ and $ThO_2$ may create oxygen deficiencies. A subsequent treatment with oxygen at a high temperature and outgassing with a liquid nitrogen trap is necessary in such cases. Without organic contaminant, for example, rutile $TiO_2$ is not reduced.

### Classification of Heat of Immersion Isotherms as a Function of Pre-Coverage

Experimental evidence for five different types of heat of immersion isotherms is given in the literature. They are presented in Figure 4. The two additional types shown in Figure 5 are suggested by vapor adsorption isotherms, but have not yet been confirmed by immersional calorimetry. By far, most of the efforts have been devoted to water as the wetting liquid. The most important impedance to the development of curves for organic liquids is the drastic effect of even trace amounts of water as mentioned earlier. Harkins (5) was the first to establish this effect for titanium dioxide into

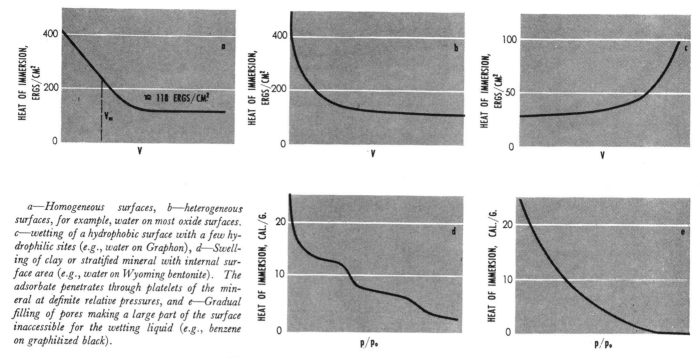

a—Homogeneous surfaces, b—heterogeneous surfaces, for example, water on most oxide surfaces. c—wetting of a hydrophobic surface with a few hydrophilic sites (e.g., water on Graphon), d—Swelling of clay or stratified mineral with internal surface area (e.g., water on Wyoming bentonite). The adsorbate penetrates through platelets of the mineral at definite relative pressures, and e—Gradual filling of pores making a large part of the surface inaccessible for the wetting liquid (e.g., benzene on graphitized black).

*Figure 4. Known types of heat of immersion isotherms.*

benzene. The results of Harkins given in Table II show that even in the presence of small quantities of water the heat of immersion of a polar solid may be increased near to that in water itself.

The curves depicted in Figures 4a and 4b are the most common heat of immersion isotherms found for polar solids in water, and also for polar and non-polar solids in organic liquids. An example of the linear decrease of heat of immersion with coverage (Figure 4a) has been observed for chrysotile asbestos in water. The isosteric heat values calculated from the adsorption isotherm showed a maximum near the monolayer similar to the differential heat of adsorption of nitrogen on copper shown in Figure 2. This is indicative of a homogeneous surface with lateral interactions between adsorbed molecules.

The exponential decrease of heat of wetting with coverage shown in Figure 1b is typical of heterogeneous surfaces. There are numerous examples of such systems.

### Immersional Wetting of Hydrophobic Solids by Water

Curve 4c is obtained in the case of a predominantly non-polar surface with very few hydrophilic sites, which is immersed in water. The interaction between the surface and water is much weaker than between water molecules themselves. On such a surface, water is usually adsorbed in patches, and the formation of clusters of water molecules around these patches at higher relative pressures is responsible for the increased heat of immersion as pre-coverage is increased. The Graphon-water system provides an example (25), and so does AgI-water (of interest since AgI is a prime ice nucleating agent).

The net heat of adsorption, which is the difference

between the heat of adsorption and heat of vaporization, is negative for such systems. Because of the low amounts of adsorption in such systems, the calculation of the heats of adsorption from multi-temperature isotherms is inaccurate. The combination of one adsorption isotherm and heats of immersion data offers a method for the computation of reliable thermodynamic quantities. The entropy of water adsorbed on Graphon is much higher than for liquid water. The area of freedom of an adsorbed molecule calculated from the entropy values indicates that there is very little interaction between neighboring adsorbate molecules when the (nominal) monolayer is adsorbed.

The isolated hydrophilic sites on a hydrophobic solid may be critical in their practical utility. Savage (20) has demonstrated, for example, that the lubricating ability of graphite is greatly enhanced by adsorbed

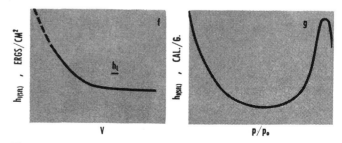

*Figure 5. New types of heat of immersion curves predicted from adsorption data. f—Weak adsorption, such as CF₄ on polytetrafluoro ethylene. Heterogeneities plus low energies of adsorption yield a heat of immersion curve which starts above the heat of liquefaction but then falls below. g—The commonly found decrease of heat of immersion is followed by a rising portion, which is believed to be due to the expansion of aggregates and possibly consequent energy release. Both these types of curves have not been experimentally observed.*

## IMMERSIONAL WETTING OF SOLID SURFACES

water on these isolated sites. Zettlemoyer and co-workers (42) have suggested that a critical hydrophobic-hydrophilic ratio (3 or 4:1) may be an important factor in the efficiency of silver iodide in ice nucleation. Several hydrophobed silicas having similar surface characteristics were found to be good nucleating agents. Such isolated hydrophilic sites are likely to be points of attack in the gradual destruction of organic coatings applied to wood, metal, and the like.

### Wetting of Clay Mineral

The type of heat of immersion isotherm in Figure 4d is usually found in clay-water systems, where a variety of processes can occur with the incorporation of water into the solid. Swelling, ion exchange, and changes due to chemical, thermal, or mechanical modification of clays and other minerals can be followed by means of heat of immersion measurements in water. The differential heat *vs.* coverage curves that can be obtained from heat of immersion and adsorption data usually show maxima corresponding to the onset of such processes mentioned above. Qualitative experiments to study the influence of particle diameter (17), firing temperature (13), and the nature of exchange sites on the heat of immersion have been carried out even before the BET method for surface area measurements was available.

Quantitative studies on clay minerals require the use of a well characterized monionic sample. The internal and external area, the water adsorption characteristics, and the magnitude of the swelling energy are needed quantities. The differential heat of adsorption as a function of coverage for bentonite is given in Figure 6 (43). The maxima correspond to the relative pressures at which the first and second water layers enter the bentonite platelets as demonstrated also by x-ray diffraction.

The constituents of the exchange sites have an influence on the heat of wetting of clays. Slabaugh (23) found that the heat of immersion of hydrogen and calcium bentonites activated at different temperatures passes through a maximum at 100 to 150° C. No such maximum was noticed in the case of sodium bentonite. It is suggested that the sodium ion is completely dehydrated at low temperatures, and as a result, the spacing between the platelets is drastically reduced, making rehydration very difficult. Calcium ions, on the other hand, dehydrate with difficulty and the complete dehydration occurs around 100 to 150° C. Similar results have been obtained by Wade and Hackerman (27) and by Brooks (6).

The isotherm in Figure 4e is generally found in the case of porous solids and possibly organic fibers. The enthalpy of immersion progressively decreases and reaches a value lower than the enthalpy of the liquid surface which should be the limiting value of the heat of immersion if no pores are involved. The filling of pores gradually reduces drastically the accessibility of the internal surface to the wetting liquid. The anomaly disappears when the loss in area is corrected using information from pore volume studies, as has been

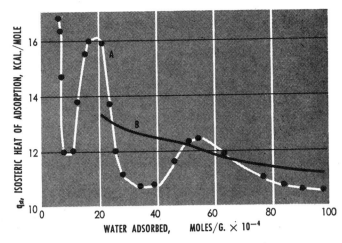

*Figure 6. Isosteric heat curves for the adsorption of water on two similar montmorillonite clay samples, a—from heat of immersion and b—from adsorption data.*

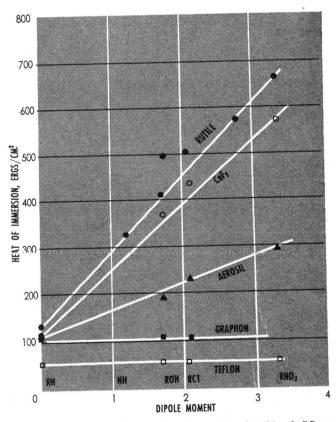

*Figure 7. The heat of immersion of a variety of solids of different surface polarity in n-butyl derivatives (allows the determination of the polarity of solid surfaces). Chemisorption must be avoided. Close-packed perpendicular array, and same distance from dipole to surface are assumed in every case.*

### TABLE II. EFFECT OF TRACE WATER ON THE HEAT OF IMMERSION OF ANATASE IN BENZENE

| Amount of Water, $\times 10^3$ Moles/Kg. | Heat of Immersion, Ergs/Sq. Cm. |
|---|---|
| 0.0 | 150 |
| 2.0 | 250 |
| 4.0 | 320 |
| 10.0 | 450 |
| 17.0 | 506 |
| $H_2O$ (pure) | 520 |

### TABLE III. HEATS OF IMMERSION OF RUTILE AND GRAPHON

| Liquid | $-h_{I(SL)}$, Ergs/Sq. Cm. at 25° C. | |
| | Rutile $(TiO_2)$ | Graphon |
|---|---|---|
| Water | 550 | 32 |
| Ethyl alcohol | 397 | 110 |
| n-Butyl alcohol | 410 | 114 |
| n-Amyl alcohol | 413 | 120 |
| n-Butyl iodide | 395 | ... |
| n-Butyl aldehyde | 556 | ... |
| n-Nitropropane | 664 | ... |
| n-Butylamine | 330 | 106 |
| n-Butyl chloride | 502 | 106 |
| Butyric acid | 506 | 115 |
| Hexane | 135 | 103 |
| Heptane | 144 | 112 |
| Octane | 140 | 127 |

found for graphite in n-propanol (24) and silica gel in water (29).

#### Average Polarity of Solid Surfaces

The heat of immersion of two solids, rutile and Graphon, in a variety of polar and non-polar liquids is listed in Table III. The heat of immersion of Graphon is essentially independent of the liquid (except water). Here, the adsorption forces arise only from London dispersion interactions. The heat values for rutile, on the other hand, vary considerably with the properties of the liquid. The heat of immersion in polar liquids is considerably higher than that in non-polar liquids; heats also vary considerably with functional groups of the liquid. A polar solid influences the orientation of the adsorbate strongly, and dipole interaction contributes highly, depending on the strength of the adsorbate dipole. An estimation of the average electrostatic field for the solid surface is possible since the net heat of adsorption is found to be approximately a linear function of the dipole moment of the wetting liquid. The heat of immersion of a variety of solids of different surface polarity in n-butyl derivatives is plotted in Figure 7. From the slope of the line of heat of immersion (or better, of net heats of adsorption obtained by subtracting the enthalpy of the liquids) vs. dipole moment, the surface force field, $F$, emanating from the solid can be estimated. The values for several solids are listed in Table IV.

The heat of immersion in water can be used as a qualitative measure of the surface polarity of solids. The adsorption of water is strongly dependent on the ability of the surface to orient the water dipoles, usually with the proton outward. For purposes of comparison the heat of immersion of some solids in water is given in Table IV. It is seen that for the solids listed the heat of immersion in water decreases with decreasing $F$.

#### Heterogeneities on Solid Surfaces

The type of intrinsic heterogeneities in a solid have been discussed in the cracking of petroleum (8, 37). In the case of solid catalysts, for instance, the heterogeneities may be responsible for their activity. Useful information regarding the energetic heterogeneity of solids can be obtained from differential heats of adsorption. For example, the nature, strength, and the topo-

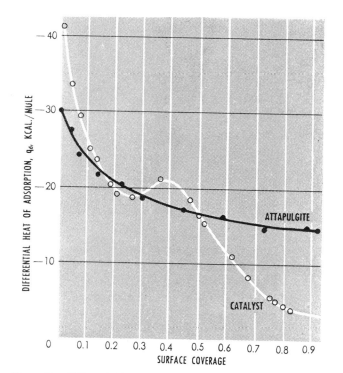

*Figure 8. Differential heat of adsorption of n-butylamine at 25° C. versus surface coverage on attapulgite clay and kaolin-based cracking catalyst.*

### TABLE IV. ELECTROSTATIC FIELD STRENGTHS AND DISPERSION ENERGIES

| Solid | BET Area Sq. M./G. | F, E.S.U./Sq. Cm. $\times 10^{-5}$ | $E_W$ Ergs/Sq. Cm. | $h_{I(SL)}H_2O$ Ergs/Sq. Cm. | Ref. |
|---|---|---|---|---|---|
| Rutile | 6.4 | 2.0 | 125 | 409 | (28) |
| Al₂O₃ (40 A. on Al) | 0.4 | 1.9 | 335 | | (19) |
| SiO₂ (Aerosil) | 120 | 1.1 | 75 | 165 | (30) |
| Graphon | 95 | 0 | 80 | 32 | (35) |
| Teflon | 9.0 | 0 | 25 | 6 | (7) |
| Iron blue (high strength) | 87 | 2.2 | 105 | | (36) |
| Chrome yellow (medium) | 6.7 | 1.9 | 105 | | (36) |
| Barium lithol (str. med. tone) | 41 | 1.7 | 105 | | (36) |
| Carbon black (short channel) | 120 | 0.7 | 105 | | (36) |

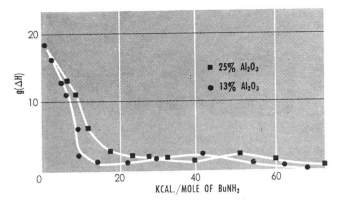

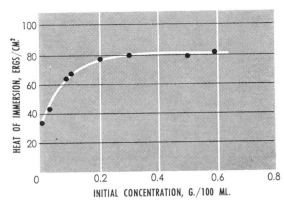

*Figure 9. Site energy distribution for two cracking catalysts. The distribution functions were obtained from values of heats of immersion into n-butylamine as a function of precoverage. The catalyst with 25% alumina showed greater catalytic activity.*

*Figure 10. Heats of immersion of Graphon into 1-butanol in water solutions. The curve is calculated on the basis of a simple model; the points are experimental.*

graphical distribution of acid sites on clays and cracking catalysts can be determined by using a basic adsorbate. As examples, attapulgite and a kaolin based catalyst were saturated with butylamine at 25° C. after initially outgassing the surfaces at 400° C. (9). The two solids were outgassed at various temperatures between 25° and 400° C. leaving behind known amounts of the amine which was measured gravimetrically. The heats of immersion were then determined as a function of pre-sorbed amine, $N_A$. The isosteric heat curves obtained from the heats of immersion according to Equation 3 are plotted in Figure 8.

The catalyst is more active initially than kaolin but its activity falls rapidly with coverage. Sites with very high energies of adsorption are usually not active in catalysis because the reactants will be very strongly adsorbed. The activity of the catalyst may be due to sites in the range where the differential heat curve passes through a maximum.

Further useful information can be obtained by differentiating the differential heat *vs.* coverage plot, although the initial results must reflect the same findings. A function $g(\Delta H)$ can be defined by the equation:

$$\frac{dN_A}{d(\Delta H_d)} = g(\Delta H) \qquad (10)$$

Such that $g(\Delta H) \, d(\Delta H_d)$ gives the number of molecules that can be accommodated on sites with energy between $\Delta H$ and $\Delta H + d\Delta H$. The site energy distribution functions are plotted for two cracking catalysts of different catalytic activity in Figure 9 (9). The catalyst with the larger number of low energy sites also had the greater catalyst activity.

### Solution Adsorption

The adsorption of solutes from solutions has been mainly followed by direct analytical methods. Although some attempts have been made to calculate thermodynamic quantities, such a method is of limited applicability in view of the many assumptions made.

Direct measurement of heats of adsorption by immersional calorimetry coupled with adsorption isotherms offers a very valuable tool for learning more about the orientation and the interaction between adsorbed solute molecules and with the surfaces.

It is advantageous to carry out the adsorption from a system where the absorption of one component from the solution is predominant. A polar solvent (such as water) is chosen for adsorption on a low energy surface such as Graphon; non-polar hydrocarbon solvents for studies on high energy surfaces.

As an example, a model which allowed the calculation of heats of immersion was developed for the preferential adsorption of butanol on Graphon from aqueous solutions (38). The specific interactions that were taken into account were:

—Dilution of the solution.
—Adsorption of butanol and the solvent water on the Graphon surface.
—Interaction between the adsorbed phases and the bulk solution.

All the above quantities could be evaluated by the measurement of an adsorption isotherm and measurement of heats of wetting of the adsorbed film at various pre-chosen concentrations. The calculated values were in excellent agreement with the experimental heats of immersion as illustrated in Figure 10. Much more work assessing various functional groups, and various solid surfaces is needed.

### Surfactant Adsorption

The heat of immersion of a homogeneous hydrophobic solid, Graphon, is greater in a surfactant solution than in water. This increased heat effect has been employed to rate the wetting ability of surfactants (21, 22, 41). A detailed study of the adsorption of sodium dodecyl sulfate (NaDS) and sodium dodecyl benzene sulfonate (NaDBS) has revealed several interesting features. The NaDS could take up one of three possible packing arrangements depending on the solution environment. The closest packing (22 sq. A. per anion) was obtained in the presence of $Ca^{++}$ ions. The heats of wetting of Graphon in NaDS and NaDBS in the absence of multivalent ions are given in Table V.

Repulsion between the head groups lowers the heat of adsorption at the higher packing densities obtained at the higher concentrations.

The measurements of adsorption can be extended to determine the heats of formation of the electrical double layer formed during the adsorption of an ionizable surfactant. In the case of surfactant having a carboxylic acid head group, the adsorbed species are not ionized at low pH, and no double layer is formed. At high

### TABLE V. SURFACTANT HEATS OF ADSORPTION ON GRAPHON

| Surfactant | Area per Anion Sq. A. | $\Delta H_{ads}$ Kcal./Mole |
|---|---|---|
| NaDS | 37 | −7.6 |
|  | 67 | −9.5 |
| NaDBS | 48 | −8.8 |

### TABLE VI. HEATS OF DOUBLE LAYER FORMATION AT GRAPHON/AQUEOUS SOLUTION INTERFACE AT 25° C.

| Octanoic Acid | | Hexanoic Acid | | Butyric Acid | |
|---|---|---|---|---|---|
| Area/ Mol., Sq. A. | $\Delta H_{DL}$, Kcal./ Mole | Area/ Mol., Sq. A. | $\Delta H_{DL}$, Kcal./ Mole | Area/ Mol., Sq. A. | $\Delta H_{DL}$, Kcal./ Mole |
| 400 | 2.4 | 400 | 3.0 | 400 | 1.9 |
| 300 | 2.0 | 300 | 2.0 | 300 | 1.3 |
| 240 | 1.7 | 200 | 1.9 | 200 | 1.1 |
|  |  | 150 | 1.7 | 150 | 1.0 |

pH, on the other hand, the double layer is developed. Comparison of the heats of adsorption at low and at high pH's at the same packing density gives directly the heats of formation of the electrical double layer. The values for heats of double layer formation obtained for the adsorption of three aliphatic acids is given in Table VI (16).

The heats of double layer formation are all endothermic and decrease with increasing coverage.

An incremental analysis of the contributions of various groups can be made by the heat of immersion technique. By comparing the heats of adsorption of the homologous series of these aliphatic acids the heat contribution per $-CH_2-$ has been found to be −350 cal./mole, and the heat of adsorption of the carboxyl group is −1.0 kcal./mole (16).

### NOMENCLATURE

| | |
|---|---|
| $\Delta H_I$ | = Heat of immersion per gram of clean solid in a pure liquid. |
| $h_{I(SL)}$ | = Heat of immersion per unit area of a clean solid in a clean solid in a pure liquid. |
| $h_{I(SfL)}$ | = Heat of immersion of a solid containing a known amount of preadsorbed wetting liquid. |
| $e_{I(SL)}$ | = Energy of immersion per unit area of clean solid in a pure liquid. |
| $e_{SL}$ | = Energy of the solid-liquid interface. |
| $e_S°$ | = Energy of the solid-vacuum interface. |
| $h_{A(SV)}$ | = Integral heat of adsorption of the vapor of the wetting liquid on the clean solid per unit area. |
| $h_L$ | = Heat of liquefaction per molecule of the vapor of the wetting liquid. |
| $\Gamma = \dfrac{N_A}{\Sigma}$ | = Surface concentration of the adsorbed species per unit area. |
| $h_{LV}°$ | = Enthalpy of unit liquid surface. |
| $q_{st}$ | = Isosteric heat of adsorption. |
| $q_d$ | = Differential heat of adsorption. |
| $s_A$ | = Entropy of adsorbed species per molecule. |
| $s_L$ | = Entropy of the liquid per molecule. |
| $\phi$ | = Film pressure at saturation. |
| $p/p_0$ | = Relative pressure. |
| $W_A$ | = Work of adhesion. |
| $\gamma_S°$ | = Free surface energy of the solid. |
| $\gamma_{LV}°$ | = Surface tension of the liquid. |
| $\gamma_{SL}$ | = Free energy of the solid liquid interface. |
| $\theta$ | = Contact angle. |
| $h_{A(SL)}$ | = Enthalpy of adhesion of liquid to solid. |
| $h_{(SL)}$ | = Enthalpy of the solid liquid interface. |
| $S_{A(SL)}$ | = Entropy of adhesion. |
| $\Sigma$ | = Specific surface of the solid. |
| $F$ | = Average electrostatic field of a solid surface. |
| $E_w$ | = Dispersion energy. |
| $cmc$ | = Critical micelle concentration. |

### LITERATURE CITED

(1) Baloga, M. R., private communication.
(2) Bartell, F. E., Suggit, R. M., J. Phys. Chem. 58, 36 (1954).
(3) Berghausen, P. E., p. 225 in "Adhesion and Adhesives," (Clark, Rutger, Savage, ed.), Wiley, New York, 1954.
(4) Block, W. M., M.S. Thesis, Lehigh University, 1964.
(5) Boyd, G. E., Harkins, W. D., J. Amer. Chem. Soc. 64, 1190 (1942).
(6) Brooks, C. S., J. Phys. Chem. 64, 532 (1961).
(7) Chessick, J. J., Healey, F. H., Zettlemoyer, A. C., Ibid., 60, 1345 (1956).
(8) Chessick, J. J., Zettlemoyer, A. C., Advan. Catalysis 11, 263 (1959).
(9) Chessick, J. J., Zettlemoyer, A. C., J. Phys. Chem. 62, 1217 (1958).
(10) Chessick, J. J., Zettlemoyer, A. C., Healey, F. H., Young, G. J., Can. J. Chem. 33, 251 (1955).
(11) Copeland, C. E., Young, T. F., Advan. Chem. Ser., No. 33, 348 (1961).
(12) Hackerman, N., API Project 47d Reports, University of Texas, 1957.
(13) Harmon, C. G., Fraulin, F., J. Am. Chem. Soc. 23, 252 (1940).
(14) Hill, T. L., J. Chem. Phys. 17, 520 (1949).
(15) Hill, T. L., Jura, G., J. Am. Chem. Soc. 74, 1598 (1952).
(16) Iyer, S. R. Sivaraja, Zettlemoyer, A. C., Narayan, K. S., J. Phys. Chem. 67, 2112 (1963).
(17) Parmele, C. W., Frechette, D. D., J. Am. Ceram. Soc. 25, 108 (1942).
(18) Rhodin, T. N., J. Amer. Chem. Soc. 72, 5691 (1950).
(19) Romo, L. A., J. Colloid Sci. 16, 139 (1961).
(20) Savage, R. H., Ann. N. Y. Acad. Sci. 53, 862 (1951).
(21) Skewis, J. D., Ph.D. Thesis, Lehigh University, 1960.
(22) Skewis, J. D., Zettlemoyer, A. C., "Proc. Third Int. Congr. on Surface Activity," Vol. II, p. 401, 1960.
(23) Slabaugh, W. H., J. Phys. Chem. 63, 1333 (1959).
(24) Tcheurekdjian, N., Ph.D. Thesis, Lehigh University, 1963.
(25) Tcheurekdjian, N., Zettlemoyer, A. C., Chessick, J. J., J. Phys Chem. 68, 773 (1964).
(26) Wade, W. H., Hackerman, N., Advan. Chem. Ser., No. 43, p. 222 (1964).
(27) Wade, W. H., Hackerman, N., J. Phys. Chem. 63, 1639 (1959).
(28) Ibid., 65, 1682 (1961).
(29) Ibid., 68, 1592 (1964).
(30) Whalen, J. W., Advan. Chem. Ser., No. 33, 281 (1961).
(31) Whalen, J. W., J. Phys. Chem. 66, 511 (1962).
(32) Wightman, J. P., Ph.D. Thesis, Lehigh University, 1960.
(33) Wu, Y. C., Copeland, C. E., Advan. Chem. Ser., No. 33, 357 (1961).
(34) Young, G. J., Bursh, T. P., J. Coll. Sci. 15, 361 (1960).
(35) Young, G. J., Chessick, J. J., Healy, F. H., Zettlemoyer, A. C., J. Phys. Chem. 58, 313 (1954).
(36) Zettlemoyer, A. C., Official Digest Federation Paint Varnish Prod. Clubs. 28, 1238 (1957).
(37) Zettlemoyer, A. C., Chessick, J. J., Advan. Chem. Ser., No. 43, p. 88 (1964).
(38) Zettlemoyer, A. C., Chessick, J. J., J. Phys. Chem. 64, 1131 (1960).
(39) Zettlemoyer, A. C., Chessick, J. J., Hollabaugh, C. H., ibid., 60, 1225 (1956).
(40) Zettlemoyer, A. C., Iyengar, R. D., unpublished work.
(41) Zettlemoyer, A. C., Narayan, K. S., "Proc. of the Fourth Int. Congr. on Surface Activity," Brussels, 1964.
(42) Zettlemoyer, A. C., Tcheurekdjian, N., Hosler, C. L., J. Appl. Math. Phys. (ZAMP) 14, 496 (1963).
(43) Zettlemoyer, A. C., Young, G. J., Chessick, J. J., J. Phys. Chem. 59, 962 (1955).
(44) Zettlemoyer, A. C., Young, G. J., Chessick, J. J., Healey, F. H., Ibid., 57, 649 (1953).

# 13

# Surface Diffusion of Adsorbed Molecules

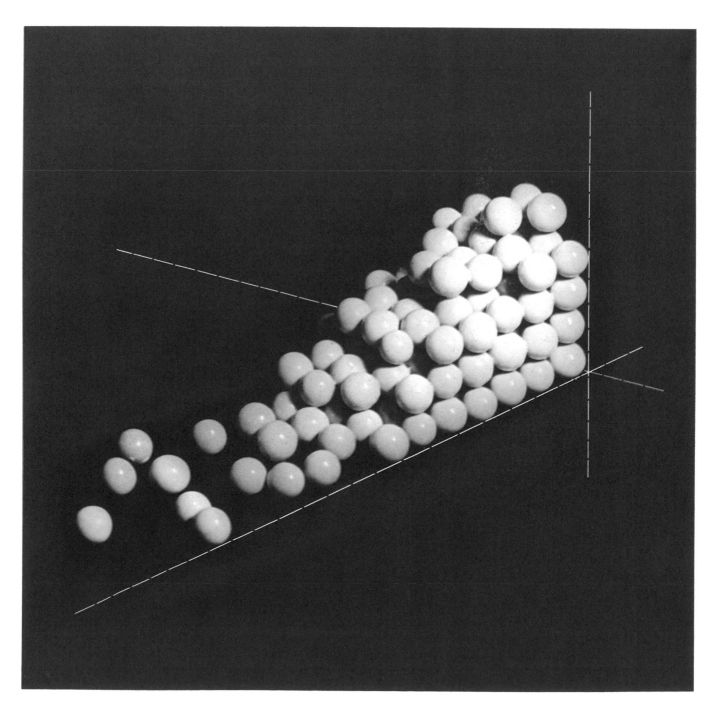

J. R. DACEY

# SURFACE DIFFUSION OF ADSORBED MOLECULES

*Gas adsorption is a dynamic process. The adsorbed molecules may return to the gas, or they may migrate to other sites on the solid surface while still in the absorbed state. This surface movement is of great importance in catalysis, in flow through porous bodies, in treatment of fibers, and even in the movement of water or petroleum under the earth*

**W**hen a solid surface is in contact with a gas, an interaction occurs which causes a concentration of the gas close to the surface. This universal spontaneous behavior named adsorption has been widely investigated for years and is the primary cause of many physical phenomena. It is important to realize the dynamic nature of this process. The molecules of the gas above the surface are moving in straight lines in all directions and at velocities described by the Maxwell-Boltzmann law. They are continually striking one another and the solid surface. The rate of collision with the surface is governed by the temperature, concentration, and molecular weight of the gas, and may be calculated by the kinetic theory of gases.

When a molecule strikes the surface it may merely reverse its direction, that is, reflect specularly, leaving with the same velocity as it approached. More often, however, when striking the surface the gas molecule loses its velocity completely and remains on the surface

for a finite time, after which it leaves in a direction and with a velocity independent of those of its approach. The ratio of the nonspecular to the specular collisions is called the condensation or accommodation coefficient, $\alpha$, and is a property of the surface and the gas combined. The length of time any given molecule remains on the surface is governed by chance, but the average time of resting, $\tau$, of a very large number of molecules is a precise figure under any set of conditions. To leave the surface, the adsorbed molecule must possess vibrational energy in the bonding direction greater than the strength of the bond. It is then free to be uprooted and to return to the gas phase. The probability of any given adsorbed molecule having energy necessary to desorb will be governed by the energy distribution law. Thus the mean free life in the adsorbed state will depend on the bonding energy and the temperature of the system. At equilibrium the rates of adsorption and desorption will be equal and the surface concentration will be given by the product of the collision rate and the adsorption life. The average adsorbed life $\tau$ is related to the heat of adsorption by the relation $\tau = \tau_o e^{Q/RT}$, where $\tau_o$ is a property of the solid surface related to the frequency of vibration of the atoms of the solid. It may be estimated by Lindemann's formula (*14*). Table I lists the mean lives in the adsorbed state for molecules with various heats of adsorption. The longer adsorbed lives are typical of chemisorption where the bonds are strong, while the shorter lives indicate the state of continuous rapid exchange between gaseous and adsorbed states characteristic of physical adsorption.

When the pressure of gas over it is increased, the surface becomes increasingly covered with adsorbed molecules. A colliding molecule may now arrive at a part of the surface already covered and its behavior will be different from when it is colliding with the uncovered solid surface. Then $\alpha$ and $\tau$ would both be altered, as would the heat of adsorption. These quantities would continue to change as multilayers built up. It is also true that, as the solid becomes more nearly covered, molecules arriving at the remaining bare patches of surface may be influenced by near neighbors, causing a lateral interaction and thus again altering $\alpha$ and $\tau$. Hence for a perfectly homogeneous surface one would expect the heat of adsorption and $\tau$ to vary with the surface concentration. Real surfaces are seldom homogeneous, some regions attract the gas molecules more strongly, have larger values of $\tau_0$, and hence are saturated sooner. This would add to the dependence of $\tau$ on surface concentration.

### Classifications of Adsorption

As I have just stated, adsorption is usually said to be either chemisorption or physical adsorption. This distinction is based mainly on the magnitude of the heat of adsorption and is not very precise. It is convenient however and widely used.

Adsorption is also classified as monolayer or multilayer. The former deals with low surface concentrations up to where the surface is covered with one layer of

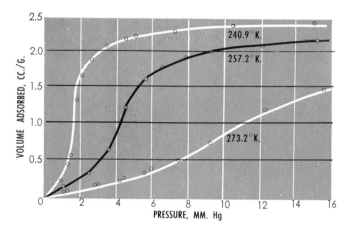

*Figure 1. Comparison of experimental data (individual points) with theoretical isotherm of a mobile adsorbed film (solid line) for CFCl₃ on boron nitride. After Ross and Olivier (40)*

adsorbed molecules and the latter with all coverage above this. The distinction here is not too exact because multilayers may begin to be built up before the monolayer is completed; hence the properties of these two types of adsorption often overlap. Capillary condensation may be considered to be a special case of multilayer adsorption where, in porous solids, the pore diameter is so small that multilayers from the sides meet at the middle completely filling the pore space with adsorbate.

Some surfaces may be pictured as an array of adsorption sites so that on adsorption each molecule occupies one site and achieves a position of minimum potential energy. For a simple uniform surface, all sites would have the same potential energy and they would occur in a regular pattern reflecting the structure of the solid beneath. Sites of more than one potential energy could occur in a regular pattern giving rise to a more complex but still homogeneous surface. On the other hand, sites of various energies could exist randomly due

to a variable solid structure, causing a heterogeneous surface. In all these cases the adsorbed molecules take up fixed positions, and although in some cases they are free to move from position to position, they are at equilibrium with the surface only when occupying adsorption sites. Such behavior is known as localized adsorption. In contrast to this, nonlocalized adsorption occurs when the molecules are stable at any point on the surface and there are no favored positions of lower potential energy. This does not mean that the surface is energetically uniform; some regions may have higher heats of adsorption than others but the adsorbed molecules are not limited to specific points of attachment.

From a dynamic point of view, adsorption is classified as mobile or nonmobile. In the former case a molecule may move about while on the surface, remaining in the adsorbed state all the time. In the latter case it does not leave its adsorbed position until it desorbs and returns to the gaseous phase. It is emphasized that localized adsorption does not preclude mobility, while a nonlocalized molecule may conceivably be completely immobile.

### Mobility of Molecules at Low Concentrations

In the simplest idealized case of nonlocalized adsorption, an adsorbed molecule would have the same energy at any point on the surface. If such a molecule could obtain momentum in a lateral direction, it would be free to move about the surface. Since there would be no barrier to lateral motion, it would not matter how great the heat of adsorption was, in all cases, once adsorbed, the molecules would be free to skate about like a two-dimensional gas. A two-dimensional pressure, or spreading pressure, would exist for such a system and a two-dimensional equation of state would apply. One would expect that an ideal gas law would be obeyed at low concentrations. At higher surface concentration, lateral interaction would require a two-dimensional van der Waals (or similar) equation of state. At some higher concentration, if the temperature were sufficiently low, condensation to a liquid would occur. Such a system would have a two-dimensional vapor pressure and critical point predictable from the equation of state.

In the case of localized mobile adsorption, for a molecule to move from one site to an adjacent one it must possess sufficient energy to pass over the energy barrier between the two sites. If this barrier is low compared to the average energy of the molecule, say less than $RT$ per mole, movement over the surface would be similar to the case of nonlocalized mobile adsorption. In fact, equations of state which predict similar behavior have been developed for both these cases.

That molecules do, in fact, exist on surfaces as a two-dimensional gas is judged to be most likely when one compares the properties predicted by this model with experimental data. Many equations of state have been developed for the two-dimensional gas, and adsorbent-adsorbate systems exist which agree with the predicted behavior. The equation below, where $\theta$ is the frac-

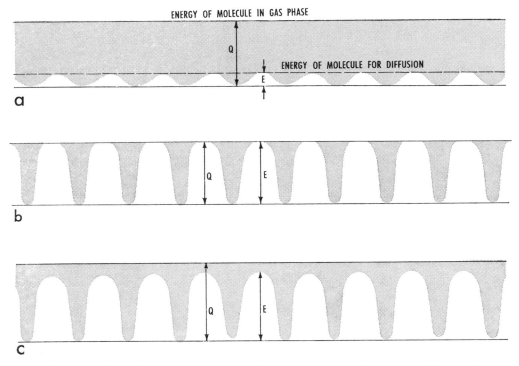

Figure 2. Energy barrier to the movement of an adsorbed molecule across a uniform surface

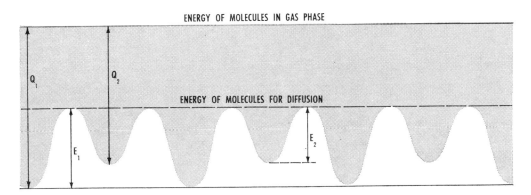

Figure 3. Energy barrier for a more complicated but still uniform surface

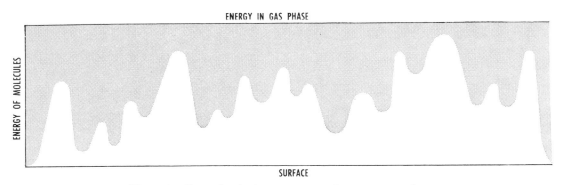

Figure 4. Energy barrier for movement on a heterogeneous surface

tional surface coverage, may be derived from a two-dimensional van der Waals equation (14):

$$p/p_0 = k_2 \left( \frac{\theta}{1 - \theta} \right) e^{\theta/(1 - \theta)} e^{-k_1\theta}$$

Figure 1 shows a family of isotherms comparing data predicted by this equation with experimental data. Ross has found similar behavior for many gases on alkali halide surfaces (38–41). Other workers have found similar results (18, 31). The critical temperature of a two-dimensional gas has been predicted by Hill to be one half of the three-dimensional case (32). Ross and others have found various values between 0.36 and 0.47 for different systems (11, 18). Supporting evidence for this model is to be found in a consideration of the entropy of the adsorbed state. Table II shows the entropies predicted for the adsorption of various models of benzene on alumina together with the actual entropies observed by Kemball (33). Similar observations have been reported by Haul for nitrogen on Spheron 6 carbon where the predicted $\Delta S$ for a two-dimensional gas was 10.0 and the observed $\Delta S$ ranged from 10.9 to 14.9 for surface coverages ranging from 0.17 to 0.90 of a monolayer (30). It appears likely that at low coverage and especially on uniform surfaces, two-dimensional gas behavior does exist.

If we do accept the reality of a two-dimensional gas, then surface diffusion of such a gas would be analogous to three-dimensional gaseous diffusion. If a concentration gradient existed, diffusion would take place in the direction that would cause the concentration to become uniform. The two-dimensional surface diffusion constant is calculated from kinetic theory to be $D_s = \frac{1}{2} \bar{v} \lambda$, where $\bar{v}$ is the mean velocity and equals $\sqrt{\pi RT/2M}$ and $\lambda$ is the mean free path, which is $\frac{1}{2} dC_s$, where $C_s$ is the surface concentration and $d$ the molecular diameter. The surface flux is then given by $-D_s \, dC_s/dx$.

For many cases of localized adsorption the energy barrier between adjacent adsorption sites is greater than $RT$, hence the adsorbed molecules cannot behave like a two-dimensional gas but must exhibit activated diffusion. Figure 2 shows ideal energy profiles of homogeneous surfaces. The energy $E$ is the activation energy the molecule must possess to pass over the barrier. Figure 3 shows a more complex but homogeneous surface when sites of two energies exist. In real cases the surface is often heterogeneous, where sites of many different levels exist (see Figure 4). There is no *a priori* reason that a high heat of adsorption should result in a high activation energy for diffusion. Values of $E$ from 0.1 to 0.8 of $Q$ have been reported for different systems. Theoretical calculations have been made for various surfaces. Table III shows experimental values for argon on potassium chloride (37) and argon on graphite (12). It is seen that graphite is a more energetically uniform surface than is potassium chloride.

When adsorption commences the high energy sites would be occupied first, and it is generally found that the diffusion coefficient increases as coverage increases—

### TABLE I.   MEAN ABSORBED LIVES

| Q, Kcal./mole | $\tau$, Secs. |
|---|---|
| 0.1 | $6 \times 10^{-14}$ |
| 1.0 | $2.7 \times 10^{-13}$ |
| 10 | $1.6 \times 10^{-6}$ |
| 15 | $9 \times 10^{-3}$ |
| 20 | 50 |
| 25 | $3 \times 10^{5}$ |
| 30 | $2 \times 10^{9}$ |

$\tau$, *the time of sitting of adsorbed molecules as a function of the heat of adsorption Q.*
$\tau = \tau_0 e^{Q/RT}$, *where $\tau_0$ for carbon is $5 \times 10^{-14}$ sec.*

### TABLE II.   ENTROPY OF ADSORPTION OF BENZENE

| Assumed Model | S | $\Delta S$ |
|---|---|---|
| 3-Dimensional gas | 59.7 | 0 |
| 2-Dimensional gas with no rotation | 26.3 | 33.4 |
| Rotation in plane of ring | 30.3 | 29.4 |
| Rotation in plane of ring and about one axis in plane of ring | 38.1 | 21.6 |
| All three rotations | 47.3 | 12.4 |
| Completely localized | 20.9 | 38.8 |
| *Experimental Values, Benzene on Alumina* | *S* | *$\Delta S$* |
| $\theta = 0.3$ | 26.5 | 33.2 |
| $\theta = 0.5$ | 29.8 | 29.9 |
| $\theta = 0.7$ | 32.9 | 26.8 |
| $\theta = 0.9$ | 31.7 | 28.0 |

*Calculated entropy of adsorbed benzene according to Gregg (29) compared with experimental values. It is seen that benzene is not localized on alumina but behaves as a two-dimensional gas.*

### TABLE III.   HEATS OF ADSORPTION OF ARGON

| Position of Adsorbed Molecule | Q, Cal./Mole |
|---|---|
| Argon on Graphite | |
| Over center of lattice hexagon | 1750 |
| Over a carbon atom | 1710 |
| Over mid-point between two carbon atoms | 1710 |
| Argon on KCl | |
| Over mid-point between two chlorine ions | 1590 |
| Over a potassium ion | 1450 |
| Over a chlorine ion | 1270 |
| Over mid-point between a chlorine and a potassium ion | 1310 |

*The heats of adsorption of an argon atom on various positions of a graphite and a KCl surface. Graphite is seen to be more energetically uniform than is KCl (12, 34, 37).*

**AUTHOR** *J. R. Dacey is Professor of Chemistry, Royal Military College of Canada, Kingston, Ontario, Canada.*

that is, as $Q$ decreases (see Figure 5). This would imply that on any given surface, energy barriers usually follow the heat of adsorption. Gilliland has suggested that when low concentrations exhibit high diffusion rates the high energy sites may have a low barrier between them due to overlapping force fields (28).

At low surface concentrations the mechanism of activated diffusion is analogous to the "random walk." During its life $\tau$ on the surface, an adsorbed molecule would make a number of slips across the surface. The time between slips is $\tau^l$ given by $\tau^l = \tau_o{}^l e^{E/RT}$. Each slip would be similar in length, but all would be randomly directed. The diffusion coefficient is related to the length of each slip, $\lambda^l$ the distance between adsorption sites, by the equation $D_s = (\lambda^l)^2/2\tau^l$ (33). The number of slips made on the average during one average lifetime would depend on the difference between $Q$ and $E$, and, if one assumes $\tau_o{}^l = \tau_o$ (which would be true for an isotropic solid), the number of slips would be equal to $e^{(Q-E)/RT}$.

At low coverage the molecules on the surface would be continually moving about in all directions but seldom meeting one another. Flow in such a system would be similar to a two-dimensional Knudsen flow where an adsorption site plays the part of a wall, and a slip across the surface is equivalent to a free flight between walls. If a concentration gradient existed, a net transfer of matter would result in the direction to equalize the concentration. This diffusion would not be due to any hydrostatic pressure but would be a consequence of the fact that the molecules are moving randomly and there are more in one place than another. The experimental evidence which has lead to the picture above, and has been used to support it, deals with the flow of gases in porous solids. This problem will be discussed below.

### Movement of Adsorbed Molecules at Higher Concentrations

As the concentration increases, at some point the adsorbed molecules cease to behave as a two-dimensional gas in the case of nonlocalized adsorption, and for the localized case the activated diffusion mechanism no longer holds. With the former, condensation to a liquid occurs usually before the entire monolayer is complete. This is especially true for porous bodies where liquids would appear in micropores before the larger porous surfaces were covered.

In the case of localized adsorption, as the adsorption sites become more occupied, a molecule finds its nearest neighbor site already filled. It then falls back to its original position or arrives on top of the adjacent adsorbed molecules and becomes a liquid-like molecule in the second layer.

As either of the above processes continues the adsorbate becomes increasingly like a liquid and would be expected to be subject to hydrodynamic laws. Depending on the over-all structure of the solid surface the change from dilute to liquid-like films occurs at different fractions of the monolayer coverage. Experimental evidence on multilayer systems indicate that they are liquid-like films but that their mobility may be smaller than bulk

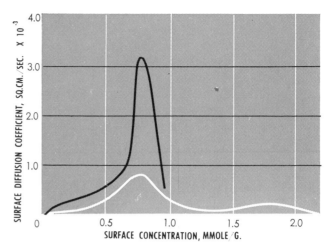

*Figure 5. The variation of surface diffusion with surface concentration, nitrogen on Spheron 6. After Haul (31)*

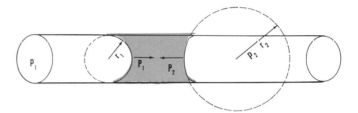

*Figure 6. Movement of a liquid within a capillary tube*

liquid. Morrison has reported that nitrogen and argon on rutile exist as thick liquid films which freeze at low temperatures to solid films. However, at low coverage, the adsorption of Argon on rutile is localized (15, 16, 35, 36). Infrared studies of molecules adsorbed on porous glass show that multilayers are liquid-like but less mobile than the bulk liquid (42). Magnetic resonance studies have yielded similar results for adsorbates on carbon black (23).

### Flow of Gases Through Porous Solids

Much effort has been directed to the study of the flow of gases through porous solids, which problem has created the main interest in the understanding of the mobility of adsorbed molecules. It was discovered early that those species which adsorbed on the walls of the pores pass through more efficiently than those which did not. For instance helium, which adsorbs very little if any at ordinary temperatures, flows through porous solids less readily than those gases which do adsorb. It was concluded that the adsorbed phase must contribute to the over-all flow.

The extent of adsorption greatly affects the rate of flow, and different mechanisms are thought to apply for greater or less surface concentration. If one considers a single pore, at one extreme at saturation pressure it may be completely filled with liquid adsorbate, while at the other extreme of very low pressure the walls would be almost denuded of molecules. Between these extremes lie three regions—less-than-monolayer coverage, multilayer coverage, and finally capillary condensation. Real porous solids contain a great many capillaries of different sizes, so that at moderate pressures the micropores may be filled while the larger ones are not yet covered by a monolayer. Obviously, the flow in various parts is governed by various laws. It is not surprising therefore that it has been difficult and confusing to find common behavior for different solids and various adsorbates. However a number of general conclusions may be reached.

There is no doubt that the most efficient way to pass a gas through a porous solid is to increase the pressure until capillary condensation occurs throughout all of the pores of the solid. The gas is then in fact transferred as a liquid by hydrostatic flow. The liquid in such a case is under a tension which is necessary to maintain the different pressures of the vapor at either end. The effective pressure which forces the liquid through the pores is very much greater than the vapor pressure difference across the capillary.

As a liquid moves through a capillary, the radius of curvature of the advancing liquid will be greater than that of the retreating end. The Kelvin equation relates the radius of curvature of a surface to the vapor pressure in equilibrium with it. For the case of flow through a capillary,

$$\ln p_1 - p_2 = \frac{2\gamma}{\rho_l} \frac{M}{RT} \cos \theta \left[ \frac{1}{r_1} - \frac{1}{r_2} \right]$$

where $p$ and $r$ are the vapor pressure and radius of curvature, $\rho_l$ the liquid density, and $\gamma$ the surface tension (see Figure 6). The tension inside the liquid necessary to maintain the curved surface varies inversely as the curvature of the surface, and directly as the product of the surface tension and the cosine of the wetting angle. Thus, the difference in tension across the length of a capillary, which is the effective pressure forcing the liquid through, is given by:

$$P_1 - P_2 = \Delta P = 2\gamma \cos \theta \left[ \frac{1}{r_1} - \frac{1}{r_2} \right]$$

Combining these equations, we can relate $\Delta P$ to the vapor pressure at each end:

$$\Delta P = \frac{\rho_l RT}{M} \ln \frac{p_1}{p_2}$$

As long as the pressure difference is small this is approximately given by:

$$\Delta P = \frac{\rho_l RT}{M} \frac{\Delta p}{p}$$

where $\Delta p$ is the difference between the vapor pressures at either end, and $p$ is their average. This can be written as:

$$\frac{\Delta P}{\Delta p} = \frac{\rho_l}{\rho_g}$$

which is equivalent to the thermodynamic condition for equilibrium of the two phases:

$$v_1 dp_1 = v_2 dp_2$$

At the other extreme, when the surface concentration is low, hydrodynamic laws cannot apply to the adsorbed molecules. If they are not localized to specific sites on the surface, or if they are localized with energy barriers less than $RT$ per mole, they will behave like a dilute two-dimensional gas. At these same surface concentrations, localized molecules will move by activated surface diffusion. These two methods of transport give rise to similar diffusion laws, although the former is more efficient for transporting matter. This fact is well illustrated by the following example given by de Boer (14). For a molecule adsorbed on the wall to traverse a capillary $10^{-2}$ cm. long and $10^{-6}$ cm. wide would require $1/150$ sec., if the molecule had velocity of $10^4$ cm./sec. and behaved as a two-dimensional gas molecule. The same molecule would require 1540 secs. if it proceeded by activated diffusion where $\tau^l$ is $3 \times 10^{-8}$ secs. and the distance between adsorption sites $3 \times 10^{-8}$ cm. For activated diffusion, $D_s = (\lambda^l)^2/2\tau^l$ while for two-dimensional gaseous diffusion it is $1/2 \bar{v} \lambda$ where $\lambda^l$ is the distance between adsorption sites in the former and $\lambda$ the mean free path in the latter. If $\tau^l$ is taken to be the average time to complete a free flight in any one direction, $\bar{v}$ becomes $\lambda/\tau^l$ for the gaseous diffusion case and the equations have the same form.

This region of low surface coverage has been studied experimentally by comparing the flow of helium, considered not to be adsorbed under the experimental conditions, with that of an adsorbable gas. The excess flow of the adsorbed gas over that calculated from the helium flow is attributed to surface flow. A considerable literature on this subject has grown mainly due to the work of the Barrer and Carmen (5-10). At coverages in the region where Henry's law holds, the diffusion coefficient is reasonably independent of concentration. As the concentration increases $D_s$ also increases, indicating that less energetic sites are now being occupied with lower energy barriers between them. As the concentration is increased further a maximum is sometimes found. This is attributed to molecules interfering with one another, since most adjacent sites are filled as the monolayer is approached, requiring a molecule to advance by entering the second layer—a more energetic process. As the second layer becomes increasingly occupied the flow rate again increases.

The activation energy $E$ for surface diffusion may be determined by measuring the temperature coefficient of the rate. With a knowledge of $E$ and $Q$, the average pore diameter, and the surface site spacing one may calculate the relative magnitude of the surface flux to the gas phase flux for different concentrations. The ratio of the calculated value to the experimental value gives an index of surface diffusion efficiency for any system. It has been found that for Saran charcoal, large molecules diffuse over the surface less efficiently than small ones. Surface obstructions, as differing from pore space obstructions, must play a part in complex solid systems (*13*). On the whole, one must conclude that flow experiments at low surface coverage support the view that activated surface diffusion is usually the mechanism of transport.

In the intermediate region between capillary condensation and partial monolayer coverage the hydrodynamic treatment of surface transport has yielded the most satisfactory agreement between theory and experiment.

Starting with the thermodynamic condition for equilibrium, and applying this to the surface phase rather than to a filled capillary, $\frac{\Delta p}{\Delta P} = \frac{\rho_g}{\rho_l}$, Flood has developed the following equation for surface flow (*19–22*):

$$Q = \frac{C}{L\eta_a} \frac{RT}{V^2 M} \left| \frac{x^2}{\alpha} \right| \Delta\alpha$$

where $C$ is a constant depending on the pore geometry, and $L$ is the length, $\eta_a$ is the viscosity of the adsorbed phase, $V$ the pore volume, and $\alpha$ the relative pressure at which $x$ is the amount adsorbed. Babbit and (more recently) Gilliland and Russell (*3, 4, 28*), using the concept of spreading pressure, have developed similar equations. The spreading pressure in the adsorbed layers, the difference between the surface tension of the bare and covered surface, is taken to be the operative force driving the adsorbate through the porous solid. Gilliland and Russell relate the spreading pressure to the adsorption isotherm and derive the following equation for surface flow:

$$N_s = \frac{-\rho ART}{k^2 SC} \frac{x^2}{p} \frac{dp}{dl}$$

where $\rho$ is the apparent density of the solid and $C$ the coefficient of resistance, equivalent to the viscosity of the adsorbed layer, $S$ is the surface area, $x$ the surface concentration, $A$ is the cross-sectional area, and $k$ a tortuosity factor. These equations have been successful in describing the behavior of many systems. Babbitt has used a similar treatment involving the same basic assumptions (*3, 4*). There is no doubt that in this region the adsorbed material is forced through the pores by forces greater than the pressure difference in the unadsorbed phase. The flow is similar to liquid flow, the outer layers sliding across each other with a viscosity-like resistance.

### Surface Mobility from Electron Emission

Gomer and Ehrlich and their coworkers have studied the effect of adsorption on electron emission with the field emission microscope. They have been able to observe the movement over the surface of molecules adsorbed on tungsten. In this way they have measured diffusion rates and activation energies. Multilayers behaved as liquids below the normal melting points. For oxygen and hydrogen, the rare gases, Gomer has reported activation energies for surface diffusion from 10% to 30% of the heats of adsorption (*24–27*). Ehrlich found different diffusion behavior on the different

crystal faces for xenon on tungsten, $E$ being 3400 and 1500 while $Q$ was 8000 cal./mole (*17*).

Finally, a few words about the engineering aspects of this subject. Certainly, in all cases where adsorption of gases and vapors on porous solids is important, the problem of surface diffusion must also be important. The problem of catalysis naturally comes to mind where several molecular species may be diffusing into and out of a porous body. Surely a full understanding of these systems must involve a far greater knowledge of adsorption on and travel over surfaces under all conditions of temperature and concentration than is now available. The problem of separating liquids or vapors by selective adsorption either for purification, preparation, recovery, or analysis—especially when rates of adsorption and desorption are important—must involve considerations of surface mobility. The physical chemistry of geological problems involving movement of water into and out of stones, sand beds, and earth or the movement of petroleum in underground locations should include flow of various kinds on surfaces. The technology of natural and synthetic fibers and their treatment for specialized uses as materials of construction involves many problems of surface chemistry, including the movement of molecules across interfaces. I am sure that this subject will continue to receive serious attention for some time and will benefit our knowledge of surface chemistry.

### LITERATURE CITED

(1) Adam, N. K., *Discussions Faraday Soc.* **3**, 5, 1948.
(2) Ash, R., Barrer, R. M., Pope, C. G., *Proc. Roy. Soc.* **A271**, 1 (1963).
(3) Babbitt, J. D., *Can. J. Phys.* **29**, 427,
(4) Babbitt, J. D., *Can. J. Res.* **A28**, 449,
(5) Barrer, R. M., Barrie, J. A., *Proc. Roy. Soc.* **213**, 250 (1952).
(6) Barrer, R. M., Gabor, T., *Ibid.* **A251**, 353 (1950); **A256**, 267 (1960).
(7) Barrer, R. M., Strachan, E. E., *Ibid.* **A231**, 52 (1955).
(8) Carmen, P. C., "Flow of Gases Through Porous Media," Academic, N. Y., (1956).
(9) Carmen, P. C., *Proc. Roy. Soc.* **A211**, 526 (1952).
(10) Carmen, P. C., Raal, F. A., *Ibid.*, **A209**, 38 (1951).
(11) Clark, H., Ross, S., *J. Am. Chem. Soc.* **75**, 6081 (1953).
(12) Crowell, A. D., Young, D. M., *Trans. Faraday Soc.* **49**, 1080 (1953).
(13) Dacey, J. R., "Solid Surfaces and the Gas Solid Interface," *Advan. Chem.* **33**, 172 (1961).
(14) de Boer, J. H., "The Dynamic Character of Adsorption," Oxford Univ. Press (1953).
(15) Drain, L. E., Morrison, J. A., *Trans. Faraday Soc.* **47**, 1023 (1951).
(16) *Ibid.*, **48**, 840 (1952).
(17) Ehrlich, G., Hudda, F. G., *J. Chem. Phys.* **30**, 493 (1959).
(18) Fisher, B. B., McMillan, W. G., *J. Am. Chem. Soc.* **79**, 2969 (1957).
(19) Flood, E. A., *Can. J. Chem.* **33**, 979 (1955).
(20) Flood, E. A., Heyding, R. D., *Ibid.*, **32**, 660 (1954).
(21) Flood, E. A., Huber, M., *Can. J. Chem.* **33**, 203 (1955).
(22) Flood, E. A., Tomlinson, R. H., *Ibid.*, **30**, 389 (1952).
(23) Graham, D., Phillips, W. D., *Proc. 2nd Int. Congress on Surface Activity* **2**, 22 (1957).
(24) Gomer, R., *J. Chem. Phys.* **31**, 1306 (1959).
(25) Gomer, R., *J. Phys. Chem.* **63**, 468 (1959).
(26) Gomer, R., Hulm, J. K., *J. Chem. Phys.* **27**, 1362 (1957).
(27) Gomer, R., Wortman, R., Lundy, R., *Ibid.*, **1099** (1957).
(28) Gilliland, R. E., *A.I.Ch.E. J.* **4**, 90 (1958).
(29) Gregg, S. J., Wheatley, K. H., *Proc. 2nd Int. Congr. on Surface Activity* **2**, 102 (1957).
(30) Haul, R. A. W., *Proc. 10th Colston Symp.*, Bristol Univ., **1958**, p. 176.
(31) Haul, R. A. W., Swart, E. R., *Z. Elektrochem.* **61**, 380 (1957).
(32) Hill, T. L., *J. Chem. Phys.* **14**, 441 (1946).
(33) Kemball, C., *Proc. Roy. Soc.* **187A**, 73 (1946).
(34) Lennard-Jones, J. E., *Trans. Faraday Soc.* **28**, 333 (1932).
(35) Morrison, J. A., Drain, L. E., *J. Chem. Phys.* **19**, 1063 (1951).
(36) Morrison, J. A., Drain, L. E., Dugdale, J. S., *Can. J. Chem.* **30**, 890 (1952).
(37) Orr, W. J. C., *Trans. Faraday Soc.* **35**, 1247 (1939).
(38) Ross, S., Clark, H., *J. Am. Chem. Soc.* **76**, 4291 (1954).
(39) *Ibid.*, 4297 (1954).
(40) Ross, S., Olivier, J., "On Physical Adsorption," Wiley, New York, **1964.**
(41) Ross, S., Winkler, W., *J. Am. Chem. Soc.* **76**, 2637 (1954).
(42) Yates, D. J. C., Sheppard, W., *Proc. 2nd Int. Congress on Surface Activity* **2**, p. 27 (1957).

# 14

# Surface-Sensitive Mechanical Properties

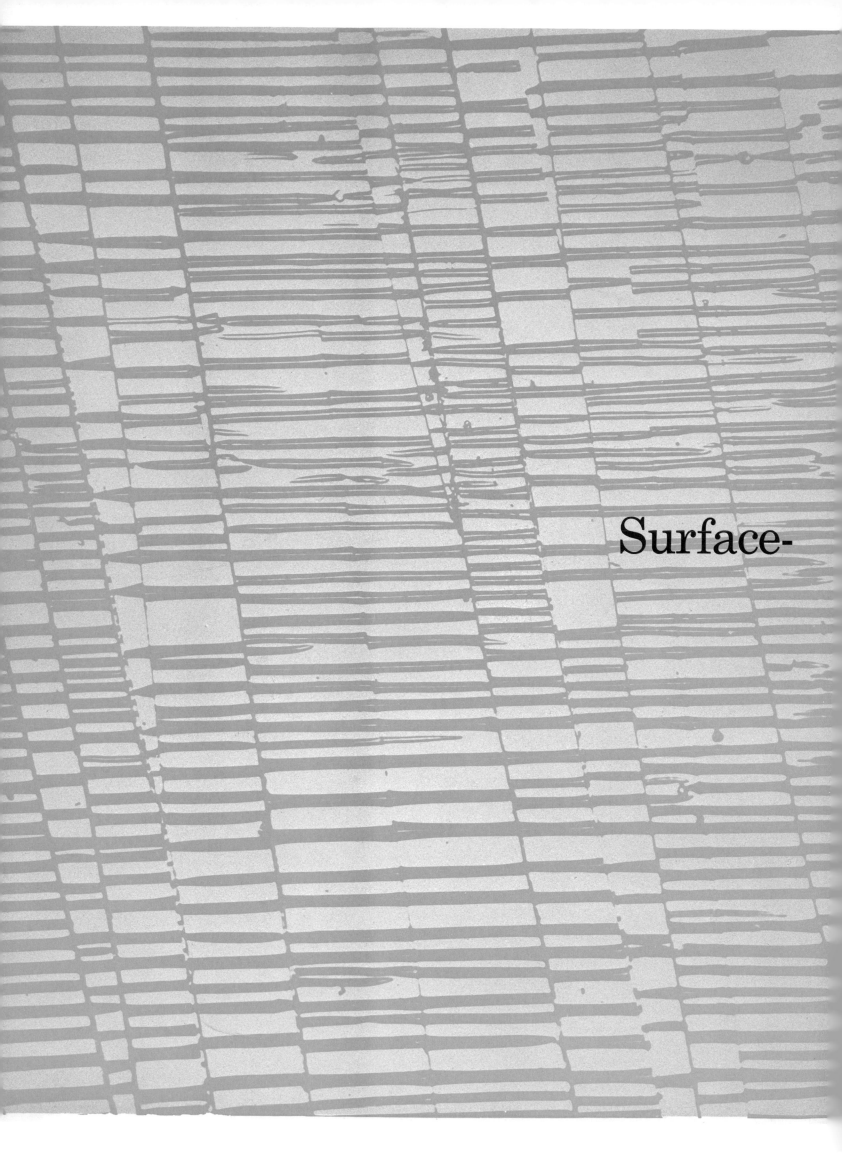

Surface-

*Surface condition and environment can significantly affect strength and ductility. Where these effects are understood, they can be used to strengthen structural materials.*

The most widely known effects of surface condition and environment on the strength of materials are the deleterious effects—notch brittleness, stress corrosion cracking, liquid metal embrittlement, and so forth. However, certain environments and surface treatments can produce markedly beneficial results. For example, Figure 1 on page 16 illustrates the significant increase in ductility observed when freshly cleaved crystals of potassium chloride are deformed in water or after immersion in water rather than in air. This phenomenon is known as Joffe's effect (*18*). Similar effects can be obtained when the rather more useful materials aluminum (*24*), beryllium (*31*), molybdenum (*8*) and tungsten (*39*) are deformed following immersion in solvent environments.

This field of research is becoming of increasing interest to materials scientists, and it is expected that a much better understanding of some of these technologically important phenomena will be obtained in the next few years. From this understanding will come increased reliability and improved mechanical properties for structural components.

To understand how and why such effects occur, it is first necessary to know something about the nature of the deformation process in crystalline materials, and to be familiar with some of the properties of the lattice

# Sensitive Mechanical Properties

A. R. C. WESTWOOD

◀

*The mechanical behavior of crystalline solids is governed by the generation, motion and interaction of the lattice-defects known as dislocations. Surface condition affects mechanical properties largely by its effect on these dislocations. The photograph opposite shows the emergence of screw dislocations from the surface of a lithium fluoride crystal after compression. The dislocations are revealed as cracks in a chromium film, vacuum-deposited on the crystal (about 600×)*

defects known as dislocations. First, then, this article will give an introduction to some elementary dislocation concepts, and then will relate these to surface conditions.

Theoretical calculations indicate that the shear strength of a crystalline material should be about $G/10$ to $G/30$, where $G$ is the shear modulus of the material (*29*). Thus, theoretically, steels should exhibit strengths of order 0.5 to 1.0 million p.s.i. In reality, of course, materials are orders of magnitude weaker than this. A zinc monocrystal, for example, starts to deform at a stress of about $G/100,000$. This discrepancy between observed and theoretical strengths of materials arises simply because real materials contain mobile structural defects.

When a real material is stressed beyond its yield stress and into the plastic deformation range, Figure 2, it does not deform by moving whole planes of atoms over each other like cards in a deck, but by moving one line of atoms in a given plane of atoms at a time. By way of analogy, consider the problem of moving a large carpet, Figure 3. One way of doing this is to pull at end $A$ and move the whole carpet at once. This is equivalent to trying to move all the atoms in a given plane of atoms at once, and is likely to require a considerable expenditure of effort! A better way is to stand at end $B$, introduce a wrinkle $W$ into the carpet, and then to shake the carpet gently until the wrinkle moves through the carpet and out of the other end. This process shifts the whole carpet along a small distance, and is repeated until the carpet is

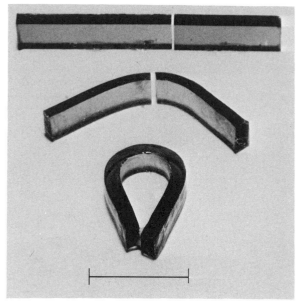

*Figure 1. Illustration of Joffe's effect (18) with irradiated potassium chloride crystals. Upper crystal deformed in air; middle crystal immersed in water for 60 sec., dried and then deformed in air; lower crystal deformed under water. The line below the crystals indicates a length of 1 cm. (Westwood)*

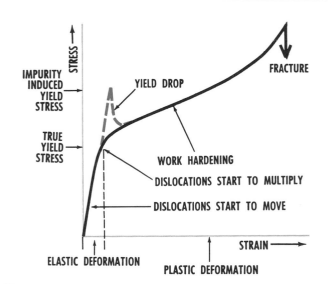

*Figure 2. Schematic of stress-strain curve for a ductile material. The amount of plastic strain before fracture is a measure of ductility*

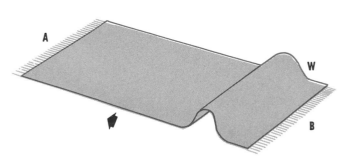

*Figure 3. Propagation of slip through a crystal is analogous to moving a carpet by moving a wrinkle*

correctly located. From Figure 3, it can be seen that at any given time, the position of the wrinkle defines the boundary between the moved and unmoved areas of the carpet. Now the shearing of one portion of a crystal over the other (like the carpet over the floor) also proceeds by the motion of a locally faulted region through the crystal. In this case, however, the "wrinkle" involved is referred to as a "dislocation." It is important to appreciate that a dislocation is a line defect, like the wrinkle, and not a point defect such as a vacant site or interstitial atom present in the crystal lattice. As in the carpet analogy, then, a dislocation line defines the boundary between sheared and unsheared areas of the crystal. Dislocations tend to move only in certain atomic planes in the crystal. These planes are known as "slip planes," and the shearing process itself is referred to as "slip."

The two principal types of dislocation are illustrated in Figure 4. When a dislocation line $CD$ lies perpendicular to its slip vector $B\ B'$, as in Figure 4a, it is termed an edge dislocation. The distribution of atoms around such a dislocation, and an indication of how this defect moves through the crystal lattice when acted upon by a shear stress, is given in Figure 5. The symbol $\perp$ is the metallurgical shorthand used to denote the position of the extra half-plane of atoms associated with an edge dislocation—i.e., $C\ C'$ in Figure 5. When a dislocation line lies parallel to its slip vector, as in Figure 4b, it is termed a screw dislocation—because then the atoms around the line $CD$ are arranged in a regular helix. In reality, most dislocations contain both edge ($E$) and screw ($S$) components, as illustrated in Figure 4c.

Dislocations are introduced into crystals during the solidification process. However, the number of dislocations so obtained which are capable of taking part in any deformation process is far too small to allow ordinary materials to deform at the rates demanded by typical testing or working operations. During deformation, therefore, additional dislocations must be either created, or generated by the multiplication of existing dislocations. It has been shown that dislocations can be created in the vicinity of such stress raisers as precipitate particles or crack tips, but most dislocations are produced by multiplication processes somewhat similar to that illustrated in Figure 7 (32). In this figure, that portion of the dislocation line lying in the slip plane is acted upon by the applied shear stress, and bows out rather like a two-dimensional soap bubble, Figure 7b. As the stress is increased, the bowing dislocation "half loop" begins to swing around the pinning points. This process continues until the line, growing and moving together behind the pinning points, eventually becomes a full circle, Figure 7(d). At this stage it breaks away from the source and becomes a freely moving dislocation loop. This loop produces a slip offset of one lattice spacing—i.e., one slip vector—as it leaves the crystal. Meanwhile, the process of joining the dislocation line to form a whole loop has also recreated the original half loop, Figure 7e. With the continued application

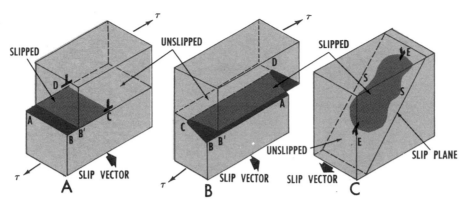

Figure 4. *Slip can occur in a crystal by the movement of (a) an edge dislocation CD from front to back, or (b) a screw dislocation CD from* right to left. *In real crystals, most dislocations contain both edge (E) and screw (S) components, as in (c)*

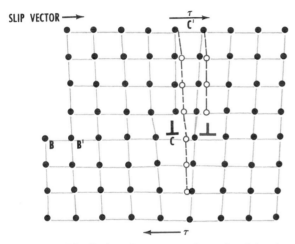

Figure 5. *Distribution of atoms around an edge dislocation. Under the action of the applied shear stress $\tau$, this dislocation moves to its right, one interatomic spacing at a time. Solid circles represent positions of the atoms before unit motion, open circles, after (9, 35)*

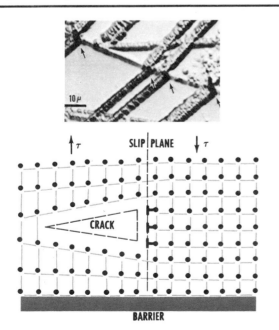

Figure 6. *Edge dislocations can coalesce to form a microcrack if piled up against some stable obstacle. Above, cracks formed in this way at a grain boundary in magnesium oxide (47), Westwood*

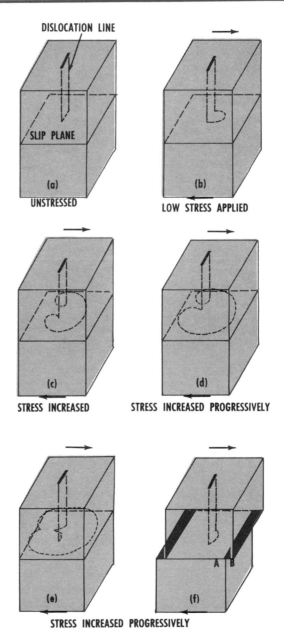

Figure 7. *Dislocations can be generated when a dislocation loop, part of which lies in a slip plane, is acted on by a shear stress. Such a generator is known as a Frank-Read dislocation source (35)*

of stress, this half loop then glides forward and repeats the whole process. When a sufficient number of dislocations have left the crystal, the offset so produced, *A B* in Figure 7*f*, becomes visible as a "slip line."

Now, since it is the motion of dislocations which governs the plastic behavior of crystalline materials, it follows that any factor which affects their motion also will affect mechanical behavior. For example, impurity atoms tend to segregate to dislocations, and can temporarily anchor them. However, when the applied stress becomes sufficient to break dislocations away from their "atmospheres" (*5*) of impurity atoms, a yield drop or yield point is observed (Figure 2). This is because less stress is required to keep the dislocations moving than was necessary to get them started. Such a phenomenon is commonly observed in mild steels and in this instance is due to the segregation of carbon or nitrogen atoms to the dislocations. Impurities also may be present as precipitated particles which can effectively impede the motion of dislocations through a crystal. This gives rise to the technologically important phenomenon of precipitation hardening, used, for example, to increase by about 50% the strength of the aluminum alloys used in airplane structures. Materials also become harder during deformation because dislocations on intersecting slip planes interact with and impede each other. This effect is called work hardening, and such hardening can be removed by heating the material to a temperature at which dislocation rearrangement occurs. The latter process is called annealing.

The fracture of materials also involves dislocations. Figure 5 demonstrated that an edge dislocation contains an extra half-plane of atoms. Figure 6 illustrates schematically what can happen if several edge dislocations become piled-up at some stable obstacle such as a grain boundary, large precipitate particle, surface film, or intersecting band of dislocations. Acted on by the applied stress, the dislocations have coalesced to produce a microcrack which can grow by the addition of extra dislocations, and then propagate catastrophically when it reaches the critical length determined by the Griffith criterion (*16*). An example of cracks formed in this way at a grain boundary in magnesium oxide is also shown in Figure 6 (*47*). In this instance, the dislocation distribution was revealed by etching the crystal in a solution containing five parts ammonium chloride, one part sulfuric acid and one part water. The electron microscope also can be used to study the distribution and behavior of dislocations in the bulk provided that specimens thin enough (about 500 A.) to allow electron transmission can be prepared. An example of a dislocation pile-up in α-brass revealed in this way is illustrated in Figure 8.

During recent years several excellent books (*3, 6, 35*) and review articles (*9, 28, 32*) have been concerned with dislocations in theory and experiment, and it is now conclusively established that for all crystalline materials possessing some degree of ductility it is the generation, motion, and interaction of dislocations which determine mechanical behavior. Thus, for surface condition and

environment to affect mechanical properties, it follows that these factors must be affecting dislocation behavior. This is the case, and they do so principally by affecting the operation of the various types of surface sources of dislocations, and by affecting the emergence of dislocations through the surface of the material. Certain environments can also affect cohesion at the surface, particularly, it is believed, at strained atomic bonds— e.g., at crack tips or near dislocations (*17, 50, 51*).

### Effects of Various Environments

A typical test specimen in an industrial laboratory may well exhibit an oxide film, certain adsorbed surface-active species (from fingerprints), a notch or two, and be surrounded by a slightly corrosive environment. However, for the purposes of this paper, the various types of surface condition and environment will be

*Figure 8. Dislocations in α-brass as revealed by transmission electron microscopy. Dislocations on intersecting slip planes are interacting at A. Magnification about 30,000× (Photograph courtesy of R. L. Segall)*

separated into six broad categories (Figure 9). Then, since a comprehensive review of this enormous field is not practical, some of the more interesting results of recent investigations will be described. In general, observations from experiments with monocrystals have been chosen because the use of such specimens optimizes surface-sensitive mechanical behavior, and the data obtained are more readily interpreted.

### Clean Surfaces and Surface Sources of Dislocations

A dislocation approaching a clean surface experiences an attraction tending to draw it from the crystal (*6*). However, opposing its emergence are two other factors. First, as an edge dislocation leaves the crystal it creates a surface step, and this requires extra (surface) energy. Second, from low-energy electron-diffraction experiments, it is known that the atomic spacing in the surface layers is different from that in the bulk (*30*). This factor is also likely to provide extra resistance to dislocation egress (*13*). Whether such factors are important in practice is not yet known, but experimental evidence does suggest that in the early stages of plastic deformation, dislocations do become tangled up in the vicinity of the surface. The removal of such tangles by chemical polishing can, in effect, restore the crystal to its virgin state. An example of this phenomenon is illustrated in Figure 10 (24). Following a prestrain of 0.5%, the chemical removal of some 0.04 inches from the surface restored yield stress of an aluminum monocrystal to its original value of about 120 p.s.i.

An alternative explanation for dislocation tangling at the surface is that the dislocations involved in yielding come from sources located at the surface. Two types of surface source have been discussed in the metallurgical literature, the "Fisher" source (12)—which may be relevant in the deformation of metals, and the "half-loop" source—known to be important in the deformation of ionic and ceramic materials (22).

The Fisher source, Figure 11, is based on the concept that a dislocation line emerging unpinned at the surface, but being pinned somewhere in the bulk (at $A$), will behave as if it were also pinned by a "mirror image" locking point on the outside of the crystal and at the same distance from the surface as the interior point. Now the stress to bow out a dislocation line so that it acts as a source is inversely proportional to its unpinned length. Thus, if $L_i \cong L_s$, then the stress $\tau_s$ to operate line $A\,B$ as a surface source will be only half that required to operate line $A\,C$, an interior source. In other words, surface sources of dislocations should be responsible for the yielding and initial plastic deformation of metal crystals.

While the existence of Fisher sources cannot be regarded as established, there is some evidence which appears to support this hypothesis. For example, it was noted that the yield stress of copper monocrystals surface-doped with about 1% zinc was 140 p.s.i., almost double the value of 80 p.s.i. obtained from un-doped crystals (1). It was concluded, therefore, that doping had interfered with the operation of Fisher-type surface sources, and that in order to yield the specimen had been forced to utilize its "harder" interior sources. When 0.005 inches was electropolished from the surface of doped crystals, their yield stress became that of un-doped crystals.

For most engineering applications, however, poly-crystalline metals are used, and for such materials surface sources are not important because most of the dislocations required are produced at grain boundaries. Figure 12 demonstrates such a process occurring in an iron-3% silicon alloy (26). The specimen illustrated was stressed just below its yield stress, heated to 150° C. to segregate carbon atoms to the dislocations, then electrolytically etched in a mixture of acetic and chromic acids to reveal the dislocation distribution. It can be seen that bands of dislocations have been emitted from the grain boundary $AB$.

For nonmetallic crystals, the effects of varying the availability and operability of surface sources can be quite spectacular. In these materials the half-loop surface source, introduced by cleaving or by any form of surface damage, often plays a dominant role in deter-

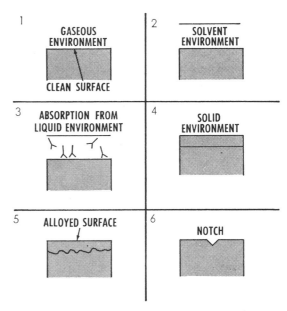

Figure 9.   The various types of surface condition and environment

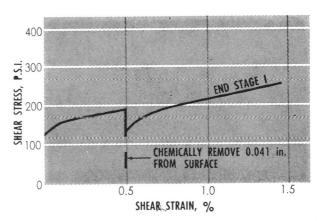

Figure 10.   The effect of chemically removing 0.041 inches from the surface of an aluminum crystal following 0.5% strain.   Note recovery of original yield stress (24), Kramer and Demer

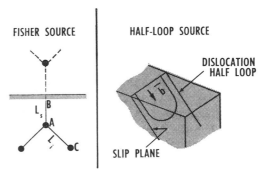

Figure 11.   Two types of surface sources of dislocations

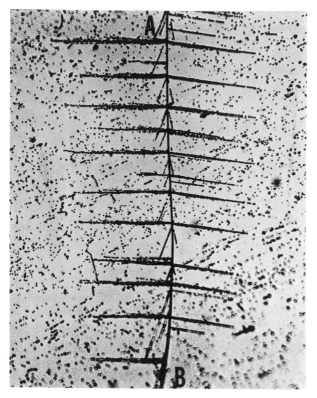

*Figure 12. Dislocations emitted from grain boundary AB in an iron–3% silicon alloy (26), Ku and Johnston*

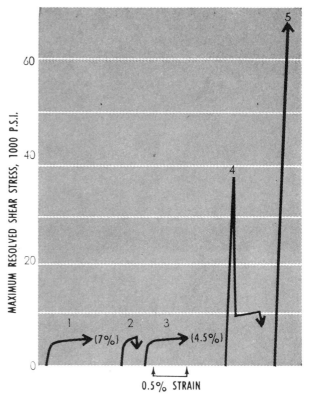

*Figure 13. Tensile stress-strain curves for carefully polished magnesium oxide crystals: (1) containing one artificially introduced surface source; (2) containing two surface sources; (3) containing many surface sources; (4) without surface sources; (5) annealed at 2000° C., cooled rapidly, polished to remove surface sources (42, 43), Stokes et al.*

mining mechanical behavior. For example, the properties of a magnesium oxide crystal can be significantly altered by controlling the type of dislocation sources available and their distribution (42, 43). This is illustrated in Figure 13. Curve 1 was obtained from an as-grown, as-cleaved crystal, chemically polished to remove half-loop surface sources introduced during cleaving, and into which was then introduced one fresh source by dropping a particle of silicon carbide onto the surface. When the crystal was stressed in tension, this source operated and dislocations from it completely filled the specimen. The yield stress, $\tau_y$ was about 5,000 p.s.i., and the strain at fracture, $\epsilon_F$, $\cong$ 7%. Curve 2 is from a similar specimen containing two artificially introduced dislocation sources. Dislocations from each source intersected and interacted to form a crack which immediately propagated, causing failure. For this specimen, $\tau_y$ again was about 5,000 p.s.i. but $\epsilon_F$ was only 0.2%. Curve 3 is from a similar specimen, but in this instance many surface sources were introduced. As before, intersecting slip bands caused cracks to form, but this time their propagation was hindered by other slip bands so that a small but useful measure of ductility was achieved: $\tau_y \cong$ 5000 p.s.i., $\epsilon_F =$ 4.5%. Curve 4 was obtained from a chemically polished crystal containing no artificially introduced and readily activated surface sources. This specimen was therefore forced to utilize harder interior sources (probably associated with impurity particles) and this

raised the yield stress to about 35,000 p.s.i. Such specimens failed after 0.1 to 0.4% strain. Finally, curve 5 is from a crystal annealed at 2000° C. to dissolve precipitate particles (interior sources), cooled rapidly to prevent their reprecipitation, and then chemically polished to remove any subsequently introduced surface sources. For such specimens, yielding and catastrophic failure occurred simultaneously at stresses as high as 140,000 p.s.i. ($\cong G/150$). Such experiments demonstrate that elimination of the usually present sources of dislocations can increase the yield and fracture stresses of oxide ceramic crystals by as much as 30 times.

### Some Effects of Solvent Environments

The effect of a liquid environment on the mechanical behavior of a crystal depends largely upon its corrosivity. If the specimen is very soluble in the environment, then enhanced ductility usually results. However if the environment is less corrosive, or such that dissolution tends to occur at certain preferred sites, then embrittlement can result.

The best known example of the effect of an extremely corrosive environment is usually referred to as Joffe's effect (*18*). In the classic demonstration of this phenomenon, a salt crystal is shown to be weak and brittle if deformed in air, but up to 25 times stronger and considerably more ductile if it is deformed in water. Figure 1 illustrates this effect with irradiated potassium chloride crystals (data of the author). The upper

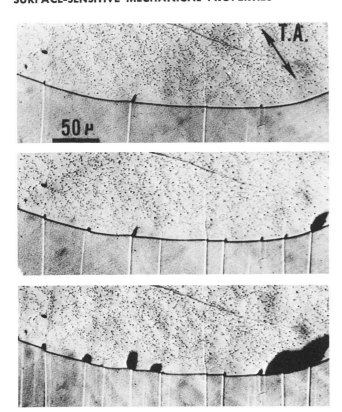

Figure 14. Cracks forming at the intersection of slip bands and grain boundary in silver chloride, during deformation in 6N aqueous sodium chloride (50) Westwood, Goldheim, and Pugh. See page 23

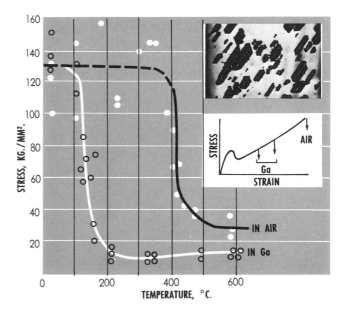

Figure 15. Embrittlement of germanium by liquid gallium. Below about 400° C., embrittlement is associated with the notch-etching effect illustrated in the upper inset. Above about 500° C. (lower inset), true liquid metal embrittlement effects dominate (34), Pugh et al.

crystal was bent in air; the middle crystal polished in water, carefully dried and then tested in air; and the lower crystal deformed in water. This apparently unsophisticated experiment in fact involves several phenomena (49), including:

—the removal, by dissolution, of pre-existing notches or cracks introduced by cleaving or mishandling (Joffe's original explanation)

—the removal, by dissolution, of pre-existing and embrittling surface films, probably of potassium chlorate or polycrystalline potassium chloride formed by interaction of the crystal with moist air (15)

—the removal of surface barriers to dislocation emergence—i.e., subsurface dislocation tangles

—the blunting of initiated cracks, reducing their propagatability.

All of these effects enhance ductility. High strength then results from the elimination of surface sources of dislocations, and work hardening.

As mentioned earlier, solvent environments can also improve the strength and ductility of metals. The fracture strength of tungsten sheet, for example, was increased from 135,000 p.s.i. to about 370,000 p.s.i. when

AUTHOR A. R. C. Westwood is Associate Director of the Martin Company's Research Institute for Advanced Studies, Baltimore, Maryland.

some 0.006 inches was removed by chemical polishing (39). This improvement was probably caused by the removal of surface notches from a notch-sensitive material. Similar effects have been observed with molybdenum (8), bismuth (4), and germanium (2, 19), and are likely to prove of value in the shaping or working of materials of limited ductility.

Of the effects of selectively corrosive environments, stress corrosion cracking is certainly the most important. This phenomenon involves a complex interplay of chemical and metallurgical factors, and remains far from well understood. However, recent work with the electron microscope suggests that for such materials as brass, failure probably occurs by preferred chemical dissolution at regions of high dislocation density, for example, at piled-up groups of dislocations near a grain boundary. Since it is known that stress corrosion cracking does not occur in pure metals, it has been suggested that a prerequisite for this phenomenon is the segregation of solute atoms to dislocations, increasing chemical reactivity there (45).

Other recent work has demonstrated that liquid metal environments can produce significant embrittlement in semiconductor materials, and Figure 15 illustrates the effect of liquid gallium on germanium (34). Over the temperature range 100° to 350° C., the fracture stress in bending is reduced from about 130 kg./sq. mm. (about 185,000 p.s.i.) in air, to about 10 kg./sq. mm. (about 14,000 p.s.i.) in gallium. It appears that this remarkable effect is caused by a combination of selective dissolution and the intrinsic notch brittleness of germanium, for cracks were observed to have initiated at crystallographic notches (upper inset) etched into the surface by the liquid metal. This observation has possible implications for the ultrahigh strength materials of the future. Such materials, while intrinsically notch brittle, are likely to be too hard to notch mechanically under ordinary working conditions, but may be notched by chemical means—with potentially disastrous results.

At temperatures above 400° C., germanium crystals exhibited true liquid metal embrittlement (see below), sometimes fracturing below the upper yield stress following measurable plastic strain (Figure 15, lower inset).

### Effects of Adsorption from Liquid Environments

According to the Russian literature (27), the presence of certain adsorbed organic polar molecules can cause significant reductions in the mechanical properties of metals—i.e., decreases in the yield stress, rate of work hardening, and stress and strain at fracture. Such reductions have been reported to occur when long-chain fatty acid, alcohol, and amine molecules area dsorbed from vaseline oil onto the surfaces of aluminum, copper, lead, tin or zinc specimens. These effects are known as Rebinder effects. To date, no Western worker has been able to reproduce the decrease in yield stress supposed to occur in a surface-active medium, but variations in the rate of work hardening of aluminum and copper crystals when tested in paraffin oil containing different concentrations of stearic acid have been observed (23). The experimental results show marked similarities with those obtained in solvent environments, and thus it has been suggested (23) that fatty acid molecules react at the surface of the metal to form metal soap molecules, and that these then desorb into the environment. The rate of surface dissolution is thus a function of the concentration of fatty acid molecules in the environment, the rate of reaction at the surface, and the rate of desorption of the soap molecules. Significantly, no effects were observed when the paraffin oil was presaturated with the appropriate metal stearate, and no effects were observed with gold crystals. It is known that gold soaps are not normally formed because the free energy required is too large (41). It has been suggested, however, that the exo-electrons emitted when a metal is deformed (25) can play a role in the soap formation process for copper and aluminum specimens (23, 40, 41).

Rebinder effects have also been observed for lithium fluoride crystals. A freshly cleaved surface of this material is clean, oxide-free, and contains the half-loop surface sources which are known to control subsequent yielding behavior. Thus it is an ideal material for examining the hypothesis that if the adsorption of surface active molecules affects mechanical behavior, it must do so because of some interaction between these molecules and dislocations where the latter meet the surface (48). From considerations of the model illustrated in the inset to Figure 16, it was concluded that, in the presence of adsorbed polar molecules, the operation of half-loop sources should be hindered and that,

as a result, the yield stress of lithium fluoride should be increased by some 50 p.s.i.—not decreased as suggested by Rebinder (27). Subsequent experiments confirmed the existence of this "adsorption-locking" effect (Figure 16) and it was found that the yield stress of lithium fluoride crystals was increased by about 25 p.s.i. However, this increase was followed by a decrease in the rate of work hardening. Metallographic observations revealed that the latter was caused by differences in dislocation distribution between specimens having locked and unlocked surface sources.

Solutions of fatty acids in water also serve as dislocation-revealing etchants for lithium fluoride, and the $C_{14}$–$C_{18}$ acids are particularly useful for they are capable of revealing the points of emergence of dislocations moving under the action of residual stresses in the crystal (Figure 17) (52). Now according to the adsorption locking hypothesis (48), a dislocation is pinned when a polar molecule adsorbs on its emerging end, but is free to move when the molecule desorbs. Thus the rate of dislocation motion, or "tracking," should be inversely proportional to the fraction of time in which the dislocation is locked by an adsorbed polar molecule. This fraction can be controlled by the concentration of polar molecules present in the environment—the higher the concentration, the greater the fraction of time a polar molecule will be adsorbed at the dislocation, and vice versa. Figure 17 presents data from observations on four individual dislocations, and demonstrates that tracking rates are greater in the more dilute solution, as predicted. These data provide an interesting example of the environmental control of an individual lattice defect.

Another important phenomenon which is believed to be adsorption controlled is embrittlement by liquid metals. This is a remarkably specific phenomenon— only certain liquid metals embrittle certain solid metals. For example, molten lithium embrittles copper and iron, but not aluminum; mercury embrittles zinc, brass and perhaps copper, but not cadmium, and so forth (37). There must be some significance to these couples, but as yet it is not apparent. A tensile stress is a prerequisite for embrittlement, and unlike stress corrosion cracking, pure metals can be embrittled. Dissolution processes are not thought to be relevant to the mechanism because a suitably prestressed specimen will break immediately if it is wetted with the appropriate liquid metal. Moreover, in general, embrittlement only occurs between metals which have limited mutual solubility. For example, iron has virtually no solubility in molten cadmium even at 700° C.—about $3 \times 10^{-4}$ wt. % (7). Nevertheless, Armco-iron is significantly embrittled by molten cadmium over the temperature range 320° to 420° C. (Figure 18) (10). In contrast with most surface-sensitive phenomena, liquid metal embrittlement is more severe in polycrystalline materials than in monocrystals.

In the past, this phenomenon has been discussed in terms of a simple reduction in surface energy associated with the adsorption of liquid metal atoms. If this hypothesis were correct, then one would expect that if the surface-area–to-volume ratio of specimens were increased, embrittlement would become more severe. In fact, the reverse is true (38). The actual mechanism remains unclear, but it has been suggested that liquid metal embrittlement is associated with the chemisorption of liquid metal atoms at certain regions of high stress or strain in the lattice—such as at cracks tips, dislocation pile-ups, and so forth, and that embrittlement occurs because cohesion is reduced locally by virtue of some electronic rearrangement (51).

Effects very similar to stress corrosion cracking and liquid metal embrittlement are also observed in non-metals—e.g., in polycrystalline silver chloride when stressed in certain complex forming environments (21, 50, 53) (Figure 14). Figure 19 illustrates the effects of concentrated aqueous sodium chloride on the time to failure of polycrystalline silver chloride specimens tested in dead-loading (53). Fracture in air and in salt solutions of concentration $\leq 2N$ was ductile and transcrystalline. In more concentrated solutions, however, fracture was brittle and intercrystalline. Now the solubility of silver chloride in concentrated chloride environments is significantly greater than that in water because of the formation of soluble complex ions of the type $AgCl_n^{-(n-1)}$ (14). Thus it was suspected that embrittlement might be due to preferential dissolution at grain boundaries, as postulated for the stress corrosion cracking of $\alpha$-brass, (45). However, when tests were performed in solutions presaturated with complex ions, the time to failure was substantially decreased—e.g., by two orders of magnitude at a stress of 500 grams/sq. mm. (700 p.s.i.) in $6N$ sodium chloride environments. Similar effects of presaturation on time to failure also were observed in concentrated solutions of sodium thiosulfate, sodium thiocyanate, and sodium bromide, etc., and it has been concluded that embrittlement is associated with the adsorption of complex ions of high (not less than 3) negative charge—such as $AgCl_4^{-3}$, $Ag(S_2O_3)_3^{-5}$ and $Ag(SCN)_4^{-3}$—at stressed grain boundaries of large misorientation (50).

### Effects of "Solid" Surface Coatings and Alloyed Surfaces

Solid surface coatings and alloyed surface layers affect mechanical behavior because they affect the operation of surface sources and thus yielding, and because they impede the egress of dislocations from the crystal and therefore affect the rate of work hardening. Fracture behavior also is affected because cracks can be formed by the piling up and coalescence of edge dislocations at the crystal–coating interface. With few exceptions, solid environments reduce the ductility of crystals, but may increase or decrease the fracture strength (49).

Figure 20 illustrates the effects of silver surface coatings on copper monocrystals (37). An electroplated-coating, 4 microns thick (mechanically bonded), did not significantly affect mechanical behavior. However, after silver was diffused into the surface by heating the specimen at 750° C. for several hours, the yield stress increased by 50%, and the rate of work hardening decreased slightly. For comparison, the stress-strain curve of a

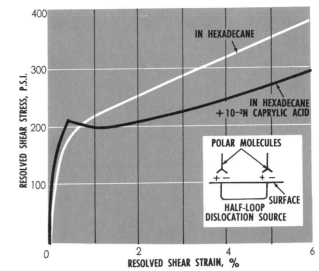

Figure 16. The effect of adsorbed caprylic acid molecules on the yielding behavior of as-cleaved lithium fluoride crystals. The inset illustrates the adsorption locking concept (48), Westwood

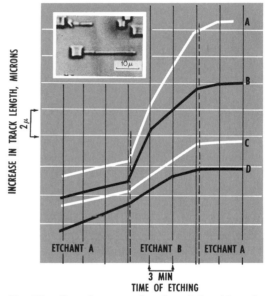

Figure 17. The effect of concentration of myristic acid on the rate of movement (tracking) of screw dislocations at the surface of a lithium fluoride crystal. The inset provides an example of the dislocation "tracks" studied (48), Westwood. Etchant A, 1.25 × 10⁻⁷N myristic acid in water; Etchant B, 0.9 × 10⁻⁷N myristic acid in water

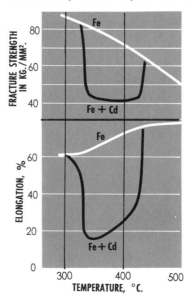

Figure 18. The embrittlement of Armco-iron by molten cadmium (10), Dityatkovsky et al.

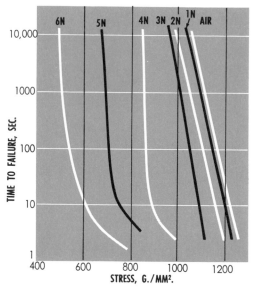

*Figure 19. Effect of applied stress and concentration of aqueous sodium chloride on the time to failure of polycrystalline silver chloride specimens tested in dead-loading (50, 53), Westwood et al.*

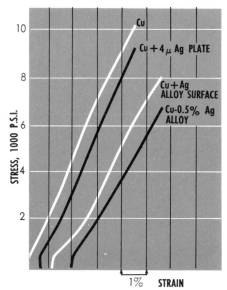

*Figure 20. Stress-strain curves for copper monocrystals of various surface conditions (36), Rosi*

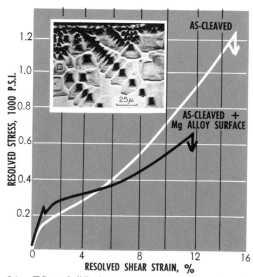

*Figure 21. Effect of diffusing magnesium into the surface layers of an as-cleaved lithium fluoride crystal. Inset shows edge dislocations piled up beneath the alloyed surface layer (46), Westwood et al.*

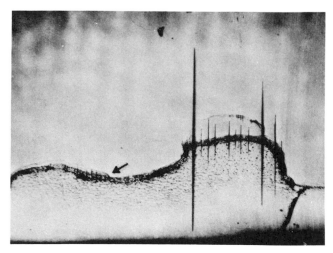

*Figure 22. Microcracks associated with a precipitate of polycrystalline sodium chloride on the tension surface of a bent sodium chloride crystal. Magnification about 17× (44), Stokes et al.*

homogeneous copper–0.5% silver alloy also is shown. This curve is virtually identical with that from the silver-doped specimen, again demonstrating the importance of surface condition in determining the mechanical behavior of monocrystals.

Similar phenomena have been observed in non-metallic crystals (46). A vapor-deposited film of magnesium 1 to 3 microns thick did not greatly affect the behavior of freshly cleaved lithium fluoride crystals. However, when the magnesium was diffused into the crystal to a depth of some 5 microns, the yield stress was increased by 50%, the rate of work hardening decreased, and the fracture stress reduced by about 50% (Figure 21). The inset to this figure shows edge dislocations piled up beneath the alloyed surface layer, and Figure 22 demonstrates the results of such piling up when the bulk material is notch brittle. In the latter, cracks have formed at the interface between a sodium chloride monocrystal and a polycrystalline sodium chloride surface-film which was produced by inefficient drying after polishing in water (44).

Solid surface films also affect creep and fatigue behavior. Figure 23, for example, illustrates what happens when a copper surface film is plated on and off a zinc crystal during a constant-stress creep test (33). Such effects are not observed when polycrystalline zinc specimens are used.

### Effects of Notches

Several effects caused by the presence, or removal, of notches have already been discussed: Joffe's effects in potassium chloride, the low-temperature embrittlement of germanium by gallium, the effect of a chemical polishing treatment on tungsten, etc., and a knowledge of the notch sensitivity of a material is essential for its correct utilization. To illustrate, during the production of rocket motor casings, catastrophic failures were occurring from small cracks in the vicinity of welds. The steel being used had been heat-treated to achieve its maximum strength of about 250,000 p.s.i. Subse-

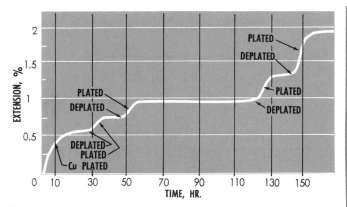

*Figure 23. Variation in creep rate of a zinc monocrystal associated with the plating and deplating of a copper film (33), Pickus and Parker*

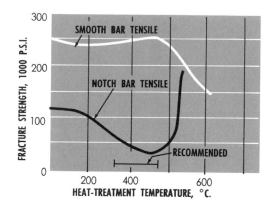

*Figure 24. Comparison of tensile strengths of smooth and notched steel specimens at room temperature (11), Espey et al. The heat treatment shown is that recommended by the supplier*

quent investigation of the effects of heat treatment temperature on the strength of notched specimens revealed that while the chosen temperature maximized smooth-bar tensile strength, it also minimized notched-bar tensile strength (Figure 24) (11).

The presence of a notch also can induce brittle behavior at temperatures for which ductile behavior might have been expected. For example, a polished crystal of silver chloride is very ductile at room temperature, and the transition from ductile to brittle behavior for such a crystal occurs at about −150° C. However, if crystals are first notched and then tested under impact loading conditions, this transition temperature rises to 70° C. (20). With sodium chloride crystals this effect is even more spectacular. Highly polished crystals are ductile above 400° C., but crystals containing a small notch fracture by cleavage to within 10° C. of their melting temperature of approximately 800° C.

### Summary

A few of the many examples of surface- and environment-sensitive mechanical behavior of materials have been described, and it has been shown that, under certain circumstances, surface condition and environment can significantly affect strength and ductility. Sometimes the effects are beneficial, for example the threefold increase in strength of tungsten sheet following electropolishing, or the eightfold increase in strength of magnesium oxide associated with the elimination of surface sources of dislocations. In other cases the effects are detrimental, for example the catastrophic embrittlement of metals and semiconductors by liquid metals, or the embrittlement of certain ionic crystals by adsorbed complexes.

### LITERATURE CITED

(1) Adams, M. A., *Acta Met.* **6**, 327 (1958).
(2) Breidt, P. J., Hobstetter, J. N., Ellis, W. C., *J. Appl. Phys.* **29**, 226 (1958).
(3) Burgers, J. M., Burgers, W. G., *Rheology* **1**, 141 (1956).
(4) Classen-Nekludova, M. V., *Tech. Phys. USSR* **5**, 827 (1938).
(5) Cottrell, A. H., "Report on Strength of Solids," Physical Society, London, p. 30, 1948.
(6) Cottrell, A. H., "Dislocations and Plastic Flow in Crystals," Oxford Univ. Press, London, 1953.

(7) Daniels, E. J., *J. Inst. Metals* **46**, 87 (1931).
(8) Davidenkov, N. N., Efimova, I. S., *Soviet Physics—Solid State* **1**, 1389 (1960).
(9) de Witt, R., "Mechanical Behavior of Crystalline Solids," NBS Monograph 59, p. 13, 1963.
(10) Dityatkovsky, Y. M., Andreyev, I. V., Gorshkov, V. F., *Phys. Metals Metallog. USSR English Transl.* **15**, 94 (1963).
(11) Epsey, G. B., Jones, M. H., Brown, W. F., *Proc. ASTM* **59**, 837 (1959).
(12) Fisher, J. C., *Trans. AIME* **194**, 531 (1954).
(13) Fleischer, R. L., *Acta Met.* **8**, 598 (1960).
(14) Forbes, G. S., Cole, H. I., *J. Am. Chem. Soc.* **43**, 2492 (1921).
(15) Gorum, A. E., Parker, E. R., Pask, J. A., *J. Am. Ceram. Soc.* **41**, 161 (1958).
(16) Griffith, A. A., *Phil. Trans. Roy. Soc. (London)* **A221**, 163 (1920–1).
(17) Hillig, W. B., Charles, R. J., Proc. Second International Materials Symposium, Berkeley, 1964, unpublished data.
(18) Joffe, A., Kirpitschewa, M. W., Lewitsky, M. A., *Z. Physik.* **22**, 286 (1924).
(19) Johnston, T. L., Stokes, R. J., Li, C. H., *Acta Met.* **6**, 713 (1958).
(20) Johnston, T. L., Stokes, R. J., Li, C. H., *Phil. Mag.* **4**, 1316 (1959).
(21) Johnston, T. L., Parker, E. R., Rept. Contract N7-ONR-29516, NR-031-255, January 1957.
(22) Johnston, W. G., Gilman, J. J., *J. Appl. Phys.* **31**, 632 (1960).
(23) Kramer, I. R., *Trans. AIME* **221**, 989 (1961); **227**, 529 (1963).
(24) Kramer, I. R., Demer, L. J., *Trans. AIME* **221**, 780 (1961).
(25) Kramer, J., *Z. Physik* **125**, 739 (1949); **128**, 538 (1950).
(26) Ku, R. C., Johnston, T. L., unpublished data.
(27) Likhtman, V. I., Rebinder, P. A., Karpenko, G. V., "Effect of a Surface, Active Medium on the Deformation of Metals," Her Majesty's Stationery Office, London, 1958.
(28) MacCrone, R. K., *Int. Sci. Technology*, No. 23, 36 (Nov., 1963).
(29) MacKenzie, J. K., quoted in Cottrell, A. H., "Dislocations and Plastic Flow in Crystals," p. 11, Oxford Univ. Press, London, 1953.
(30) MacRae, A. U., Germer, L. H., *Ann. N. Y. Acad. Sci.* **101**, 627 (1963).
(31) Mathews, C. O., Jacobson, M. I., Jahsman, W. E., Ward, W. V., WADD Tech. Rept. 60-116 (1960).
(32) Parker, E. R., "Mechanical Behavior of Crystalline Solids," NBS Monograph 59, p. 1, 1963.
(33) Pickus, M. R., Parker, E. R., *Trans. AIME* **191**, 792 (1951).
(34) Pugh, E. N., Westwood, A. R. C., Hitch, T. T., unpublished data
(35) Read, W. T., "Dislocations in Crystals," McGraw-Hill, New York, 1953.
(36) Rosi, F. D., *Acta Met.* **5**, 348 (1957).
(37) Rostoker, W., McCaughey, J. M., Markus, H., "Embrittlement by Liquid Metals," Reinhold, New York, 1960.
(38) Rozhanskii, V. N., *Soviet Phys.-Solid State* **2**, 978 (1960).
(39) Schroder, K., Packman, P., Nash, G., Weiss, V., Syracuse Univ. Res. Report No. MET. E 1040-0164F (January 1964).
(40) Smith, H. A., Fort, T., *J. Phys. Chem.* **62**, 519 (1958).
(41) Smith, H. A., McGill, R. M., *J. Phys. Chem.* **61**, 1025 (1957).
(42) Stokes, R. J., *Trans AIME* **224**, 1227 (1962).
(43) Stokes, R. J., Johnston, T. L., Li, C. H., *Phil. Mag.* **6**, 9 (1961).
(44) Stokes, R. J., Johnston, T. L., Li, C. H., *Trans. AIME* **218**, 655 (1960).
(45) Tromans, D., Nutting, J., "Fracture of Solids," p. 637, Interscience, New York, 1963.
(46) Westwood, A. R. C., *Phil. Mag.* **5**, 981 (1960).
(47) *Ibid.*, **6**, 195 (1961).
(48) *Ibid.*, **7**, 633 (1962).
(49) Westwood, A. R. C., "Fracture of Solids," p. 553., Interscience, New York, 1963.
(50) Westwood, A. R. C., Goldheim, D. L., Pugh, E. N., *Disc. Faraday Soc.*, **38**, 147 (1964).
(51) Westwood, A. R. C., Kamdar, M. H., *Phil. Mag.* **8**, 787 (1963).
(52) Westwood, A. R. C., Opperhauser, H., Goldheim, D. L., *Phil. Mag.* **6**, 1475 (1961).
(53) Westwood, A. R. C., Goldheim, D. L., Pugh, E. N., "Grain Boundaries and Surfaces in Ceramics," Plenum Press, New York, 1965, in press.

# Index